NT Co

FOR

For a complete list of volumes and individual titles available in the Connections *series, see page 641*

NT Connections 2007

NEW PLAYS
FOR YOUNG PEOPLE

Baby Girl

The Black Remote

A Bridge to the Stars

DeoxyriboNucleic Acid

Red Sky

Ruckus in the Garden

Scary Play

Show and Tell

A Year and a Day

ff

faber and faber

First published in 2007
by Faber and Faber Limited
3 Queen Square, London WC1N 3AU

Typeset by Country Setting, Kingsdown, Kent CT14 8ES
Printed in the UK by CPI Bookmarque, Croydon, CR0 4TD

A CIP record for this book is available from the British Library

978-0-571-23898-9

2 4 6 8 10 9 7 5 3

Contents

Introduction

Connections is a new plays laboratory where anything can happen. The litmus test is the quality of the scripts and this year's are exceptional – all written by writers at the top of their game. There are tales of loss and corruption, cover-ups and breath-stopping risks. Settings include the street, ancient and magical gardens, a small town in Sweden and a hot alien landscape. Collectively the plays demonstrate that, for a young person, the big wide world can be a testing place, whether you're inside or out.

In Glyn Maxwell's play *The Black Remote* Polly is having a bad night. Her parents have gone away 'to find themselves', her big sisters are out on the town, and she's left alone with a brand new enormous sleek plasma-screen TV and four remote controls – a white one that does this, a grey one that does that, a silver one that does the other, and a black one – well no one knows what that does. Enter her curious friend Norman, who picks up the forbidden black remote and starts rapidly surfing the channels. As anyone who's done that knows well, this will cause the TV to explode and strange winged creatures to burst out of the screen and take over your house. Meanwhile, a beautiful firework display has begun on the Great Meadow, a fabulous fair is in full swing, everyone's being lovely and life is suddenly perfect. Is this anything to do with the creatures in Polly's house, and what will happen if she lets them out? And they really, really, want to get out . . .

More strange happenings await the pupils of Riverdale Comprehensive and St Nectan's grant-maintained schools when, in David Farr's *Ruckus in the Garden,* they find themselves in the garden of Cecil Fortescue on a school trip. A brawl is inevitable, as is customary when these two schools meet. Magic waits amidst the topiary in the form of Cupid, who brings about transformations romantic, revealing and hilarious.

John Retallack's adaptation of *A Bridge to the Stars* by Henning Mankell is a story about a boy and a town. Joel is eleven and lives alone with Samuel, his dad. Joel has no friends. So he forms a secret society. All his adventures happen in the middle of the night while the town sleeps. He searches for a dog he has glimpsed, a dog that is 'headed for a star'. He never finds the dog but he finds Rolf instead. Rolf is new to the town and has very different ideas to Joel. Rolf believes a secret society must create fear and he sets out to terrorise a lonely woman. Joel finally has the courage to defy Rolf, but he risks his life to do so. In a gripping climax, Joel is stranded a hundred feet up on an icy railway viaduct in the middle of the night . . .

In another time and another place, ten-year-old Kal and his mates (Mal, Ro, Tilly, Jaz and Boff) are having a sleepover round Kal's to celebrate his birthday. As the night draws in, the kids indulge in an age-old pastime: scaring the living daylights out of each other. Kal tells the story of a local house, said to be haunted by the ghost of a man who once lived there with his ageing mother and his pet monkey. As a boy, Kal's dad and his mates snuck into the very same house, only to come screaming out again when they found something absolutely terrifying in the upstairs bedroom. Kal challenges his friends to do the same and, with varying degrees of reluctance, they disappear into the night. Meanwhile, Kal's much put-upon eight-year-old sister Lou has been listening at the door. Despite the fact that Kal told her it was his sleepover and babies weren't allowed to take part, Lou sneaks after the gang. *Scary Play* by Judith Johnson follows the ten-year-olds (and Lou) as they creep into the haunted house and each of them faces up to their own unique fear.

Facing up to things or not is only one of the themes in Dennis Kelly's chilling new drama. If you're a teenager and you do something bad, really bad, what should you do? Tell your parents? Tell the police? Tell a teacher? No, you should do exactly what adults do – cover the whole thing up and hope no one finds out. *DeoxyriboNucleic Acid* is about a group of teenagers who are brought together by the act of doing something bad. But when things begin to unravel their newfound sense of solidarity begins to crack.

Baby Girl by Roy Williams is about Kelle, who is thrteen years old and, to the shock of her best friend Danielle, still a virgin. Now if Danielle knows, then the whole school knows, and Kelle isn't having that, even if it means sleeping with creepy Nathan who smells like old people. Getting off with a 'yat' like Kelle is just the kind of street rep Nathan needs if he is to be a 'wide boy' like his big brother Richie. But neither of them counted on Kelle getting pregnant and Richie falling in love. Now Kelle's mum wants to throttle her, Nathan is cruising for a bruising if his antics have ruined Richie's chances with the lovely Josie, and Danielle thinks the baby should be called Lady Sovereign.

A Year and a Day by Christina Reid is a very different story of teenagers falling in love. A travelling storyteller and a girl meet in a land devastated by war and famine. The storyteller remembers and conjures a long-long-ago land of people and plenty – a beautiful garden inhabited by the Kritters of the land, the trees and the water. And the humans come to the garden: two tribes who worship different gods. The storyteller's tale of the corruption and loss of the ancient garden is a love story that becomes a never-ending tale of old ghosts who haunt the earth –

a legend with the warning 'Don't be seduced by the music. Don't look back.'

Laline Paull has written the first-ever *Connections* farce. In *Show and Tell* grumpy and seriously hormonal best friends Oli and Jo, constantly arguing identical twins Alex and Toby, and nerdy no-mates Bunce become obsessed with the secret life of their sexy new supply teacher, whom they are convinced is involved in the world's oldest profession. In between trying to get off with each other, shaking off weird and clingy parents and making an earth-shatteringly important documentary, they find there's high jinks to be had in a gang that gets it completely wrong . . . and the hamster is still alive.

Bryony Lavery's play *More Light* was part of the second cycle of *Connections*. Now, a decade later, she has written *Red Sky*, a thrilling new companion piece. In a hot, alien landscape, Ross, Tark and Luce, three argumentative archaeology interns, are cataloguing the latest artefacts. Near them, a gaping dark hole marks the entrance to a recently opened tomb. On the trestle table, under a baking sky, stand a fragile paper bird, a richly-jewelled ceremonial robe and an axe made of human bone . . . What happens when you pillage the graves of the long dead?

The writers workshopped their plays here at the National with our Young Company. Once they were ready, hundreds of schools, colleges and youth theatres from the UK and abroad sent their director to work on the play at an autumn retreat hosted by the Stephen Joseph Theatre in Scarborough. A new play normally has a solo first outing with the writer usually being part of the rehearsal process. So on the writer's part being involved in this enormous laboratory is a great act of faith. They're going to see their play taken in many different directions, and so it's vital they get to work with the directors who are going to be premiering their work. Over a long weekend these directors are able to begin their rehearsal process in the best way possible, by asking the questions they need to ask the writer in sessions facilitated by a team of National Theatre-associated directors. Notes on these workshops appear following each of the plays.

The plays will be premiered in March 2007. All will be visited by one of the team from the National in their own venue (listed at the back of this book) and in many instances the writers themselves. If you have as many as forty productions of your play presented in one month alone it's going to be impractical to see all of them. But the companies produce show-reels and writers get ample opportunity to see different approaches, which might lead to some minor adjustments to their scripts. Most shows will transfer to one of the major partnership venues as part of the *Connections 07* season, launched in April at the Royal and Derngate Theatres, Northampton, and continuing to Hampstead Theatre; Nuffield Theatre, Southampton; Lyric Hammersmith, London; Brewery Arts Theatre, Kendal; Arcola Theatre, London; The Garage and Playhouse Theatres, Norwich; Everyman Palace Theatre, Cork; Teatro Litta, Milan; Bath Theatre Royal; Castle Arts Centre, Wellingborough; National Theatre, Norway; Stephen Joseph Theatre, Scarborough; Cultergest Theatre, Lisbon; Newcastle Theatre Royal; Lowry Theatre, Salford; Bristol Old Vic; Brighton Dome; and the Lyceum Theatre Edinburgh. The season culminates at the National in July, when each of the plays will be presented and this fabulous new anthology will be launched. I hope you get to see them, but if you don't and you'd like to be part of the next Connections Laboratory, check out the website on the back of this book.

SUZY GRAHAM-ADRIANI
National Theatre, January 2007

BABY GIRL

Roy Williams

Roy Williams's work for the theatre includes *Sing Yer Heart Out for the Lads*, *Slow Time* (National); *No Boys Cricket Club* (Theatre Royal Stratford East); *Starstruck* (Tricycle); *Lift Off*, *Clubland*, *Fall Out* (Royal Court); *Local Boy* (Hampstead); *The Gift* (Birmingham Rep); *Souls* (Theatre Centre); *Night and Day* (Theatre Venture); *Josie's Boys* (Red Ladder); and *Days of Significance* (RSC). His plays for television include *Offside*, *Bredrens* and *Babyfather* (BBC); and for radio, *Homeboys* and *Tell Tale* (BBC). He received the John Whiting Award and the Alfred Fagon Award in 1997 and an EMMA award in 1999 for *Starstruck*; the George Devine Award in 2000 for *Lift Off; the Evening Standard* Charles Wintour Award for Most Promising Playwright in 2001 for *Clubland*; and the BAFTA Award for Best Schools Drama in 2002 for *Offside*.

Author's Note

This play is for my mother, Gloria Williams, and all other single mums, everywhere. You guys are the best.

To the Kelles, Nathans and Richies of this world: I honestly believe you belong to the best generation this country has ever seen. There is so much you can learn, and more that you can teach. Know what you are worth, go get what you are worth. You are loved.

ROY WILLIAMS

Characters

Samantha (Sam)
twenty-six

Kelle
thirteen

Danielle
thirteen

Nathan
thirteen

Yvette
eighteen

Richie
eighteen

Josie
seventeen

Setting

Various locations

APRIL

Sam enters, hovering, singing along to 'Hung Up' by Madonna which is coming from the radio. Kelle, her daughter, enters, wearing an extremely short skirt. Sam turns the radio off.

Kelle Yeah, what?
Sam I don't think so, somehow.
Kelle Oh Mum!
Sam No, no, no.
Kelle What?
Sam Don't you 'Mum' me.
Kelle Oh sorry, Sam!
Sam Oy!
Kelle Well, which one is it, Mum or Sam?
Sam Kelle?
Kelle What?
Sam I'm not playing.
Kelle At what, Sam . . . I mean Mum?
Sam You winding me up.

Kelle sighs.

I know all of the tricks, yeah. I did it with your gran.
Kelle Is it?
Sam Yes it is. And do you know what? I was better.
Kelle Do I look like I'm playing any tricks?
Sam Yes you are.
Kelle All I want to do is wear my skirt.
Sam No way.
Kelle Ain't that short.
Sam You sure?!

Kelle Yes.

Sam Lie bad. Look at it, it's a belt. You want every boy round here come at you like dog?

Kelle Do already.

Sam Well, they're pervs, man.

Kelle Deh boys.

Sam I am talking about the older ones.

Kelle Yeah well, they're pervs.

Sam That is what I just said. I see no reason at all in putting it on a plate for them. Wear your longer one.

Kelle Are you deliberately trying to shame me?

Sam Stop yer whining.

Kelle You used to wear skirts like this.

Sam Who told you that?

Kelle Gran.

Sam Yer gran has an enormous mouth.

Kelle You turned out alright.

Sam Not at first. When I was thirteen, I was standing right where you are, sweetheart, listening to yer gran, giving me a hard time about the way I dress, and I was handing her the same look you're giving me now. Did I listen, did I fuck!

Kelle You did actually see me, standing here?

Kelle giggles. Sam cannot help but smile a little herself. She knows she shouldn't.

Kelle Yu nasty gal, yu!

Sam (*trying hard not to laugh*) Kelle!

Kelle Dass yu dat! Nasty, dirty gal!

Sam Stop it.

Kelle So, who yu on wid it now?

Sam No.

Kelle Come, gal. Come on!

Sam (*gives in*) Sean, from *EastEnders*!

Kelle Oh!

Sam You know!

8

Kelle Yes!

Sam Dat bwoi is . . .

Kelle Fine!

Sam That bwoi is mine.

Kelle Oy, oy . . .

Sam/Kelle . . . buff bwoi!

Kelle We're waiting fer yu.

Sam Never mind Walford, son.

Kelle Cross that river now.

Sam Get that fine arse over here.

Kelle At once.

Sam Believe.

Kelle My mum loves you up.

Sam Mad up.

Kelle Completely!

Sam Seriously!

Kelle She's all wet for yer.

Sam Hey!

Kelle What?

Sam What! What you mean, what?

Kelle Just messing.

Sam Crossing the line, Kelle.

Kelle Chill out, man.

Sam Chill out, Mum.

Kelle Sorry. I thought we were having a laugh.

Sam It's enough.

Kelle Why you have to spoil it?

Sam Kelle!

Kelle You love to spoil it.

Sam Do as yer told for once.

Kelle I don't know why you love to feel guilty, Mum. Mum?

Sam What?

Kelle Don't fix up yer face like that. Makes you look ugly.

Sam Less of it.

Kelle Fix up yer face then.

Sam Christ!

Kelle You need to learn how to chill. Oh, Mummy. (*Gives her a hug.*)

Sam Oh, Mummy now, is it?

Kelle We're alright. Aren't we?

Sam Course.

Kelle You love me?

Sam It's disgusting how much I love you. My sweet little girl.

Kelle If I'm so sweet, you gonna let me wear the skirt then?

Sam sighs.

All the other girls are wearing skirts like these. You want me stand out?

Sam Quite the opposite.

Kelle So let me.

Sam Let me think about it.

Kelle That means yes, cheers.

Sam I've thought about it, that means no.

Kelle That couldn't be more funny if you tried, you know.

Sam Is it?

Kelle Hate you.

Sam And I love you.

Kelle You think I don't know?

Sam No.

Kelle I know.

Sam What do you know?

Kelle You want it for yourself.

Sam Step!

Kelle Auntie Gina's hen night is coming up, you want teif it, stay out all night, get pissed on vodka straights, and sex up man.

Sam You're crossing the line again, Kelle.

Kelle It's what you do.

Sam Not no more. When was the last time I ever done that?

Kelle You're nicking my clothes, though.

Sam Bwoi!

Kelle Don't know why. Nothing of mine looks good on you. This skirt won't look good on you.

Sam I'm not after your bloody skirt.

Kelle You ain't got the legs for it anyhow.

Sam (*offended*) Say what?

Kelle You deaf?

Sam Excuse me, Miss Big Mouth, But I happen to have great legs, better than yours.

Kelle Whatever.

Sam No whatever about it. (*Pulls up her skirt, rubs her leg.*) Feel that, *smooth*.

Kelle (*rubs her own leg*) Smoother. *Smoother.*

Sam Lickle child.

Kelle Come then.

Sam Come then what?

Kelle I come wid you to Auntie Gina's hen night, dress up, then we'll find out who man loves up most, me or you. And I bet it's me. You see, you were fine in your day, Mother, but yer time is passing, time to make way for the young.

Sam Young? First off, I'm twenty-six.

Kelle Yes, old.

Sam Second, you hanging out with me and Gina is never going to happen. Third, and most important, even if you did come out with us, when I get going wid man, you won't stand a chance against me. I've seen man start wars to get to me. So why don't you just jog on before I pin yer.

Kelle Gal love herself.

Sam It's a simple fact.

Kelle You talk the talk.

Sam I walk the walk.

Kelle Is it?

Sam Believe . . . (*Realises what she is doing.*)

Kelle What? (*Sucks her teeth.*) What?

Sam I'm doing it again.

Kelle Don't pussy out now.

Sam Why am I so stupid?

Kelle You ain't stupid.

Sam What am I doing?

Kelle Hanging out wid me.

Sam This chat is over, young lady. I'm not playing any
more.

Kelle Mum?

Sam Stop it, Kelle.

Kelle Why?

Sam I'm not one of yer mates.

Kelle You'd make a brilliant mate – I wish you were my
mate.

Sam Well, I'm not, darling.

Kelle I could tell you things.

Sam Anyone can be yer mate, sweetness, only I can be
yer mother.

Kelle Well, stop teifing my clothes and make up then.

Sam I wasn't . . . alright, I was.

Kelle (*smug*) You see!

Sam You'd give aspirin a headache.

Kelle Gimme what I want.

Sam Oooh! Alright!

Kelle Nice.

Sam Wear the bloody skirt.

Kelle Cheers, Mum.

Sam I'll never get used to it.

Kelle You know what it's like, you remember what it was
like.

Sam Look at you.

Kelle Why? Do I have a spot?

Sam No, precious.

Kelle Don't lie to me, shit, man.

Sam You haven't got a bloody spot! Shut up for a minute, I'm trying to tell you something. Listen to me. Kelle?

Kelle What?

Sam You're changing. Right before my eyes. You've got bigger tits than me.

Kelle (*brags*) I know. Shame.

Sam You were such a beautiful little baby.

Kelle Oh, man.

Sam I wish I could have kept you like that for ever.

Kelle I'm fine. We're fine. Whatever happens.

Sam Nothing is going to happen. Understood?

Kelle Yeah, yeah.

Sam You hearing me?

Kelle I'll be alright.

Sam Right.

Kelle I think I'm pregnant, Mum. I know I am.

Sam How do you know?

Kelle Done the test, course!

Sam Don't get lippy.

Kelle Ain't.

Sam Pregnant?

Kelle Yep.

Sam You?

Kelle Duh!

Sam Well, that is just fucking lovely, ain't it, Kelle?

MAY

A park bench. Kelle enters with her best friend Danielle, who is pushing a pram.

Danielle (*shouting to someone offstage*) Will you leave her alone, Leon? Don't make me come over deh and slap you, yeah? Little shit.

Kelle Easy girl.

Danielle Got too much to say for himself.

Kelle He's only eight.

Danielle Deh the worst ones.

Kelle Nuff times Mum wanted to kill me when I was eight.

Danielle Come like his dad, Leon.

Kelle He ain't nuttin like Cameron.

Danielle Glad to hear it, Cameron's baby father to this one – (*Points to pram.*) – not him.

Kelle I thought this one was Glen wassisname.

Danielle Glen wassisname? Mum wouldn't touch Glen wassisname Would you touch Glen wassisname?

Kelle No!

Danielle Besides, yer thinking Ben, but it ain't Ben either.

Kelle I thought yer mum grind him.

Danielle Course she grind him. Probably grinding him now. But when she thought she was, she wasn't. False alarm.

Kelle So, whose that one?

Danielle Dan!

Kelle And that one?

Danielle Ian!

Kelle Right.

Danielle Get it?

Kelle No offence, Danielle, but yer mum's had nuff men!

Danielle She's a ho, ennit?

Kelle Can't say that.

Danielle Just did. I got half-siblings spread out, man, so like you say, nuff men!

Kelle Speaking of which, how's yer own man?

Danielle What, Richie? (*Smiles.*) Yeah, he's alright.

Kelle Ain't dash him yet?

Danielle No, but almost.

Kelle Oh yes?

Danielle Forgot my birthday the other week.

Kelle Shame.

Danielle He tried to make it up to me by taking me out to Nando's. I goes, alright, you carry on. Afterwards, when my mum was out, he wants to go upstairs, you get me? I poured cold water over that dream. We made up for it the night after, though. As soon as I showed him where it was, though.

Kelle He didn't know?

Danielle Not at first.

Kelle Soff.

Danielle Oh leave him, man, he's sweet. He's my little teddy. Whenever I think about him, I just want to eat him. You know?

Kelle He's a man, though, he should know where it is.

Danielle Not all man though. They love to talk big, that's their problem. Mind you, it was in the back of his car at the time.

Kelle Car? Richie have car?

Danielle That's what I said.

Kelle How can he afford to have a car?

Danielle Ca' him work.

Kelle Where?

Danielle Morrison's. Leon! You see my fist! See, I ain't at all like you, Kelle, I don't for boys, cos none of them would know where to put it, guaranteed. Least wid a man, you get double the chance.

Kelle So eighteen make a boy man?

Danielle Of course.

Kelle You don't think it's disgusting?

Danielle No. Who tell you it was?

Kelle Mum – that's when she weren't flinging herself at me, calling me all sorts.

15

Danielle Well, she can chat – how old was she when she
  had you?

Kelle Exactly.

Danielle Deh you go.

Kelle That's why she was flinging herself at me.

Danielle (*clenches her fist*) Thin ice, Leon, no joke!

Kelle Going on about I'm wasting my life, blah, blah,
  blah! Just like she did. Like she hates me or summin –
  I mean, how am I supposed to react to that?

Danielle Yer so lucky.

Kelle How so?

Danielle Having a baby, summin to cuddle, they are so
  nice to cuddle. So soft.

Kelle (*going along with it*) Yeah!

Danielle Ain't good when they grow up to be like these
  lot, you know. I'm gonna kill that Leon. Ugly little
  runt. Ain't never gonna be a mum. Sorry.

Kelle 'S'right.

Danielle I'd only be a mum if they stay little. Stay like
  babies, nice and soft.

Kelle Yeah, believe.

Danielle You know what this means?

Kelle What?

Danielle Can tell that Jasmine to step off now. Always
  calling you virgin.

Kelle I know, I can hear her.

Danielle Many times I came close to bussing her head for
  you.

Kelle Bitch ain't worth it.

Danielle Bitch is worth it. Calling you virgin.

Kelle Well, I was.

Danielle Ain't the point. She got too much to say for
  herself, always have. I bet she was a virgin – I mean,
  who would touch that, honestly? She is so hard up to
  be sexed, yeah, you know who I saw her chatting to in
  the playground, making moves and shit?

Kelle Tell me.

Danielle Nathan, Richie's brother.

Kelle (*disgusted*) Oh no!

Danielle Can you imagine?

Kelle Seriously?

Danielle For trut.

Kelle No!

Danielle The shame of it.

Kelle Nathan.

Danielle Total.

Kelle Well, I suppose someone has to.

Danielle Desperation.

Kelle Incarceration.

Danielle I don't think I've ever in my days seen a boy as broc as that. I don't know how him and Richie wound up as brothers.

Kelle Butters.

Danielle Why don't you tell Jasmine on Monday? Tell everybody?

Kelle I can't.

Danielle Why not?

Kelle It's my business, Danielle.

Danielle Yeah, but yer gonna get nuff perks at school. Time off when you want it, teachers making a fuss, no more PE, you lucky sket! You had better not forget me, Kelle, telling you.

Kelle What do you mean?

Danielle You know when yer feeling sick and that. Tell the teacher you want to go home, and you want me to take you. I'll have afternoons off.

Kelle What if I'm really sick?

Danielle Then I'll take you home ennit? But you had better be really, really sick.

Kelle As oppose to just sick?

Danielle What you saying, man? I don't get it.

Kelle Nuttin, don't matter.

Danielle I can't wait to catch the look on Jasmine's face, man.

Kelle I don't know if I'm telling anyone, Danielle.

Danielle Oh come on, man, it'll be funny.

Kelle Mum don't want me to.

Danielle Yer mum needs to chill, quick style!

Kelle Look on her face, man, she hated me.

Danielle Stop worrying. You got me.

Kelle For ever and ever?

Danielle Believe!

Kelle Good.

Danielle Still so lucky. You know I ain't asked, yeah?

Kelle About what?

Danielle Who the baby father is?

Kelle Oh, right?

Danielle Well?

Kelle Well what?

Danielle Who?

Kelle Thought you weren't gonna ask me.

Danielle I knew I weren't gonna ask you, cos I knew you were gonna tell me, so I wouldn't need to ask you, but since we've been sitting out here all afternoon, and you still haven't told me, even knowing I was never gonna ask you, which is kind of shitty by the way if you don't mind me saying, so now, after waiting for you to tell me, ca' I'm getting bored, and I'm dying to know, I have to ask you.

Kelle Ask me what?

Danielle Yer not funny, Kelle.

Kelle No one you know.

Danielle Bet it is.

Kelle Bet it ain't.

Danielle Is it someone in our class?

Kelle No.

Danielle Someone in our school?

Kelle No.

Danielle Alright, don't tell who it is, tell me who it ain't.

Kelle That's the same thing, Danielle.

Danielle Ain't.

Kelle Don't worry yerself.

Danielle Too late. You might as well.

Kelle I ain't even told Mum, she'll go mad.

Danielle Yer mum is always mad, no offence. Kelle?

Kelle No.

Danielle Kelle?

Kelle Stop bugging me.

Danielle Who am I going to tell?

Kelle Everybody.

Danielle Excuse?

Kelle Yer mout is as big as a car, girl.

Danielle Hey, it's you for me, me for you, you forget?

Kelle No.

Danielle Coulda fooled me. (*Looks.*) Where is that little fool now? Hey, Leon, where I ca' see you, yeah? What? Awright, you see what happen when you get grab up by some paedo, don't come running to me. I'll tell Mum, then she'll beat you, go beat you senseless! What are you crying for? I ain't coming to you. Go stand there and cry for all I care, you little girl.

Kelle It was just a boy, Danielle.

Danielle At our school?

Kelle No!

Danielle Another school.

Kelle Yeah

Danielle Which one.

Kelle It's miles away.

Danielle Which one, girl?

Kelle Isaac Newton.

Danielle Thank you.

Kelle Happy now?

Danielle How you get a boy from there?

Kelle Remember when they came to our school, to play football?

Danielle Oh yeah, oh yes! I know who it is now

Kelle (*getting worried*) You do?

Danielle Of course. The pretty one, the goalkeeper. He loved you up, trying to get yer digits all day. It was him? Thought you didn't like him.

Kelle Course I liked him.

Danielle Obviously. He looked like Ashley Cole, ennit?

Kelle Yeah.

Danielle Which is weird ca' he was the goalkeeper, and Ashley Cole don't play in goal. Still looked like him, though. Oh, Kelle, yer so lucky.

Kelle Will you stop saying that?

Danielle But if he looks like Ashley Cole, then there's you, yer baby's gonna be so pretty. Prettiest baby in the whole world! Oh, let me hold her first, please!

Kelle Alright.

Danielle You promise?

Kelle I promise.

Danielle Yes!

Kelle Why don't you have it?

Danielle If it's a girl, yeah, and if she's as pretty as I think she will be, you better believe I'm having it. I'm running outta the hospital wid it, never see me again. I ain't lying!

Kelle Mad!

Danielle Or I'll make Richie get me pregnant.

Kelle I got pregnant first, don't copy me.

Danielle Richie don't look like Ashley Cole, but he's half-decent – we'll have a nice baby, but it won't be as pretty as yours, so relax.

Kelle But it'll just be . . .

Danielle What?

Kelle Too weird.

Danielle Us two, pushing buggies?

Kelle Yeah?

Danielle Gonna have to do it sometime.

Kelle Says who?

Danielle Says everybody. You act like you don't want it.

Kelle I don't know anything, dread.

Danielle You for me.

Kelle Me for you.

Danielle See, that's one thing you know.

Kelle We stay true?

Danielle Course.

Kelle No matter what happens? What we say?

Danielle For real, Kelle – now will you please chill?
   (*Giggles.*) Ashley Cole?

Kelle You won't tell no one, yeah?

Danielle Fingers on lips. I have to say, I can't believe how
   smart I am.

Kelle How so?

Danielle I knew it was a boy. Even before you told me.

Kelle How could you possibly know for sure?

Danielle Ca' if it was a man, you wouldn't get pregnant.

Kelle Explain?

Danielle Where is the boy going to get the thing from?

Kelle What's a thing?

Danielle See, even you don't know.

Kelle Don't laugh.

Danielle Everyone knows, Kelle.

Kelle So tell me.

Danielle What they have to put on ennit, the condom.
   Boy can't buy them, not allowed.

Kelle He coulda nicked it.

Danielle Yeah, but he didn't use it, Kelle, cos he's a boy.

Kelle He didn't want to wear one, he said. He hated
   them.

Danielle Yep, boy!

Kelle Girls don't get pregnant when it's their first time he said.

Danielle Boy! And a stupid one at that. Richie would be howling if he was here.

Kelle Oh, you think so, do yer?

Danielle I know so.

Kelle Me as well.

Danielle Me as well what?

Kelle That you know yer smart, girl.

Danielle Believe. But thank you.

Kelle You for me.

Danielle Me for you. We done that, you crazy bitch.

Kelle I know, I just like to hear it.

Danielle That's it now, yer mind's gone. Come like my mum, her hormones going all mad and shit. Talking rubbish, eating weird food, that's gonna be you. It's getting cold – you done?

Kelle I'm done.

Danielle (*calling the kids*) Alright, come, you lot, it's home. If Mum thinks I'm cooking again, she's making a sad mistake. *X-Factor* is on! See the one last week, the guy who can't sing?

Kelle None of them can sing.

Danielle He was the worst, so funny!

Kelle Yeah, I'm up for that.

Danielle It's funny.

Kelle What now?

Danielle I always thought it woulda bin me who got pregnant first.

Kelle Don't say I'm lucky, yeah.

Danielle Alright, I won't, but you should be happy at least!

Kelle Why you?

Danielle Man love me up, ennit, can't help that. You seen the way they hang around the school gates for us,

every day, what are we supposed to do, ignore the way they look? Even the male teachers are doing it, they think we don't know, but we know. And they know we know, they like it. Mr Bannister is always leaning over, looking down.

Kelle He's a right grandpa, though.

Danielle So? He's still a man. The way you were carrying on, I thought it mighta been a teacher who got you pregnant or summin.

Kelle All the man teachers in our school are ugly, Danielle.

Danielle I know – point?

Kelle Well, how could you think . . . errgh! As if!

Danielle What about Mr Richards.

Kelle Except him.

Danielle Don't you think he looks like Justin from *Hollyoaks*?

Kelle (*suddenly realising*) Yeah!

Danielle No, he can look down me, I'll 'low dat.

Kelle Every girl in school will 'low dat!

They laugh.

Danielle Oh, so you found yer happy face at last, keep it there. (*Shouts.*) Leon? What you standing there for? Bring dem!

Kelle You think he's deaf?

Danielle He will be.

Kelle Seriously.

Danielle Ain't bothered, seriously. Hey, it's gonna be alright. you know.

Kelle Tell my mum.

Danielle I will. Ashley Cole!

Kelle I'm lucky!

Danielle Nuff benefits now.

JUNE

Nathan's living room. Kelle enters, followed by Nathan.

Nathan Hey!

Kelle What?

Nathan Feet. (*Kelle moves one foot.*) Kelle?

Kelle Yeah?

Nathan Move yer feet off the coffee table.

Kelle Awright, ease up. I'd thought you'd be glad to see me. Aren't you glad to see me? Bye den.

Nathan I am glad to see you.

Kelle Good boy. (*Giggles.*)

Kelle puts her feet up on the table again.

Nathan You have to put yer feet up?

Kelle Yes.

Nathan Careful.

Kelle What is it?

Nathan An ornament, one of Mum's, put it back.

Kelle Alright.

Nathan Is that where you found it?

Kelle Yeah, I think. You tell me, dread. Wass the problem?

Nathan She don't like anyone touching her things. Do you have to pick up everything?

Kelle I don't see yer mum here. Maybe we should wait for her.

Nathan Are you seriously mad?

Kelle You don't want her to know she's going to be a grandmother?

Nathan Never.

Kelle Don't make me buss yer head, yeah.

Nathan (*giggles*) Come on then.

Kelle Don't laugh at me.

Nathan Or what?

Kelle I will buss yer head.

Nathan In your condition?

Kelle It's only three months.

Nathan Can you feel it?

Kelle Moving? Yeah, starting to. Mum said she couldn't feel me at all – she got worried, thought I was dead or summin.

Nathan Shouldn't say that.

Kelle Ease up. Like you care.

Nathan I do care.

Kelle So?

Nathan Yer stupid.

Kelle I'm stupid?

Nathan You said it wouldn't happen.

Kelle How was I to know?

Nathan Well, it ain't my fault.

Kelle Don't start acting the big man, Nathan! Yer lucky I gave you the time of day. You know what the girls say about you in school? That yer broc, yer butters, yer ugly as sin. You smell like old people!

Nathan So, why did you come to me for?

Kelle Ca' I ain't no virgin! You were the first that come along, it coulda bin any boy. If I only waited five minutes, it woulda bin Richie.

Nathan You as well. Every girl in that school wants to sex Richie.

Kelle Cos he's *fine*.

Nathan And I ain't.

Kelle Believe!

Nathan You musta liked me.

Kelle No.

Nathan To do it.

Kelle I said no.

Nathan What is so wrong about me?

Kelle You smell like old people.

Nathan I do not smell like old people.

Kelle You gonna cry?

Nathan No.

Kelle Soff.

Nathan You don't think I'm nice?

Kelle No.

Nathan Not even a little?

Kelle No, no, no.

Nathan I ain't told anyone.

Kelle You better not have.

Nathan That's nice, me not saying anything. I coulda told nuff people.

Kelle Then you'd be dead.

Nathan You would have to catch me, you and yer big belly.

Kelle (*chuckles at the thought*) I'd catch yer.

Nathan See!

Kelle See what, you fool?

Nathan Yer smiling! I made you laugh.

Kelle So?

Nathan Well, that's a nice thing as well, ennit?

Kelle Alright Nathan, yer nice.

Nathan I remember when you first said it to me.

Kelle I've never said it to you.

Nathan Yes you did.

Kelle Well, don't keep me hanging, man – when?

Nathan When we were in Year Five, you were eating yer packed lunch, yer dropped yer apple, it rolled on the floor, I picked it up for you – you said I was nice.

Kelle bursts out laughing.

Nathan What? Don't laugh.

Kelle That was it?

Nathan Yeah, you made me feel really happy.

Kelle Sorry, Nathan, but I don't remember that.

Nathan Well, I do. I always thought you were nice, Kelle.

Kelle Yes, Nathan, whatever.

Nathan I'm serious.

Kelle Whatever.

Nathan I hated the way them older boys would always look at you, and say things about yer skirt as you come out of school. Always making moves.

Kelle Yer brother Richie does it.

Nathan I ain't my brother.

Kelle Believe!

Nathan Don't do that.

Kelle I'm teasing.

Nathan I'm telling you something! I felt sorry for yer, for all yer.

Kelle You felt sorry for us?

Nathan Yes.

Kelle And you call yerself a man?

Nathan It was like, you were too nice for that.

Kelle Yer too soft.

Nathan Fine, I don't care.

Kelle Don't tell me you love me, Nathan.

Nathan I wasn't going to.

Kelle Good. Cos I will just laugh in your face. What you think this is?

Nathan If you hate me so much, yeah . . .

Kelle Did I say I hated you?

Nathan Why you here, why you telling me?

Kelle I don't hate you. You think I'd be afraid to say it, if that is how I felt? I ain't afraid of you, I ain't afraid of no one. So shut yer noise.

Nathan Alright.

Kelle You had a right to know, that's it, okay?

Nathan Coulda lied. You didn't have to come here.

Kelle So, why am I here then, genius?

Nathan You tell me.

Kelle You think I'm into you, is that what your stupid mashed up brain thinks? Oh my daze, you do, ennit? Nathan!

Nathan I'm just asking a question.

Kelle Listen, yeah, listen carefully. It was just sex.

Nathan Alright.

Kelle Eejit!

Nathan Don't matter anyhow.

Kelle Good. I know it don't matter, that's alright then.

Nathan If Mum finds out, she won't want me have anything to do with it.

Kelle Mums always chats, deh mums.

Nathan Yeah, but she'll go mad. You shoulda seen the look on her face when Richie tell her he got another girl pregnant.

Kelle At the end of the day, it don't matter what she says, don't you think?

Nathan It does to her.

Kelle Yer the father, ennit.

Nathan It's unreal when you say it like that. Scary and shit.

Kelle What do you want to do?

Nathan I thought you didn't like me.

Kelle Look at my face, Nathan. I know it's fucking scary. You think it's just you? Well it ain't. It was an orange.

Nathan What?

Kelle You picked my orange, not an apple. I don't like apples.

Nathan I knew you remembered

Kelle Probably why I chose you. I knew you wouldn't tell.

Nathan Thought you wanted Jasmine and them to know yer not a virgin.

Kelle I want them to know I'm not a virgin, but I don't want them to know who did it to me.

Nathan Oh, right.

Kelle Stupid.

Nathan I ain't stupid.

Kelle Sound it.

Nathan I'm scared, man

Kelle You already said that, now move on.

Nathan I'm thirteen, man, that's weird.

Kelle What do you want to do, Nathan?

Nathan I don't know.

Kelle Look at me.

Nathan I'm not supposed to know, am I? Be honest. Cos I'm Nathan, who smells like old people. The ugly one. What am I supposed to know about anything, Kelle?

Kelle I said look at me.

Kelle takes Nathan's hand and places it on her belly, so that he can feel the baby.

Nathan No.

Kelle Keep yer hand there.

Nathan I can't! (*Pulls his hand away.*)

Kelle Soff!

Nathan I ain't like you, Kelle.

Kelle What you know about me? You don't know nuttin about me.

Nathan Shoulda got rid of it.

Kelle You want die?

Nathan I wanna go college and shit. It's what me mum says.

Kelle Yer mum's a ho. She should learn to keep her nose out.

Nathan Kelle?

Kelle Yer soff, Nathan.

Kelle tries to go. Nathan blocks her path.

Kelle Step outta the way.

Nathan No.

Kelle Move.

Nathan places his hand on her belly.

Kelle Don't touch me.

Nathan I can't feel nuttin.

Kelle What, you don't think it's in there? It's in there, Nathan, trust.

Nathan Boy or girl?

Kelle I don't bloody know! What – you want go inside, have a look? You can't tell yet.

Nathan I know you don't know.

Kelle So, why ask?

Nathan What do you *think* it will be, a boy or a girl, that's what I meant.

Kelle Oh!

Nathan Jesus!

Kelle A girl. I want a pretty baby girl. I want to call her Lady Sovereign.

Nathan No you ain't.

Kelle Excuse?

Nathan That's a shit name.

Kelle You want die? What you want, I bet it's Jordan, or summin?

Nathan 'S right.

Kelle Oh, so you do wanna die.

Nathan Better than Sovereign.

Kelle Lady Sovereign, you deaf? Besides, ain't even up to you.

Nathan It is.

Kelle I juss want yer dough.

Nathan Dough?

Kelle I gotta buy a buggy, nappies, dummies and shit, the whole shebang. Gonna go mad in Mothercare.

Nathan (*getting really worried*) Is it?

Kelle Believe.

Nathan Oh, shit.

Kelle Yes, Nathan, shit.

Nathan Wish I was dreaming.

Kelle I bet. Me as well.

Nathan But I was saving up to buy an iPod.

Kelle Aw!

Nathan Why don't you get rid of it?

Kelle Ca' it's mine, and I wanna love it!

Nathan I don't. I don't, Kelle. I don't want it.

Kelle Like I say, it ain't up to you. Ugly little runt.

Nathan You said I was nice.

Kelle I changed my mind. Anyhow my baby is as butters as you, I'm gonna throw it at you.

Nathan Don't care.

Kelle You will care. Cos my baby will be beautiful just like me, and I'm gonna hug it every day!

Nathan What about me, I might wanna hug it?

Kelle You just told me a second ago to get rid of it, you ain't hugging shit.

Nathan Kelle?

Kelle You said.

Nathan Yeah, but if you have it, I still wanna hug it.

Kelle Juss pass yer dough to me every month.

Nathan Ain't fair.

Kelle Life's a bitch. Don't make me call CSA, Nathan.

Nathan I'm too young.

Kelle Yer mum and dad ain't.

Nathan This ain't funny, Kelle.

Kelle Oh shut up. Look at my face, you fool. I was joking.

Nathan Seriously?

Kelle You should know me by now. Don't want yer money. I just wanted you to know.

Nathan Shouldn't say that.

Kelle Seriously though, you wanna hug it?

Nathan Yeah, if you don't want get rid of it.

Kelle I don't.

Nathan Don't you want go college?

Kelle Yeah.
Nathan With a baby?
Kelle (*unsure*) Yeah.
Nathan What are we doing, man?
Kelle I don't bloody know. Shut up!
Nathan Call me, yeah? Come see me.
Kelle You love to think I do.
Nathan Because you do.
Kelle Whatever.

JULY

Yvette and Richie are standing by one of the doors. Loud garage music coming from inside.

Yvette Yu owe me money. Ninety squid ought to do it.

Richie laughs.

Yu think this is joke, Richie?
Richie What have I done?
Yvette Yu got no brains, ennit?
Richie What have I done? Juss tell me please.
Yvette Yu had a visit from the police, or I should say I did. Six in the morning, right. Me and Chantelle wake up to their breaking down the door. What you laughing at? Boy, you best tek that smile right off yer face.
Richie Or what?
Yvette Oh, you think you can play me again?

Baby cries.

Is that what your wurtless tiny little brain really thinks?
Richie Chantelle's crying.
Yvette I got ears.

Richie Well, feed her or summin then.

Yvette Never mind her, don't worry yerself about her. My front door is missing.

Richie What am I supposed to do?

Yvette Hundred pound please.

Richie Where am I suppose to get that?

Yvette I don't care.

Richie Well, you best wait.

Yvette How much you have in yer pockets?

Richie I ain't got no money, man.

Yvette Empty yer pockets.

Richie Get off.

Yvette Don't play bad man wid me, Richie.

Richie Yu think yer so bad cos you got yer big bad army brother living wid you now.

Yvette Just be thankful it ain't him standing here right now.

Richie I took him once.

Yvette Oh yes?

Richie I'll take him again.

Yvette You're such a big man, Richie.

Richie Believe.

Yvette It was a lucky punch. Don't let it go to your head, you fool.

Richie I still remember how tings were before him. Do you?

Yvette I said empty yer pockets.

Richie (*turns out a twenty*) Twenty, thass all.

Yvette Bare money.

Snatches it.

Richie Hey!

Yvette Now you owe me eighty.

Richie Thass all I got.

Yvette Yu best go tief some more then.

Richie Come outta my range, you don't know nuttin about me. I was doing some jobs with my Uncle Sean, decorating.

Yvette Did I ask for yer life story?

Richie Will you bloody feed her, please?

Yvette Yu do it. Yer the baby father. She always shuts up when you do it.

Richie feeds his daughter.

Richie She's getting big.

Yvette Believe. Yer good wid her.

Richie Shut up.

Yvette All she does is scream, she loves to scream. Not that you would know.

Richie Alright.

Yvette Mister Part-Time Dad.

Richie You done?

Yvette Gimme a fifty.

Richie I ain't got a fifty. I told you, I'm brassic.

Yvette You had better not be giving any to that Debbie bitch.

Richie No.

Yvette I don't care what she says, that kid ain't yours. Too ugly to be yours.

Richie I ain't seeing her.

Yvette So what you steal now?

Richie Nuttin.

Yvette So they kick down my door for the fun of it. Yer lucky I didn't tell them where yer living now. Maybe I should.

Richie Sorry.

Yvette Excuse me.

Richie Sorry, right?

Yvette One more time?

Richie Alright you know what, you can step.

Yvette Yu had me worried there, for a minute I thought you said sorry.

Richie Fuck it then.

Yvette Too late, you already said it. Apology accepted.

Richie Well, now I'm taking it back, yeah.

Yvette For you to take back, I would have to give.

Richie Juss gwan.

Yvette Did you ever spend a day at school?

Richie Yes.

Yvette I meant in school, Richie, not hanging round school gates, chasing young yats in short skirts.

Richie You were the finest youngest yat with the shortest skirt in that school.

Yvette Don't start.

Richie It's true.

Yvette All I wanted was some fun.

Richie We had fun.

Yvette Fun ended when the words 'Condom's split' left yer lips. (*Points at baby.*) Now look.

Richie Ain't my fault.

Yvette Is it mine?

Richie Bored now, go.

Yvette I'll gwan, when I feel like gwan.

They both want to laugh, but do not.

So, who are you seeing now?

Richie No one.

Yvette Don't lie. How old is she? You better watch yerself, Richie.

Richie I am watching myself.

Yvette You're gonna land yourself in it.

Richie What am I, a paedophile?

Yvette Technically, you are.

Richie No I'm not, I see them on tele, they're nothing but dirty, fat old men. Does that look like me? Don't think so!

Yvette You are so thick it's untrue.

Richie She's a woman if you must know.

Yvette You, going out wid a woman?

Richie Yes, problem?

Yvette She blind?

Richie She's beautiful.

Yvette Sounds like yer loved up.

Richie Maybe I am. Yeah.

Yvette She love you?

Richie Dunno.

Yvette You dunno? You telling me you ain't asked it, yet? (*Roars with laughter.*) Well, what is this world coming to? Richie don't know, Richie too scared to ask!

Richie Fuck off, man.

Yvette You come like yer brother.

Richie I'm waiting.

Yvette Yer waiting?

Richie Yes, cos some yats are worth the wait.

Yvette Oh, so she's a yat now, not a woman.

Richie I meant woman.

Yvette I know only too well what you meant.

Richie No you don't, cos, as usual, Yvette, you love to run yer mouth off. Kelly Holmes couldn't keep up wid yer mouth.

Yvette Bullshit, Richie.

Richie Bullshit what?

Yvette Bullshit you. Bullshit about you chatting about love. Bullshit.

Richie Jealous, Yvette?

Yvette Richie, she can do whatever to yer, you understand, cos I ain't bothered. Gimme back my baby.

Richie My baby as well.

Yvette I could throw a stone and hit a better daddy than you.

Richie You see, you think yer funny, Yvette, but you ain't.

Yvette Who said I'm joking?

Richie You're boring me, time to leave.

Yvette With pleasure.

Richie So hurry up.

Yvette Bitch!

Richie Ho!

Yvette Dawg!

Richie Sket!

Yvette You ain't got no woman.

Richie Whatever you got, don't care.

Yvette You wouldn't know what to do with a woman.

Richie Look at my face, ain't bothered!

Yvette You best fix up.

Yvette places the baby back in the buggy.

If the police come back, I'm telling them where you live.

Yvette leaves. Richie waits a moment before ringing the front doorbell next door. No answer. He rings again, still no answer. Richie is about to give up when Josie (black, late teens) answers her door. Richie does not see his brother Nathan coming up the stairwell.

Richie Awright?

Josie Hello.

Richie I was about to go.

Josie I was on the phone. Yu want the keys, right?

Richie Right.

Josie goes inside.

Nathan Oh come on, Richie.

Richie Go play wid traffic.

Josie returns.

Josie There you are.

Richie Cheers.

Josie It's really good of you.

Richie No worries, we'll have it looking all nice.

Josie Yu can help yourself to tea and that.

Richie We will.

Josie I had better get back to my phone call. Thanks, Richie.

Richie Later.

Nathan (*mimics*) 'Thanks, Richie.'

Richie Hey little man, that's enough.

Nathan (*mimics*) Later!

Richie I know yer mouth is big, Nathan, but you have to show the whole world?

Nathan Richie man, you didn't check her face? She was going, 'Richie, if you don't start chripsin me soon, my pussy gonna catch fire.'

Richie What would you know about pussy? What would you ever know?

Nathan More than you think, bruv.

Richie You think I don't know what the kids at school say about you? (*Sniffs.*) They're right – you do smell like old people.

Nathan I don't.

Richie Take yer arse inside and have a wash, please!

Nathan Look. Stop telling me what to do.

Richie I will do what I like, when I like! What you up to tomorrow morning?

Nathan Sleeping.

Richie No yer not.

Nathan Yeah I am, it's Saturday.

Richie You can hang wid me. I'm decorating her room, you can help.

Nathan What I know about painting? What do you know, for that matter?

Richie How hard can it be? Up and down with a brush. Just like Uncle Sean taught us.

Nathan How much? (*Richie grunts.*) I ain't working my arse off for free.

Richie Fifteen.

Nathan Twenty-five.

Richie Shut up.

Nathan Twenty then.

Richie Twelve.

Nathan Yu said fifteen.

Richie Yu call yerself a hustler? Yes or no.

Nathan Alright.

Richie Out here at nine. Don't be late.

Josie comes out of her flat with a rubbish bag. She shoves it down the chute.

Nathan You know her name yet?

Richie Josie.

Nathan You ain't got a chance, bruv.

Richie Who ask you?

Nathan She's a woman.

Richie I got eyes.

Nathan You like girls.

Richie Well, maybe it's time I stopped fooling around with young girls and found myself a woman.

Nathan I bet you mess up.

Richie Excuse, but why am I even discussing this with you? What do you know about women and girls? Who was that yat I saw you with? How much did you have to pay her to even talk to you?

Nathan Didn't pay her.

Richie You telling me she's your girlfriend?

Nathan Yes.

Richie In your dreams.

Nathan She is!

Richie You wouldn't know what to do with her, you little freak!

Nathan I would know, I do know. I have!

Richie Excuse?

Nathan She's pregnant.

Richie You joke.

Nathan So, I do know what I'm doing.

Richie You the man!

Nathan Yeah!

Richie laughs.

Don't laugh.

Richie You stupid little spas.

Nathan Just like you, now.

Richie You ain't nuttin like me. What's Mum gonna say?

Nathan Don't tell her.

Richie You won't be her favourite any more.

Nathan I ain't her favourite.

Richie Coulda fooled me.

Nathan Don't tell her, Rich, alright?

Richie Wass it worth?

Nathan Watcha want?

Richie Guess?

Nathan My PlayStation 3.

Richie And?

Nathan All my games.

Richie And?

Nathan You ain't having my laptop. Oh come on, Rich?

Richie Yes, dog, beg, thass how I like it.

Nathan What else you want?

Richie That MP3 player you got should cover it.

Nathan Alright then.

Richie Well?

Nathan Well what?

Richie Go get 'em.

Nathan What are you gonna do with them?

Richie Don't worry yerself. Hey little man? Yer secret is safe with me, for now.

AUGUST

Sam is in her bedroom, getting ready for a night out.

Kelle Mum?

Sam Mum? Sorry, love, there's no mum here. Mum is having the night off. All that is left is Sam. Sam with the legs! That's what yer dad used to say. You don't mind if I wear your dress do yer? Course you don't, sis! It was way too sexy for you anyhow. I thought I told you to take it back, like you listen to a word I say. What am I, yer mum?! I'm glad you didn't take it back. It looks right on me, don't you think? It gives out just the right signal. I am a dam waiting to burst. Poor sod, whoever he is, won't know what's hit him, cos I feel like chicken tonight! You don't mind me talking like that? Course you don't – after all we're sisters! I'm really loving this, it's liberating, it's funny, I feel young again, bring it on! Borrowing your lip gloss, alright? I'll take you out next time, I promise. When you've dropped yer load. Then we'll find out who is the best at checking men. Course we already know, ca', gal, I'd wipe the floor wid you. I got plenty, I am stacked. Yer gran's babysitting, don't argue, done deal. Don't give her any lip. Listen to me, I sound like yer mother. Not when I walk through that door I won't. Sam is back! Lock up yer boys, mums! I shall be back, whenever.

Kelle Mummy?

Sam Oy, don't call me that. Stop calling me that. You make me sound old.

Kelle You are old.

Sam I am twenty-six, Kelle! Twenty-bloody-six, who's gonna be a grandmother! I gotta call *Guinness World of Records*. Do you have any idea how that feels? Any? Call me Mummy again, I'll knock you out.

Kelle My belly hurts.

Sam Of course it hurts, you're four months pregnant, you've got a little person growing inside of you. You think my belly didn't hurt? You were kicking me all the time – yes you, Kelle, you! Relentless or what? Kelle? What is it? (*Watches her cry.*) Yes! Setting in now, isn't it? Scary, isn't it? I tell you already.

Kelle I'm scared.

Sam Don't tell me that, you Kelle, don't you dare, don't you ruin up my night! I mean it.

Kelle Why do you hate me?

Sam I don't hate you. I don't like you sometimes, but I don't hate you.

Kelle Do you love me?

Sam It's disgusting how much.

Kelle Then help me.

Sam I am helping you. I've been helping you since you was born. See this roof, over our heads?

Kelle Put yer arm around me, then, come on. Give me a cuddle, tell me it's going to be alright.

Sam But it's not going to be alright, Kelle – ain't no point in me lying to yer.

Kelle You bitch!

Sam It's gonna be hell. Every day. No money, no life, just you and that. For ever!

Kelle You did alright.

Sam Yeah, and look at what I did? Turned you into me, you stupid little ho!

Kelle Mum!

Sam Oh, but it's alright for you to cuss me? Calling me bitch?

Kelle Tell me what to do.

Sam You got no brains.

Kelle Stop it.

Sam If you think I'm looking after it . . .

Kelle Ain't asking you to.

Sam Alone, Kelle, you will be all alone!

Kelle Why you so mean, you love it or summin?

Sam It's what happened to me. Yer dad, shitbag that he is, couldn't run fast enough. I ain't lying.

Kelle I don't want to be alone.

Sam Come here.

Kelle Oh, Mum!

Sam takes Kelle in her arms. For a moment, Kelle feels safe, until she can feel her hair being pulled backwards by Sam.

Kelle Mum, what you doing? That hurts!

Sam Who's the father, Kelle?

Kelle Stop it Mum.

Sam Tell me.

Kelle (*breaking free*) Get off me!

SEPTEMBER

Richie is on the landing with Josie.

Richie So, you like it, then? The wallpaper?

Josie I don't like it, I love it. I can't thank you enough.

Richie All part of the service.

Josie I'm hopeless at DIY, always have been.

Richie Just call me if you need anything else, shelves putting up?

Josie I will, you can count on it.

Richie Dass alright then.

Josie It really looks good.

Richie Told you.

Josie St Catherine's.

Richie What?

Josie St Catherine's School. You used to go there.

Richie Yes. You went St Catherine's? Don't remember you.

Josie Don't expect you to. You were a year above me. I was just an average little girl – pigtails, glasses.

Richie What happened to the glasses?

Josie Contacts, love.

Richie I don't remember you, you remember me.

Josie Yep.

Richie But I was a nobody too.

Josie Liar.

Richie What was that for?

Josie England versus Holland. Under-Fifteen game.

Richie Shit.

Josie Whole school came to watch you.

Richie Ain't thought about that in years.

Josie You scored three goals.

Richie Four.

Josie I kept expecting to read about you, back papers, playing for Arsenal or summin.

Richie Arsenal!

Josie What happened?

Richie Messed up my knee thass what happened. You wanna know what that is like?

Josie Do I want to?

Richie No.

Josie Must have been awful, you were so good.

Richie I got over it.

Josie Big man, Richie Adams.

Richie Dass my name. Listen, yeah . . .

Josie Yes?

Richie I'm normally good at this.

Josie Just not today?

Richie It's you.

Josie Me?

Richie It's like yer too good to be real.

Josie I'm just me, Richie.

Richie You want go out?

Josie I'd love to.

Richie Cool.

Josie You took your time.

Richie Yeah, well, you know . . .

Josie I kissed you once.

Richie You kissed me?

Josie Yes.

Richie Explain.

Josie You had a party in your house, yer fourteenth or summin.

Richie You were there?

Josie Half the school was there. You were dancing with Clare Tyler.

Richie Clare Tyler? Oh man.

Josie She weren't that big.

Richie She was big.

Josie Yes.

Richie So how did you end up lipsing me?

Josie You asked me to dance.

Richie Then what?

Josie Nuttin, that was it.

Richie What were you wearing?

Josie Short blue dress. It was my sister's.

Richie Open back?

Josie Yes.

Richie I saw you.

Josie I know.

Richie I saw the back of you. Kept wanting to know who that was. I was following you all round the flat, trying to see what you looked liked, couldn't, too many people in the way.

Josie Well, it was a party.

Richie That was you?

Josie That was me.

Richie And I let you go?

Josie For Clare Tyler.

Richie Things could have been different.

Josie Yes, you wouldn't be a baby father to three kids at the age of seventeen.

Richie Don't believe everything you hear.

Josie Is it true?

Richie Guess I didn't grab you in time. I shoulda done, with both hands. You know how it is round here.

Josie No, I don't.

Richie There's nothing to do.

Josie That's an excuse.

Richie There's nothing I can do.

Josie You can do anything.

Richie You bin chatting to my mum?

Josie You know.

Richie Maybe, whatever – I dunno.

Josie That's a start.

Richie (*smiles*) Who are yer, man?

Josie I'm Josie.

Richie No, I mean who are yer, the way you chat and shit like you know . . .

Josie Know what?

Richie Everything.

Josie I know what I know.

Richie See, that's what I mean. In all my days, I've never known a yat to chat the way you do.

Josie Maybe cos I ain't no yat?

Richie What I meant was, yeah . . .

Josie I know what you meant

Richie No you don't. It's a force of habit.

Josie So, change. I should go.

Richie No, stay.

Josie Dat you barking orders?

Richie Please. What do you want from me? Just tell me, I'll do it.

Josie When I'm with someone, it's for keeps, Richie.

Richie Alright.

Josie Do you understand?

Richie Yes.

Josie You sure? Playing around with schoolgirls ain't right for you.

Richie You think yer that special?

Josie Yes. I am.

Richie Believe.

Josie If you want to come wid, you might have to cut some ties. You can do that?

Richie I want you. It's like I can't breathe whenever I think about you. I can do that.

Sam enters.

Sam Yo? You, excuse me?

Richie You want summin?

Sam Nathan Adams.

Richie Bit young for you.

Sam Funny. Does he live here?

Richie What you want him for?

Sam That's my business.

Richie Mine as well, he's my brother.

Sam Oh, so yer the nasty piece of shit he takes after.

Richie What you say?

Sam You must be deaf?

Richie You must be well dizzy, chatting to me like that.

Josie Richie, don't.

Sam Yes, Richie, don't.

Richie Go step, you mad old cow.

Sam Old? I'm twenty-bloody-six!

Richie And mad?

Josie What is this about? What do you want?

Sam That little brother of yours has been dipping his pen into the wrong ink.

Richie Seriously?

Sam My little girl?

Josie How old is she?

Sam Thirteen!

Richie Seriously, yeah – it was definitely Nathan?

Sam See my face, how serious you think I am?

Richie And there was me, thinking he was lying.

Sam Trust me, he ain't.

Richie So, what do you want me to do?

Sam This is between me and him.

Richie What you expect? He's only a boy.

Sam Anyhow, he forced himself on her.

Richie Eh, my brother don't do that.

Sam No, but you do.

Richie Shut yet mout.

Sam Hanging round the school gates, like some dog.

Richie Don't listen.

Josie Is that true?

Sam Watch his face now – go on.

Josie Richie?

Richie What? Look, it's just a bitta fun.

Josie I've got a sister who's fourteen.

Richie I wouldn't touch her.

Josie How do you know?

Richie I'd know. I wouldn't. I'm wid you now.

Josie pulls away.

What? Josie?

Josie I can't do this.

Richie Oh, come on.

Josie Leave me alone, please.

Sam You get dash, boy

Richie Piss off, you old skank!

48

Sam Call me old again, see what I do.

Josie You should go.

Sam Yeah, and who is you, telling me?

Josie Sounds like yer little girl needs you, why don't you go to her, eh?

Sam Tell yer brother I'm coming for him.

Richie Ain't interested – step!

Sam leaves.

Richie Josie?

Josie I can't.

Richie Come on, man.

Josie Just leave me alone.

Richie You might as well be telling me to cut my arm off – I can't do that, girl.

Josie It's just like you said, Richie, you can't be anything else.

Richie I can be, with you.

Josie No!

Josie goes inside. Richie also goes into his flat. He comes back shortly afterwards, dragging Nathan out with him. Nathan is wearing nothing but a T-shirt and boxer shorts.

Richie See, see what you've done?

Nathan What? I haven't done anything.

Richie Course you can't, cos you can't see anything beyond yer own little world.

Nathan Rich?

Richie Don't look at me like that. Like you think I'm gonna let you off. I don't like you. I can't stand you. The minute I laid eyes on you. You make me sick, bruv.

Nathan What did I do?

Richie What you always do, pretend yer summin you ain't. Well, yer gonna find out now. Mum's only the beginning.

Nathan No, you promised!

Richie I lied!

Nathan Well, gimme back my laptop!

Richie Shut up, just shut up! It's all yer fault.

Nathan What is?

Richie I was mad up for her. First girl ever to do that to me! Ever! Do you understand? I said do you understand, Nathan?

Nathan (*terrified*) Yes.

Richie Liar.

Nathan I'm not.

Richie You think I'm scary? Wait till Mum gets hold of you.

Nathan Don't, Richie, please.

Richie Why should I get all of the shit? It's your turn now, bitch!

Nathan I just wanted to be like you.

OCTOBER

Kelle is in the park with Danielle.

Kelle Well, come on then.

Danielle Come on what?

Kelle You know you want to.

Danielle No I don't.

Kelle Lie bad.

Danielle I ain't lying.

Kelle I can see it all over yer face, girl.

Danielle No you can't.

Kelle So, if I say his name, you won't do nuttin – is that what you're telling me?

Danielle Go on then.

Kelle You sure?

Danielle Yep.

Kelle Nathan. Nathan! NA-THAN!

Danielle is pulling every muscle in her body not to laugh.

Nathan!

Danielle cannot take it any longer. She bursts out laughing.

Danielle I'm sorry, I'm so sorry.

Kelle Bitch. That's what you are, a low down bitch!

Danielle Oh come on, Kelle man.

Kelle Who have you told?

Danielle No one, what do you take me for?

Kelle Big mouth, skank!

Danielle Dat ain't fair. Girlfriend?

Kelle So, who knows my business at school?

Danielle You should be asking who *doesn't* know?

Kelle Oh, man.

Danielle Nathan?

Kelle Don't you bloody laugh no more.

Danielle I weren't, I swear.

Kelle One more smirk, and I'm gone.

Danielle Alright. But Nathan?

Kelle Danielle?

Danielle I'm not smiling, you see me smiling, look at my face. Relax, girl.

Kelle Alright.

Danielle Nathan, though.

Kelle I know.

Danielle Why him?

Kelle He was there.

Danielle Of all the brers you coulda picked, man, bare boys sniffing round you, girl. Buff boys!

Kelle They wouldn't come near, they think I'm a virgin!

Danielle But, Nathan?

Kelle I know, Danielle, I bloody know.

Danielle He musta forced himself. Ennit?

Kelle No.

Danielle The bastard.

Kelle I said no.

Danielle You don't have to be scared.

Kelle Clean out yer ears.

Danielle Just tell me the truth.

Kelle He did not force himself. I forced myself – on him.

Danielle But, Nathan?

Kelle I'm gonna bust yer head.

Danielle Only thing yer gonna be busting is yer water.

Kelle All over you if you ain't careful.

Danielle Just tell me, why him?

Kelle (*smiles*) He picked up my orange for me.

Danielle What?

Kelle I told him he was nice.

Danielle Nice?

Kelle He is nice, Danielle, give him a chance.

Danielle I can't help it if the boy is bare ugly. What if the baby looks like him?

Kelle What you saying, Danielle, you saying you won't cuddle my baby?

Danielle No.

Kelle No, you wouldn't, or no, it ain't true?

Danielle Well . . .

Kelle What?

Danielle It depends.

Kelle Lie bad.

Danielle Sorry.

Kelle It don't matter what you think, Danielle, it don't matter what anyone thinks. Cos it's my baby yeah, no one else's, and I'm gonna cuddle it every day, no matter what it looks like.

Danielle I wanna cuddle it. I do, I really do, honestly, no matter what it looks like . . .

Kelle Say his name, girl.

Danielle Nathan, Nathan, Nathan!

Kelle Thanks, yeah.

Danielle Whatever.

Kelle You for me?

Danielle Me for you.

Nathan appears, his face all bruised.

Kelle Oh man!

Danielle What you walk into?

Kelle His brother's fist.

Danielle Richie do that?

Kelle What you think of yer man now?

Danielle Him say why?

Kelle There's no excuse for it, Danielle, guy's wired, off his bleeding head.

Nathan Says it's all my fault.

Kelle For being nuttin but a dog?

Danielle Easy.

Kelle He's a dog, Danielle, wake up!

Nathan I only wanted to be like him.

Kelle But yer not like him, are you, Nathan? Cos you picked up my orange for me.

Danielle Oranges? What oranges? What you chatting about, Kelle?

Richie enters.

Danielle (*pleased to see him*) Alright, Richie?

Kelle Danielle, you have no shame.

Richie Shoulda known you go hide out with girls.

Kelle Why you beating on him?

Richie Is this her? You got taste, bruv, I give you that.

Danielle Richie?

Richie See me talking to you?

Danielle (*crushed*) No.

Richie If things were different, it coulda bin you and me, baby girl.

Kelle I'd rather have him than you.

Richie Now I know yer lying.

Kelle See my face?

Richie Mum wants you home. Now!

Kelle Say no.

Nathan (*to Richie*) No.

Richie Say what?

Nathan I'm staying out.

Richie You heard what Mum said.

Nathan Don't care.

Richie She don't want you hanging wid this skank.

Kelle This skank is gonna slap you if you keep this up.

Richie This yat is tougher than you, Nathan.

Nathan I ain't going wid you.

Richie Just shut up and come.

Nathan No, Rich.

Richie Don't get me mad.

Nathan Leave me!

Kelle You heard.

Richie If you don't shut up . . .

Kelle What, you gonna hit me?

Danielle Richie man, you can't.

Richie I can do what I like. Home!

Nathan No.

Richie Ain't got time for this.

Richie tries to grab Nathan. Kelle gets in the middle.

Kelle Leave him!

Richie You think I won't lick you down, pregnant or not?

Kelle What will that make you?

Richie Step out, bitch.

Kelle Yer the bitch.

Richie Step!

Kelle Ain't even a man.

Richie I won't ask again.

Kelle Yer a boy, Richie. Least Nathan know where mine was first time. Makes him a man in my book. Danielle said you didn't know where hers was. (*Chuckles.*) Is that true, Richie? Is that true? How sad are you . . .

Richie gives Kelle a violent shove.

Danielle Don't push her, man.
Richie What you gonna do? What you have to say?
Danielle She's pregnant.
Richie Do I look as if I care?
Danielle Wass the matter wid you?
Richie You wanna stay out here, Nathan? Wid the girls?
Nathan Yes, that's what I want to do.
Richie Batty boy. Yer so stupid. I got three kids, yeah, you think you'll make a better daddy than me? Do you? Are you that dizzy?
Nathan Like you always say, Rich, I ain't like you.
Richie Stay, then.

Richie leaves.

Danielle Kelle, you alright, girl?
Kelle No.
Nathan Wass wrong?
Danielle She's having the baby, fool, what you think?
Kelle Get my mum.
Danielle Juss sit down girl, relax.
Kelle (*screams*) I want my mum!

NOVEMBER

Kelle is in hospital, along with Sam and Danielle. She has given birth to a beautiful baby girl.

Danielle Well, pass me it.
Sam Pass you it? This is a baby, Danielle.

Danielle I know what it is.

Sam So, mind yerself.

Danielle But she promised me! Didn't you promise me, Kelle?

Sam Promise you what?

Danielle I'm the first to hold it . . . the baby. Didn't you promise me? Tell her, Kelle, don't just sit there, man.

Sam You leave her alone

Danielle I'm just saying. Kelle?

Sam I don't care what she or you said. It's her baby, and she's gonna be first to hold it.

Kelle I don't wanna hold it.

Sam Kelle?

Kelle I don't.

Sam Stop it.

Kelle I hate it.

Sam Come on now.

Kelle No, Mum, no.

Sam Say hello to yer daughter.

Kelle Don't bring her to me, don't. I don't want to see it.

Danielle But Kelle, you should see her though. She's really beautiful, I ain't lying to yer, man. You sure Nathan's the daddy? I mean . . .

Sam Shut up, there's a good girl.

Kelle It's all her fault.

Danielle Mine?

Kelle Hers, that baby.

Sam Your daughter.

Danielle Lady Sovereign.

Sam What?

Danielle Her name ennit.

Sam Lady Sovereign, her name?

Danielle Yeah.

Sam Did you put her up to that?

Danielle No! It was her idea.

Sam Anyhow. Yer daughter, Kelle.

Kelle She ain't my daughter.

Sam Don't say that.

Kelle I don't want her.

Sam Kelle!

Kelle I don't want to be like you. Danielle, take it.

Danielle Excuse?

Kelle I said you could have it. So take it. I don't wanna see it. Take it, man! The stupid little thing.

Sam She's not a pair of shoes, Kelle.

Kelle I said take it, Dan.

Danielle Are you sure?

Sam Are you thick or summin?

Danielle No.

Sam Get out.

Danielle No, I'm staying.

Sam Well stand over there, just keep away from me, and the baby!

Nathan enters.

Sam Oh look, it's Moron Number Two.

Danielle Yer mum is so rude, Kelle.

Kelle Nathan, man, what you doing here?

Nathan I dunno.

Sam Out.

Kelle Leave him, Mum.

Nathan I just wanted to . . .

Danielle What, you want to see it?

Sam What have I told you about this?

Nathan Boy or girl?

Kelle Girl.

Danielle Lady Sovereign.

Sam Yes, alright.

Nathan Can I see her?

Kelle You can have her.

Sam Kelle. That's enough. (*To Nathan.*) Well, dopey, do you want to hold her or not? What's the matter with him?

Danielle (*shouts*) Nathan!

The baby starts crying.

Sam Oh, well done, Danielle.

Danielle Me?

Sam (*to Nathan*) Well, come on, hold her, then get out. And you tell yer mum from me, she starts slagging me off again in public, we're gonna have words.

Danielle (*hands the baby over*) Here, hold her head – careful, yeah.

Nathan Alright.

Danielle Well? Pretty, ennit?

Nathan Yes.

Danielle Takes after yer mum obviously.

Kelle So, take her and go.

Sam Just ignore her.

Kelle I mean it, why won't anyone believe me?

Nathan Mum wouldn't let me anyway.

Sam Are you crying? Is he crying?

Nathan hands the baby over to Kelle.

Kelle No, no, keep her away from me.

Sam Shut up now, Kelle, I bloody mean it!

Sam takes the baby. Nathan walks away.

Sam Where's he going? Oy, where do you think you're going?

Nathan I can't do this, Kelle.

Sam Do you think she can?

Nathan I'm sorry, I'm really sorry.

Nathan leaves.

Sam Bring him back.

Danielle (*calls*) Nathan? Come back, you fool!

Kelle See, Mum, you see? If he can't do it, if he's allowed to run off, why can't I? Why can't I?

Sam Cos yer the mum.

Kelle I don't wanna be a mum.

Sam You ain't ready?

Kelle I know I ain't ready, believe! All I wanted was for them to stop calling me virgin. You don't know what it's like.

Sam I don't know what it's like? Oh, you Kelle, you stupid little cow.

Kelle Mum!

Sam You are. Sorry.

Kelle Well, what about you, then? When you had me, what was your excuse?

Sam Same reason as yours, I suppose.

Kelle Deh you go then. Yer as bad as me.

Sam I know. But that doesn't change a thing. It's not going to make this little one go away.

Kelle I don't love her, Mum. I hate her.

Sam You think I loved you? I couldn't stand the sight of you. You were as ugly as hell. Crying all the time, shitting yerself twenty-four seven. I never knew so much crap could come out of one little arse.

Kelle Easy.

Sam I used to leave you behind sometimes, all by yourself, at night, so I could go out with my mates. I would scream at you, shake you by your fat little arms – I wanted to kill you.

Kelle Mum?

Sam Cos it was all yer fault.

Kelle Put the brakes on.

Sam I blamed you for ruining my life. When you was coming outta me, I felt like I was being cut in half, thought I was gonna die.

Kelle Stop it.

59

Sam I just wanted to flush you down the toilet, like you never existed.

Kelle Why are you doing this?

Sam Cos you're gonna feel all of that, and more with her – you will, I swear to yer.

Kelle So, yer saying I get rid of it then, give it up?

Sam No.

Kelle What you mean, 'No' – what you saying to me?

Sam You hang in there, my darling. What do you think I have been doing? One day at a time, yeah.

Kelle I can't.

Sam You can. You bloody will. Too late now. Cos as much as you hate her, there are gonna be times you love her. You'll lie down in front of a bus for her. I knew I loved you for certain when you were two years old. I had the flu, lying in bed, you came in, on yer little fat legs.

Kelle Why you love to keep saying I was fat?

Sam You put a wet flannel on my forehead and gave me a kiss. Oh, I wanted to eat you alive.

Kelle Don't remember that.

Sam Yer gonna have those times.

Kelle I don't want to have those times.

Sam You can do this, Kelle, yer gonna do this. Now, take yer baby and hold her. Kelle!

Kelle Alright. Love to shout.

Kelle reluctantly holds her baby.

Sam Hold her head, like the midwife taught you. She's beautiful.

Kelle Whatever.

Sam Takes after her gran.

Kelle Yer not funny.

Sam I'm a twenty-six-year-old grandmother, Kelle. Being funny is on the bus. It's long time. Bleeding tragic is what it is.

Kelle Then why're we bothering for?
Sam Cos we have to.

Kelle lifts up her baby's little fingers.

Sam See? One day, yeah.
Kelle Whatever. Her fingers are so tiny, man.

Sam tuts.

What?
Sam Lady Sovereign!

Blackout.

Production Notes

Roy grew up in a single-parent family with no support from his father, and this play is a tribute to his mother. Although times were sometimes tough, they weren't bleak. He feels that kids can often be made stronger by feeling the need to look after a parent. That parent is normally the mother, as she cannot walk away as fathers often do.

Part of the inspiration for the play came from Roy overhearing two thirteen-year-old girls discussing sex. They spoke frankly, using strong sexual language, and it became clear that both were having sex and were extremely interested in who else of their age was doing so. The 'race' to lose their virginity at such a young age led Roy to consider how this can lead to a cycle of early sexual encounters and pregnancy. In *Baby Girl*, Kelle is pregnant at thirteen just as her twenty-six-year-old mother Sam had been.

The language of the play is owned by the youth and the street, not by a particular race. So first try reading the dialogue as if written in your own accent, if that differs from the text. But avoid changing the language of the play as it will alter the meaning. Particular words may not be in use in your region, so make every effort to stick with Roy's slang usage on the page. Here are some of the words that may be unfamiliar:

bare   (as in 'bare money') lots of
batty   homosexual, gay
brassic   without money, broke
brers   friends, boys

broc   ugly, unattractive
buff   sexy, attractive
butters   ugly, unattractive
bwoi   boy
chirpsin   chatting up someone, flirting with
dash   to break up with, dump, get rid of
digits   phone number
dread   friend, mate
grind   have sex with
long   boring
sket   whore, slut

The play is set in a variety of locations, but the set should be as simple as possible since the weight of the location is in the dialogue. How you present the time scale is up to you. Avoid blackouts.

In terms of music Roy feels current hip-hop may be too obvious, and asks you to think more creatively about the use of music. Don't overuse it.

We can't stress strongly enough that all the parts have been written to be played by actors of any race.

Kelle is pronounced with a long 'ee' at the end, as in other spellings of the name such as Kelly. No character names should be abbreviated unless this is specified, as it will change the rhythm of the lines.

Sam's frustration over lost opportunities due to her situation is tinged with sadness, and this is exposed through subtle humour. Sam may worry about having to look after Kelle's baby, but she knows that ultimately she will force Kelle to take responsibility herself. It's this act that could be the making of Kelle, allowing the play a hopeful ending.

Kids are bombarded by the things they are told they must have right now. This need to belong through having

material possessions is also true of sex. Young people are racing to lose their virginity without thinking through the consequences. Roy is fascinated by this latest young generation, but concerned that a fast-food mentality could lead to self-destruction.

APRIL

One of Kelle's objectives in the scene is to get permission to go out wearing her miniskirt, but she manipulates the situation to achieve a more important objective – to find the right moment to tell Sam she is pregnant.

There is so little age difference between Kelle and Sam that it's as if they are growing up together. It's difficult for either character clearly and consistently to define their roles as mother or daughter, and they can switch from moment to moment from mum-and-daughter to just being mates. Decide which of these relationships Sam and Kelle are playing at any given moment.

When Kelle finally reveals she is pregnant, this is a big revelation. Try having her play it lightly – find the right weight for her sharing this information.

MAY

Danielle, the oldest of five children, all from different fathers, is looking after her siblings. Three are playing in the park and one is in the pram. Danielle and Kelle use the kids playing in the park to aid in their discussion of something quite heavy. Danielle is playing mum to her siblings. She and Kelle play their adult roles in a variety of ways. Their role-playing consists of bravado mixed with fear. It is important, throughout the play, to use

these contrasts and to discover how these young people can appear to turn on a penny.

Have the actors describe a very clear picture of what the children offstage are doing at any particular moment. Recreate this offstage picture so that it serves to highlight or contrast with the action onstage.

Danielle sees Richie as a boyfriend; they would likely see each other a couple of times a week. Richie will be seeing other girls behind Danielle's back. When Danielle suggests that Richie does not know where 'it' is, she is referring to the clitoris: this is not bravado, but an honest revelation to her mate.

Danielle might be tempted to be the first of her friends to get pregnant, as her mother did. But she has had to take on so much responsibility within her family that she seems to have made the decision to break the cycle.

Kelle does not want to admit that Nathan is the father simply because it may spoil her image. Nathan is the unattractive one at school, and at the mention of Nathan Kelle should try overplaying disgust for him. As the scene progresses, and Kelle wishes to divert Danielle's attention away from Nathan as the father, have the actor clearly define and play the diversionary tactic she is using at each turn.

JUNE

This is the first time the audience sees Nathan. Make sure his name is well placed. Nathan and Richie are full brothers and live with their mum.

Nathan and Kelle will have seen each other at school, but this is the first time they have been alone since he has

learned of the pregnancy. Both Nathan and Kelle are aspirational figures. Nathan does not want to be just like all the other boys, and Kelle is intelligent and sees a future for herself.

Kelle does remember picking up the orange, just as she picked Nathan to lose her virginity to.

The contrast between the complex character objectives and tactics and the inability of these characters to express themselves adequately need to be realised.

Kelle wants to feel safe with Nathan, even if this is subconscious, and the more rocky the scene becomes, the harder she has to work for this. Nathan also represents her internal struggle, so from beat to beat what she consciously wants constantly changes. She has difficulty articulating her feelings.

Nathan really wants Kelle as a girlfriend, but he sees fatherhood at his age as the worst possible scenario and is therefore undergoing an internal struggle. Don't make Nathan the hero of the play. He makes bad decisions as well. It's worth asking how aware each character is of how they are feeling at a particular moment – how quickly they change tactic, want, emotion. The age of the characters is shown through extremes of emotion.

Roy's writing doesn't appear to be complex, but it is. It's important to mine all of the relationships, subtext, character, etc., before trying to achieve the rhythm of the piece.

EXERCISE 1   *Read the text and note the objectives and tactics of each character.*

Lose the text and improvise the scene with the characters attempting to get what they want.

EXERCISE 2   This is to be used during the stage of rehearsal when the actors have worked on the text and made some choices but are not yet off-book.

The actors playing the scene give their scripts to a 'feeder'. The feeder stands behind the actor and reads out manageable chunks of text to the actor. It is important that the lines are fed flat, with no inflexion.

The actor then plays the line. This allows the actor to do so without the panic of trying to recall the words. The rhythm will not be achieved in this exercise. It's a good bonding experience for the company, as everyone takes part.

JULY

Two new characters are introduced nearly halfway through the play. Make sure both names and identities are clearly placed.

Yvette is the mother of Richie's second child, and their baby, Chantelle, is eight to twelve months old. Richie sees Chantelle regularly, as he and Yvette get on quite well. The suspicions that Richie is a thief are true.

Nathan looks up to Richie. Although Nathan is able to make fun of Richie in this scene for his behaviour towards Josie, he does ultimately feel the need to impress Richie. This is why he reveals that he is to be a dad. Unfortunately, this merely provokes Richie's blackmailing.

To some extent Richie does also want what Nathan has – youth and freedom. It is this desire that holds him back, even when he discovers that he has sincere feelings towards Josie and that a relationship with her has true potential.

EXERCISE   *Improvise the backstory between Richie and Josie (e.g., the school party).*

Discuss how familiar or unfamiliar this makes the two characters to each other when they meet in the play.

AUGUST

It's not necessary to create a real stairwell – Nathan's entrance can be cheated. This interior scene can be placed by use of indoor costume. Many of the characters are at home and so will be dressed in something more casual and comfortable (e.g., Richie in a robe or pyjamas).

This is a character-driven play, and therefore it's doubly important that the actors and director empathise with the characters.

You will need to unearth Sam's pain. At this moment, she feels incapable of being a mother, as Kelle has fallen pregnant despite her efforts, which Sam sees as not good enough; this speech comes from her pain. If Kelle sees this pain, maybe Sam can teach her some sort of lesson.

EXERCISE   *Read Sam's speech at the start of the scene first at Kelle, as a means to teach her a lesson.*

Read again with Sam directing the anger at herself.

The act of Sam pulling Kelle's hair comes from the same painful place as the earlier speech. The act must be painful for Kelle as it comes from a place of deep love and anger within Sam. Again, these characters find it difficult to express themselves and therefore feel self-hate.

In terms of the practicalities of Kelle's growing bump, Kelle can play a good portion of the script physically by placing the weight in the gut, in the centre.

SEPTEMBER

Richie sees Josie as almost unattainable. She is the beauty of the estate, has class, but will not fall pregnant at a young age and will certainly go on to have ambitions and a career.

The stakes must be kept high. Richie must feel he is in love with Josie, and that by the end of this conversation they are at a point they have not reached before. The repercussions of Sam's interruption are massive. This spurs Richie on to a harsh and violent treatment of Nathan.

Richie's line about 'thinking he was lying' is far more cruel if he plays it as if he really did believe Nathan was lying when he said Kelle was pregnant.

OCTOBER

Just before this scene Richie and Nathan have had a row at home. Nathan has left and Richie has followed him. When Nathan first enters, he thinks he has lost Richie, so that when Richie arrives we should see a physical change in Nathan.

Decide who knows about the pregnancy at this stage. We know the families do. Sam and Nathan's mother have had a confrontation, but it is likely that the nature of their relationship is beginning to level out.

Decide how much Kelle has come to terms with her pregnancy, how Nathan's mum reacts to it. There is likely to be a shift at this point from Nathan being the favourite to Richie, as we learn by following Nathan that he is doing their mum's bidding.

The shove must be violent enough for Kelle to fear for the well-being of the baby. Richie ultimately leaves when Kelle shames him by pointing out that he does not even know where the clitoris is, reminding us of the status a young person achieves from their sexual knowledge.

NOVEMBER

The baby has the highest status in the room. The scene can start with the baby in a cot or being held by Sam. In rehearsal, play with the spatial dynamics in regards to the relationship between each person in the room and their relationship with the baby.

EXERCISE   *Try the scene with a variety of extremes with regard to the baby.*

Have the actors looking at the baby at all times.

Have them never looking at the baby.

Now have them looking at the baby first with adoration, then in fear.

Workshop facilitated by Indhu Rubasingham
with notes taken by Kelly Wilkinson

THE BLACK REMOTE

Glyn Maxwell

Glyn Maxwell's plays include *The Lifeblood* (Riverside Studio/Edinburgh: British Theatre Guide's 'Play of the Fringe' 2004), *The Forever Waltz* (New York/Edinburgh, 2005), *Anyroad* (Bridewell, 2000), *Broken Journey* (Hen and Chickens: *Time Out* Critics' Choice, 1999) and *The Best Man* (Edinburgh, 2004, and now a film). His poetry has won numerous awards, including the Geoffrey Faber Memorial Prize for *The Nerve* (2004). His latest book of poems, *The Sugar Mile* (2005), deals with the London of the Blitz. His novel *The Girl Who Was Going to Die* is to be published in 2008. He has also written opera libretti, travelogues and for radio. He divides his time between Sussex and New York, where he is poetry editor of *The New Republic*.

Author's Note

When I was young I heard the mythological tale of
Pandora's Box, and saw it frighteningly illustrated by
horrid giant biting insects flapping out into the world with
these words blazoned on them: HUNGER, POVERTY,
HATRED, IGNORANCE, VIOLENCE, SICKNESS, GREED . . .

All the evils of the world, of course – a female's fault
again, this time a little girl's curiosity, so even harsher and
stupider a tale than the one in the Garden with the Snake
from central casting and the Tempted Temptress and the
kindlier sex trashed for eternity.

In the version I read, what was left in the box when the
horrified Pandora brought down the lid was a little creature
named *Hope*. But even this consolation was removed
when I read a different version which described the last
creature as *Vain Hope*, or *False Hope*, or *Futile Hope*.

To spare the creature whose survival darkens the world:
is that hope or futile hope?

Here's some more channel-surfing with a black remote.

Stanley 'Tookie' Williams, the convicted murderer who
founded the bloodthirsty Crips gang in Los Angeles,
became over a quarter of a century in prison a tireless
advocate against violence, writing children's books aimed
at saving the young from the life he'd led. The Governor
of California considered mercy for a weekend, then had
him put to death with poison.

The mother of Anthony Walker, hacked to death by racist
thugs in a Liverpool park, said she had no choice but to

forgive them, and hoped that in prison they would reflect upon what they had done.

Faint light still glowing in the empty box.

GLYN MAXWELL

Characters

Polly
the youngest sister

Sally
the eldest sister

Charley
the middle sister

Norman
Polly's friend

Glimmer
Leach
Nono
three winged creatures

A Moving Statue

More Moving Statues

Crowd

Place
Hereabouts

Time
Nowadays

Darkness.
  Light. A big flat black screen standing somewhere.
  Three sisters: Sally, Charley, Polly.

Polly
  What do you mean they've gone?
Sally
                                I mean they went,
  they went to FIND THEMSELVES.
Polly
                      What do you mean,
  to FIND THEMSELVES, but they can FIND THEMSELVES
  here, they wake up *here,* and they leave *here;*
  they work *there,* they come back *here* –
Charley
                                Well, exactly.
  Their days are meaningless as yours or mine.
  I don't expect them back here in a hurry.
Polly
  They've *gone* in a hurry, though.
Sally
                      I don't expect them
  any time soon and d'you know how much I care?
Charley
  This much?
Sally
              Are you mad?
  This much. I don't care because I'm free.
Charley
  I care *this* much, I'm showing it with my fingers.

77

Sally
  You are but I'm not looking, I'm so free
  I'm looking somewhere else.
Charley
                              I'm so free
  I'm going to find myself.
Sally
                        What's there to look for?
Charley
  Least I *know* there's nothing. You don't *know*
  there's nothing, you still think there's something.
Sally
                                              Me?
  I do *not* think there's something, do you mind?
  I know for a fact there's nothing,
  I known that, like, *forever*, no returns,
  I dance all night, I'm so aware there's nothing
  the sky goes light again and I'm the only
  thing in the world that's going.
Charley
                              I'm not even
  in the world, you know where I am? I'm nowhere.
Polly
  'Gone to find themselves . . .'
  Did they say goodbye?
Charley
                        They wrote goodbye in a note.
Polly
  Mum and Dad?
Charley
                    They wrote it down in biro,
  in capitals.
Sally
              WE NEED TO FIND OURSELVES.
Polly
  But Sally, did you *see* them lose themselves?

78

Did you see them when they left, did they look lost?
Sally
    I can't remember everything. I'm free,
    do you mind, I got to go.
Polly
                            But did *you* see them,
    Charley, did you see them?
Charley
                        Might have done,
    don't think it really matters, what you see,
    what you don't see, it's subjective, as I see it.
    I'm off, my Krew and me, we're hanging out
    tonight at the Level Krossing.
Sally
                        The Level Krossing!
    Cos no one's asked you anywhere.
Charley
                            Dead right.

    We're no one. Nowhere's where
    we go. That's philosophical.
Sally
                        My dates
    are clubbing down the Kaves.
Polly
                            Have I got dates?
Charley
    Course not, you're just a kid, you don't have dates.
Sally
    Who needs *you* anywhere?
Charley
                        They made a list.
    They stuck it in the hallway, it's long.

    It's very long.

Sally
    It's a list of Things To Do.

79

Charley

                          It's a list of Things
Not to Do, you'd better make a start
on not doing *any* of the things. Each thing
takes ages not to do.

Polly

                        It's so long
I can't see where it ends . . .

Sally

                            It never ends.

Polly

Did they sign it *Mum and Dad*?

Charley

                                How could they sign it
if it never ends? That's philosophical.

Sally

I am *so* out of here.

Charley

                    I been gone ages.

They're gone.

Polly

How could they make a list so long
    when they had to leave in a hurry?
How could they write down everything
    when they had no time to stay?
It's quiet without them here.
It's quiet with only me, it's why I'm talking.
I ought to write things down but writing things
is quiet, it's mega quiet.
So nothing's written down about me really,
nothing's been remembered. But they do say
everyone in the end is always famous,
for something, for a while, for some moments.
Maybe they'll last forever, those moments.
Meanwhile it's pretty quiet. But there's this.

The big flat black screen somewhere.

It's so brand new it's still
black. It's so brand new I can see my face
wondering what it does.
It doesn't say a thing but . . . MADE IN CHINA.
What does it say about it?

She looks at the list, follows it out of sight.
  Norman comes in through a window.

Norman
Polly. I'm here. It's Norman. I've arrived.
Oh, look at that . . . it's there . . . it wasn't there . . .
and now it is, that's choice, that's bang on time.
I am in the presence of newness,
flat, black, wideness. Everything you have ever
owned is a heap of junk forever. For this . . .
is the new flat black wide XL8-Kobra-Klassik.
Polly
Is that what it is?
Norman
                    Fact is, it's cutting edge,
I bought the magazine *Cutting Edge*, just now,
and they left the cover blank in case this happened.
And now it's happened. Wow. I am reduced
to one word: 'Wow'.
Polly
                    I don't think that's a word.
Norman
Words are, I don't know, words are one thing,
served their purpose maybe, who knows,
but fact is this is the new flat black wide screen
XL8-Kobra-Klassik, it's cutting edge,
it's where we are, it's . . . No. There are no words.
You can hear the actual language
throwing in the . . . you know . . .

Polly
                                             Towel.

Norman
                                                The towel.

Polly
  I'm not allowed to touch it.
  It's the Ninth Thing Not To Do.
Norman
                              Where are your parents?

Polly
  It doesn't say.
Norman
                    Where are your sisters?

Polly
                                             Gone.

Norman
  Good. That means we're free.
Polly
                              That's what *they* said.
  We can't all be.
Norman
                    I think you'll find we *can* be,
  what with the way things are, for example, progress,
  market forces. Where are your remotes?
Polly
  Where are my what?
Norman
                         Your remotes,
  you know, your things, your what's the word: *dobbers*.
Polly
  That isn't a word either.
Norman
                              It is now,
  I say it, so it is, it's home grown,
  it's organic.

Polly
> But I'm not allowed to touch it.

Norman
You're not allowed to *touch* it, but remotes
can touch it for you.

Polly
> They keep them all down here . . .

Norman
Down the back of a sofa?

Polly
> I think you'll find
they're in their usual places, there's a white one,
a silver one, a grey one, a black one.

Four remotes.

Norman
Cool, in business, literally, we're booming.
Now what does what?

Polly
> What?

Norman
> Look at your list.

Polly   Remote, remote . . . the white one's on and off,
brightness, volume, contrast –

Norman
> And that black one?

Polly
The grey one's music, we could hear some music.

Norman
No thanks, I got my own I just downloaded.

Polly
We could listen to it.

Norman
> Got it on random play.

Polly
We could hear it.

Norman

It's my playlist, Polly, fact is
it's personalised, okay? What's that black one?

Polly

The silver one's the DVD, the video,
the curtains and the blinds.

Norman

Yeah, and the black one?

Polly

I'm looking . . . Do Not Smoke, Do Not Skateboard,
Do Not Waste Time, Do Not Waste Space,
Do Not Keep Secrets, Do Not Tell Secrets,
and here, the Ninety-Ninth Thing Not To Do is:
DO NOT USE THE BLACK REMOTE.

Norman

You serious? It says that? All those rules?
What is this, olden times?
'Once upon a time' – did someone say that?
No, we're here and now, we won the war,
we're free.

Polly

What war did we win?

Norman

It was, it was – I don't know, it's all behind us.
We're over it. You know, they have statues,
they hold some kind of silence and the old folks
wear flowers.

Polly

DO NOT USE THE BLACK REMOTE.

Norman

Why not?

Polly

It doesn't say.

Norman

It doesn't say?
Is there a Hundredth Thing?

Polly

Not To Do?

Yes. It says . . . DO NOT ASK WHY NOT.

Norman

Are they serious?

Polly

They went to find themselves,

so I can't tell.

Norman

They can't be serious.

What's the worst that could happen? Dot dot dot . . .
Sure, there's a malfunction, well, we say,
or rather, *you* say when they're back, it's the new
flat black wide screen black new
XL8-Kobra Klassik, it's cutting edge,
you gonna get teething problems. Slide it over.

Polly

I don't think we should use it. Here's the grey one,
we could watch a DVD.

Norman

I've seen 'em all.

I've seen 'em *and* the sequels *and* the prequels.

Polly

Or a video.

Norman

It's not Victorian days,

Polly, it's cutting edge. Or let's just watch
the blinds go up and down.

Polly

Alright.

Norman

I was joking.

Polly

Oh . . . 'cause you just press this.

Norman

I was being sarcastic.

I want the black remote.
We need the black remote.

Polly

It says DO NOT USE IT.

Norman

It means *Polly,* DO NOT. Ah ha, d'you see?
It's not addressed to me. *My* mum and dad
have found themselves, they never leave a note,
they never leave the house. Fact is, I creep out
every night, and every night I'm making
more and more of a noise just so they'll ask me
Where do I think I'm going? but there's silence.
Nothing but clocks ticking. Mum and Dad
just sitting there in memory of something.
So I say it to myself, I say, 'Norman,
where do you think you're going?' and I say, 'Norman,
I'm going round to Polly's, try and stop me,'
and I wait for his response, and there's no response,
so I go. You get it? Freedom.

Norman has the black remote.

Polly

It says DO NOT USE IT, Norman.

Norman

What it says is
DO NOT USE THE BLACK REMOTE and *you're* in total
compliance, Polly.

Polly

What am I in total?

Norman

Switch on, use the white one.

The television is on. White noise.

Polly

Everything's broken.

Norman
                    It's only the Big Bang.
Somewhat old news.
Polly
                        I'm going to play with the curtains.
Norman
No, I need your input. INPUT.
Let's try that one.
Polly
                    It feels like now we're flying
an aeroplane we've stolen.
Norman
                        Cutting edge,
Polly, no one said it would be easy.
Polly
No one said anything, they just skedaddled.
Norman
Welcome to our galaxy, you could say.

BBC1 News: clear.

Okay, now we have news, and the white one,
the white one's dead.
Polly
                    It still affects the volume.
Norman
Turn it up.
Polly
                But it can't change the channel.
Norman
Only the black one can.
Polly
                    Don't use it, maybe.
Norman
It even *smells* new, that's the scent of choice.

He starts to change the channels. BBC2, ITV1, C4 . . .

In the old days this was all they had, four channels,
can you believe? They also had these great black
boxes for their music, and they sometimes
went into big rooms to watch these people
acting out whole stories, real people,
you couldn't pause or rewind, or fast-forward,
they had no scene-select,
and incredibly you had to watch in silence,
and listen to their story, not your *own*
story like now, like digital, organic,
but some old story *they'd* been practising.
There was nothing you could affect,
and you had to hope the actual real people
knew what they were doing. Like as if!
History, I heard that in. More volume.

*Satellite channels, cable channels, anything, surfing
faster, louder.*

Polly
> I don't think it's very helpful
> to change it quickly, Norman.

Norman
>   There's so much,
> how else do you get through it?

Polly
>   I can't see
> what anything quite is.

Norman
>   It's a free choice,
> fact is, it's clean, you make your own selections
> instead of like, you know, like people in power
> telling you what to watch.

Polly
>   Nobody's ever
> told me what to watch.

Norman
                    Subliminal,
    that's the key, messages, messages,
    kind of like fascist messages and you're like
    completely in the dark.
Polly
                    What messages?
Norman
    See, it's working.
Polly
                    Slow down, slow down . . .

Everything going by, faster, dizzier.

Norman
    I can see why no one wants you
    using this, it's typical of Them.
Polly
    Them? My mum and dad?
Norman
                    Those are the names
    they go by but you never really know.
    Think of a fact you know, Polly, go on . . .
Polly
    I've got one.
Norman
                    Have you? Good. Well it's not true.
    Try again. Same thing. That's not true either.
Polly
    I was thinking about my birthday.
Norman
                    You can't trust them.
    Nothing you think is true, not just you
    personally, Polly, you, you're just a pawn
    in the game they play. That's how fast we're moving.
Polly
    Chess is quite a slow game.

Norman

                        Look, it's not chess.
You're a pawn in a game of, I dunno, like, boxing.
Sorry to be the bringer of that news.

Anything, anything, things we have now.

Polly

Norman, please slow down, I'm getting dizzy!

Norman

You want to live on a 'farm', you want to ride
a 'bi-cycle', you want to use a 'land-line',
you do that, Polly, this is the Here and Now,
and it goes like this . . .

*Chaos of colliding sound, over which three voices
tune in and out, overlapping, fading, rising, as if the
chaos is spawning three voices.*

Glimmer

no, but it's hell the life they look at you
and he's a star they say he's got it all
he's got the looks the talent got the money
sure I live the dream but the dream is hell

Nono

really, whatever . . .

Glimmer

they look at you they want a piece you know
that's all they want don't want the real you
like who's the real me? I ask myself
and people are asking that who is he really
deep down well that's for me to know it's hell

Nono

really, whatever . . .

Glimmer

the life they look at you and he's a star
they say he's got it all the looks the money

the girls the talent sure I live the dream
but the dream is hell

Leach

would I say I'm happy excellent question Susan
I am in of myself but am I happy
with what I see around me? different answer

Glimmer

he's got the looks the talent got the money

Leach

Susan take the Lakeside I was born
at the Lakeside I'm a Lakesider Susan

Nono

really, whatever . . .

Leach

I walked those hills as a boy I walked those hills
the air was pure and fresh there was a sense
of community those days you knew your neighbour

Glimmer

like who's the real me? I ask myself

Leach

Susan it's all going it's all gone now

Nono

really, whatever . . .

Leach

Susan where's it gone I'm a Lakesider
through and through it's gone would I say I'm happy

Glimmer

deep down well that's for me to know it's hell

Leach

excellent question Susan

Nono

really, whatever . . .

Norman

Polly, I can't stop it!

Polly
> Look there's smoke,
I don't think smoke is good!

Norman
> No it's very bad,
it won't go where it's meant to!

There is too much, too fast, too loud.
> *Crescendo. Bang. Smoke.*
> *From the ruins of the XL8 Kobra-Klassik, three*
winged creatures: Glimmer, a star; Leach, a purist;
Nono, a nobody.

Polly
There's – monsters on the carpet.

Norman
> That is so –
unrealistic. Something's – malfunctioned.

Polly
When they – when they find themselves,
my mum and dad, they will kill me.

Norman
It's – cutting edge – I – no one . . .
said it would be easy.

Polly
Can the white one switch them off?

Norman
> The white one's dead.
The black one's dead.

Polly
> I can't affect the curtains.
There's no music. None of the remotes
do anything. I press, but they're still there,
these . . . three.

Norman
> It's a whiteout, it's a meltdown,
it's a downturn, it's a shortout,

it's not like digital, those things are – like –
errors, it's like *we have encountered a problem
and must shut down* . . .

Polly

They're breathing,
they've wings.

Norman

It's only totally illegal
for them to come.

Polly

They weren't supposed to come.
We weren't supposed to touch it.

Norman

You weren't.
I blame you in a way. You hear that, Polly?
In a way I do.

Polly

We have to put them back.
They don't belong.

Norman

It's a blowback, it's a pitfall –

Polly

Norman, will you stop
saying what things it is, 'cause what it is
is not like what you say!
Say there are three winged animals right there.
Say they just fell out of the great new
flat wide black new screen and it's very broken.
Say they don't look friendly.

Norman

Now you've done it.
They were just hallucinations, now you've done it.
Now they exist! Satisfied, are we?
That there's monsters in the world? And all the time
the evidence was, there wasn't? There are.

You'd better do something, Polly, something soonish,
or soon. Nowish. Now.

Polly

Where – where have you come from, wingèd creatures?
What were you doing in there?
What do you want in here?

Glimmer

                 What do I want?

Norman

It spoke!

Glimmer

         What do I want, what do I want . . .?
Same as everyone else, I want respect,
I want privacy, I want dignity, but no,
you people always after me with your questions,
your 'love and devotion', yeah, call that devotion?
I was safe in there, safe from you parasites.
I am a star, an artist. Is it too much
to ask to be left alone?

Polly

              He says he's a star!

Norman

I've never heard of him.

Polly

              But he's from TV!

Norman

He *came* from the TV.

Polly

           Yes, exactly!

Glimmer

A safe house, a getaway,
that's how I figured this, a hideaway,
but the same old people and the same old questions
day in, day out. I wish, you know what I wish?
I wish I was nobody, I wish I was *you*,
I actually do, I actually wish I was you.

Norman
  Her, or me?

Glimmer
            I wish I was run of the mill.

Norman
  She's run of the mill, I'm not. I don't mean that
  rudely, Polly, it's just –

Polly
                Wow. Are you famous?

Norman
  You said 'wow' wasn't a word.

Polly
                You look a bit famous.
  Look, he ignored my question, and he's wearing
  sunglasses indoors! I think I've seen you
  in loads of brilliant things!

Glimmer
            They mean nothing.
  It's work. I am an artist.

Polly
          That police thing,
  where you catch the murderers, and that hospital thing
  where you save the dying ones, he's in *everything*!
  He was in that film where the world was going to end
  and people needed him but he had to battle
  this evil thing, and then he said, 'It's showtime!'
  and the Earth was saved!

Glimmer
                It's nothing, just a pay cheque.

Polly
  He looks the part, *and* he doesn't care, *and* he's rude!
  Can I have your autograph please? See that, Norman?
  As if I wasn't there! And he's in my house!
  I met somebody famous and my sisters
  missed it all!

Norman

What about the others?

Glimmer

These parasites? They follow me about
like sheep.

Norman

What do you want here?

Glimmer

No more questions.

Leach

What do *I* want here?
Same as I want anywhere. I want beauty.
I want grace, and beauty, purity, and love.
I want the world I used to know.

Norman

Well, Polly,
a little bit more higher-class than your
big celebrity, no?

Polly

But *he* isn't famous,
talking like that, how could he be?

Leach

Who wants
fame in a world like this?

Norman

That's very true.

Leach

Who'd want to shine in a sewer?

Norman

You hear that, Polly?
True, and a bit like poetry, so actually
mega-true, we did that once in English.

Leach

I have found an oasis here.

Norman

He's found an oasis,

he means that as a metaphor, he means
in the desert of our culture.

Polly

         I got that.
Why have you got those wings?

Norman

Ask your celebrity why *he's* got wings.

Polly

He's not taking questions now.

Leach

         I have broken wings.

Polly

Are you an actual monster?

Norman

        Now who's rude?
This is a – *Thing* – of quality and breeding.

Polly

Yes, but it's got wings.

Norman

       They're broken wings.

Leach

For a broken world.

Norman

      Yes, for a broken world,
that's the point he's making.

Polly

        What's that one?

They look at the third creature.

Glimmer

He's nobody.

Leach

    He's nothing.

Polly

      Little creature,
what are you?

Norman
> They already said, he's nothing.

Polly
What's your name?

Nono
> No, no . . .

Polly
Nono is your name?

Nono
Don't want to be . . .

Norman
> Don't want to be what?

Nono
Don't want to be no trouble.

Norman
Well, you're a lot of trouble, you all are.
Polly's in deep trouble, aren't you, Polly?
She'd be the first to admit. She was warned, you see.
DO NOT USE THE BLACK REMOTE, they said. And
   now this.
I'm trying hard not to say 'I told you so'
but it's quite a battle.

Polly
> Did you hear a bang?

They look out. Glow of distant fireworks.

Polly
Beautiful, look, fireworks . . .

Norman
Fireworks, but why?
I can't see any reason.

Polly
> There, and there,
and there – that's three displays on the Great Meadow,
near and far and very far. Ooo, crimson,
crimson and gold!

98

Norman

But why?

Polly

And gold and blue!

Norman

And by the light two people are approaching . . .

Polly

But that's impossible, it's my two sisters . . .

Norman

Why are there fireworks?

Polly

Why are my sisters coming?
We have to hide these – Things! If they see the Things
they'll know you used the remote!

Norman

It's *your* remote,
Polly, I just happened to be passing.

Polly

It doesn't matter! Things – don't be afraid!
But we have to hide you now!

Norman

Where can we hide them?

Polly

Well . . . well . . . we have to think of places
my sisters never go . . . They never eat,
so *you* (*Glimmer*) go in the kitchen. They never read,
so *he* (*Leach*) goes in the study. And nobody *ever*
goes in the attic, so the little one (*Nono*) goes there.
(*To Glimmer.*) Sir, may I escort you to your suite?

Glimmer

Hey there, girl, assistant,
am *I* supposed to carry my own things?

Polly leads Glimmer out.

Leach

I hope I have a view, can I see the Lakeside?

Norman
  You can when it's clear.
Leach
              Then I rather hope it's cloudy,
  for it's ugly now and I wish to draw the curtains.

  Norman leads Leach out. Fireworks. Nono moves
  towards their light and looks out. He hears Polly
  coming back and cowers again.

Polly
  And I'm taking you upstairs, then up a ladder,
  but it's very peaceful there.
Nono
                  It doesn't matter.
Polly
  You're very easy, aren't you?!
Nono
                      No no.
Polly
  This way then, you, Nono, Nono . . .

  Sally and Charley with two sacks. Norman.

Sally
  It's Norman from next door.
Charley
                  How are you, Norman?
Norman
  You don't have to pretend. I know you think
  I'm nobody, just Polly's little friend.
Sally
      You're a special friend to Polly.
Charley
                      She needs friends.
  We've not been friends at all, have we, Sally?
  We hope to make amends.

Sally
                              Because we love her.
Norman
  Look, I've heard your sarcasm before
  and it doesn't fool me, frankly. I expect
  you're wondering what happened to your new
  flat wide black new screen and why it's now
  a bashed-in empty smouldering sort of wreck.
Charley
  I hadn't noticed.
Sally
                    Oh. Well, I don't mind.
  Waste of money.
Norman
                    What???

  Polly.

Polly
  Why have you come back? Why are there fireworks?
Sally
  Why are there fireworks?
Charley
                          Why, because they're lovely.
  Everyone likes them, everyone from the town
  is watching them tonight. Whole families,
  mothers, fathers, sisters, brothers,
  everyone has a picnic –
Sally
                          A midnight feast!
Charley
  Even the Lakesiders, who have nothing
  lovely in their lives.
Sally
                    It's only you
  who's missing the excitement! There are stalls,

and rides and games to play, it's the greatest fair
that's ever come!

Polly

                There's a fair?

Sally

                                And an astro-glide
where you take all night to reach the end!

Charley

                                      There's a pool,
it's called an infinity pool because it seems
to meet the horizon. Only it truly does:
you can swim right through the horizon and be home
by morning.

Sally

                There's a bouncy castle!

Charley

                                  A whole
bouncy palace.

Sally

                A bouncy cathedral!

Norman

I'm sorry, look, but that's unfeasible.

Polly

I don't know what he means but I'm sure he's right.
Why is there a fair and a great pool
and fireworks and an astro-glide? It's way past
bedtime!

Sally

        We don't know.

Charley

                        We've no idea,
but we wanted you to know.

Polly

                      I can *see* the fireworks,
so *that* bit's true. Oh, the rockets are so bright
it looks like day, it looks like day in the distance!

Norman

There are towers on the horizon, what are they then?

Sally

Roller-coasters, tallest on earth.
You move so fast you're younger when it's over!

Norman

Nonsensical.

Charley

And we thought, as we were here,
we'd fetch some things we have that we don't need
and take them to the fair.

Sally

There's a great marquee
where all the food and books and clothes you bring
are free to the Lakesiders!

Charley

They have nothing.
No food, no books, they scavenge in the litter
we dump beside the lake.

Norman

Well, we know that,
and it's very sad of course, but why do *you* care?
You've never cared before.

Charley

That's not enough
to stop me caring now.

Sally

And there's no time
to worry about why – these folks are hungry!

Charley

These people have no books and they wear rags,
and look at how *we* live! The shame of it.

Sally

I'm off to the kitchen! – Where is it again?

Polly

Er . . . let me do that for you! I know the way!

Charley
I'll fill my sack with books. – Do we have books?
Norman
I know where, let me do that!

Polly and Norman go with the sacks.

Sally
How did we know, we were suddenly new!
Charley
It was suddenly good to be me and you.
Sally
A time went missing.
Charley
An hour or two.
Sally
When we got to the place we were going to!

Different light, music coming.

It was dark in the world, it was noisy and grey,
and everyone what they wanted to say!
Charley
We sat in the ashes, the sun went red,
and nobody cared what somebody said.

*The fair starts to build up around them, as if built of
rhymes: it gets brighter and brighter.
People: rich people, poor people – all is harmonious.*

Sally
Then a time went missing,
Charley
An hour or more,
Sally
And something was where
Charley
There was nothing before

Sally
And the sky went green
Charley
                              And the ground was gold
Sally
And everything else
Charley
                        Was a thing to behold,
Sally
And we suddenly know, and we suddenly see
Charley
It is suddenly good to be you and me!
Sally
A time went missing,
Charley
                              An hour or three,
Sally
When we turned to the people we wanted to be!

The fair. Very bright. The time of your life.
  Polly and Norman bring the sacks, and the sisters
give out food, books to the poor.

Polly
Like Christmas but it's much too warm for Christmas!
Norman
Like a holiday but happening where we live . . .
Polly
Like a big surprise and everyone kept the secret!
Norman
You can touch and see and hear it but it's not
possible to believe . . .
Polly
                        But the creatures,
the things that came, *they're* not possible either.
Norman
They're unrealistic, yes, but if I saw them,

They *must* be real, I'm of sound mind.
Polly

                                        We saw them!
Norman
I think there's a connection.
Polly

                        I don't think
it's fair they miss the fair.
Norman

                        Think about it:
everything was the same, then, suddenly . . .
Polly
Everything was different.
Norman

                        There's a connection.
I think it's down to us.
Polly

                  What do you mean,
it's down to us?
Norman

                  I think it's down to us,
what's happened here. I think what happens next
is up to us.
Polly

            You said it was down to us.
Is it up to us or down to us?
Norman

                              It's both.
Polly
I'm on a roller-coaster but I'm just
standing here.
Norman

            It was the black remote.
They said DON'T USE IT, didn't they, but we did,
our own initiative, my initiative really,
and the town got better. There was once a garden,

apparently, and Romeo and Juliet
were in it and they had to eat these apples,
or not, I can't remember – anyway, God,
we did him in Religious Studies, *he* said
DON'T DO THIS OR THAT but they did do it,
so he made some changes.

Polly

                          Do you maybe think
God sent those creatures? Also, a second question,
do you think we could get some candyfloss?

Norman

                                        God?
God's history, don't you know, and candyfloss?
Everything is available. I believe
we have unlocked the door to a better life,
you and me. Well, technically me and you,
I probably take the credit here. I believe
that I, Norman W. W. Jones,
have unlocked the door to a better life.

Polly

                              It's a life
where *I* know someone famous, someone famous
knows me! But look how I've treated him, he's locked
in the kitchen, they should be here!

Norman

                          If they were here
they'd tell the world it was I,
Norman, I and my black remote, who unlocked
the door to a better life.

Polly

                          I'm going to fetch him.
I can be like his helper, can't I, carry his things,
organise his time, he is an Artist.

Norman

I'll meet you at that statue. I shall stand there
observing this new life that I have wrought.

People will pass by and say thank you,
Norman, for these changes.

Polly

                                At the statue!
My star beside the statue!

Polly goes.
There is a Statue, a person painted who is very still.
It gets tired of being still and moves away. Things of
the fair go with it.

Norman

Statue, you can't move, you're a statue,
you're made of stone – come back, it is I, Norman!

Norman follows the Statue.
Darker. Polly at her house. Faint singing from
above.

Polly

Hello? Who is that singing?
Is it the star who's singing? Sir, it's me,
Polly, I've come to tell you that the town
is very bright tonight, and you'd enjoy it
if you came along. There's a fair,
there's candyfloss, I could buy you a stick of it, sir,
with my pocket money except it's all for free,
everything's for free but I could simply
give you my pocket money, only perhaps
you have what you need. It's lovely singing, who is it?

Is it you, Mr Lakeside Man?
The fair is full of Lakeside people, I saw them
for the first time – I mean, I've always seen them,
but I've never seen them happy. You'd be happy
to see them changed like that. Is it you singing?

Nono?

The singing stops and we see Nono high up. His wings have grown.

It was very nice, that singing.
Nono
                                    It's nothing.
Polly
What did you say?
Nono
                              It's nothing.
Polly
Would you like to come to the fair?
There's rides, there's candyfloss.
Nono
                                        No, I'll stay here.
Don't want to be no trouble.
Polly
                                    It's no trouble,
we can *oooh* at the Roman candles,
we can *aaah* at the Chinese rockets –
did I say there's candyfloss?
Alright. I'll let you be. If you change your mind . . .

Glimmer.

Glimmer
Am I on?
Polly
            I'm sorry?
Glimmer
                        Am I on? I should be on.
Polly
Yes, yes, you're on, you're on!
Glimmer
                                    I'll keep them waiting.
They waited all night to see me, they can wait
another hour.

Polly

                  To see you, how do you mean?

Glimmer

Hold this. I need to focus.

Polly

                      There's a fair,

Sir, a marvellous fair.

Glimmer

                  I need to be centred.

Polly

I thought we could go together.

Glimmer

                    Oh, did you,

hit the red carpet, right, be seen with me?
Good for your profile, eh? Got some product
out this summer?

Polly

                  I thought we could be friends.

Glimmer

Just 'friends', like keep 'em guessing? Yeah, why not.
Sign this, it's a disclaimer.

Polly

                 What's that?

Glimmer

What *I* say happened happened, what *you* say
didn't, it's pretty standard.

Polly

                Oh, I see,

I'm quite new to the business.

Glimmer

                It's a nightmare,

it's hell on earth.

Polly

        But don't you ever enjoy it,

being a star?

Glimmer
> I was born to be a star.
It's natural, I was chosen. It's *people*
I've got some problems with, the kind of losers
who follow me around. I say get a life.

Polly
I think you'll like the people now, and the life,
everyone seems much nicer.

Glimmer
> Right, *seems* . . .
I know what they're really like. Where's my limo?

Polly
We'll walk, it isn't far. Where are the others?
I don't want them to miss it!

Glimmer
> Bad idea.
Piece of advice. Don't let them out of this house.
They're parasites, they're poison.
You bring them, the deal's off.

Polly
> Okay, I'll leave them.
Can't miss what you never knew!

Glimmer
> I tell you – losers.
Okay, shades on. Watch out, world. It's showtime.

They go. Nono starts singing again.
> *The Moving Statue passes by, the fair comes with
him, Norman in his wake. The Statue halts.*

Norman
Look, I'm out of breath, can you not stop?
There, that's better, that's more like the statues
I'm used to. You're supposed to just stand there,
were you not told? And *mean* something, yes,
for example, what, perhaps you won a battle, or
invented something, or maybe you're from a story,

like a fairy tale? You're not supposed to move.
I don't have to follow you. You're like, the past,
you understand, you stand there meaning something,
so just keep still, it's me who moves around
and changes – a mover and shaker, that's me,
I'm always on the move, and . . . er, shaking.

Polly.

Polly
Norman, who are you talking to?
Norman
                                This statue,
it moves around.
Polly
                        Are you feeling alright, Norman?
Norman
Top of the world.
Polly
                        I lost him!
Norman
Lost who?
Polly
                I lost the star, he was right beside me,
I thought he was – I was telling him all about
the films I've seen him in and then I asked
would he like some candyfloss and I turned round
and he wasn't there.
Norman
                                Where are the other two?
Polly
I left them there, he said they were poisonous,
and he ought to know, he's a star, he's in the business,
it's hell on earth.
Norman
                        You've been made a fool of, Polly.

There's nothing wrong with those two, those are
   creatures
of quality, your 'star' is the whole problem.
He's shallow and he's selfish and he never
blames himself for anything. It's *your* fault.

Polly
But I like him, and I lost him!

Norman
                     Look, he's probably
over there, at the market.

Polly
                    There's a market?

Norman
Sure there's a market, everything's for sale.

Polly
I thought everything was free, and I never got to
eat my candyfloss.

Norman
                Everything free?
Not in this town . . .

Polly
             There was a tent, a marquee,
they collected food, and books. You were there,
you saw it with me!

Norman
             Here come your sisters.
I saved up all my savings.

Sally with food, Charley with money.

I'll have a hot dog please.

Sally
             They're not for sale.

Polly
See? They're not for sale, they're free gifts
for the people of the Lakeside, aren't they, Sally?

Sally
No. They're not for sale because I want them.
Polly
But you never eat!
Sally
                          I don't want them to eat,
imbecile, I want them to increase
their value.
Norman
                 Look, I'm starving. Here's a pound.
Sally
A pound? And he says he's starving!
Charley
                                  Some people . . .
Norman
Two pounds, mustard and ketchup.
Sally
                                Just like that,
thrown in? Mustard's ninety-five, it's scarce,
do you mind, my dealer says it's like gold dust.
Polly
You have a mustard dealer?
Norman
                       I need mustard.
Do you have an onion dealer?
Sally
                     Might do.
Norman
I need them, for the flavour.
Charley
                     Some people . . .
Polly
Charley, don't you remember, you had a sack
it was full of books we didn't need –
Charley
                     Hello,

hey presto, look at them now.

She waves money.

Polly
                          You charged money
to the Lakeside people?
Charley
                          Idiots can't read,
what kind of a market is that? No, I flogged them
to something called a 'library', where these people
hand out books for nothing. Must be a tax dodge.
Anyway, I've enough for sixty goes
on the Mega-Slide.
Polly
                          But I thought
the rides were free.
Charley
                          Everything's *free* with you,
isn't it? Gimme a handout, gimme a hand,
I'm poor, sob, I'm sick, boo-hoo, I'm starving,
ahhh . . . well, that's not the way we do things
in the free world.
Sally
                          Hey little sister, look,
look what I got . . .
Polly
                          You have some candyfloss!
Sally
At a special family discount, eight quid
for a stick of it.
Polly
                          I don't have eight quid.
Norman, have you got anything?
Norman
                                    Look, Polly,
see it my way. If I buy you candyfloss,

it's all very nice, it's all very nineteen-sixties,
but (a) I'm out of pocket, right, and (b)
I don't *like* candyfloss so in terms of profit
it's a bust, and (c) I need those liquid assets
to invest in my own portfolio. For example
there's a Mega-Slide, she said so.
Sally

                             And a Splashworld.

Norman
   There's a Splashworld?
Sally

                   Don't think I even mentioned
Candyfloss Canyon.
Polly
                 Candyfloss Canyon?
Sally

                          Look,
they built it while we stood here. Time is money,
children.
Charley
         Polly, I understand your mindset,
I know where you're coming from, I was young once,
and when we're young sometimes
we have sweet little thoughts about how lovely
life could be if it all just floated by
and settled in your lap, but you know we grow,
we put all that behind us.
Polly

                   But I saw you,
you were giving things away, there were fireworks –
where are the fireworks now?
Sally

                      They're in the Skydome.

Polly
   The Skydome?

Sally
> It's behind you.

Polly
Oh my word!

Sally
> The Skydome you can enter
for only thirty quid, or if you're a member –
is it sixteen, Charley?

Charley
> Eighteen.

Sally
> Eighteen.

Polly
I don't have eighteen quid, I don't have eight quid,
I've two pounds forty-one.

Sally
> Look, you're my sister,
and I must be mad to do this, but here,
have these ketchup sachets.

Charley
> Here's a book
I couldn't sell, take it, no, don't thank me,
just take it.

Polly
> *Insects of Antarctica* . . .
It's very short.

Charley
> I don't suppose you've heard
it's the thought that counts.

Polly
> Yes . . . of course, thank you.

Sally
Charley look, it's beginning.

Polly
> What's beginning?

Sally
  The show, don't you know anything?
Norman

                            There's a stage,
  they've built a stage in this last minute, it's huge,
  it must be for an orchestra.
Sally

                        I told you,
  it's for the show.
Polly

                      What happens in the show?
Sally
  Do I have to explain it all?
Charley

                        It's simple, Polly.
  It's called Star Aid, it's the brainchild of this guy,
  there, that's him projected on that cloud,
  it's his idea.
Polly

                  Norman, it's him, the star,
  I *know* that man!
Sally

                      Yeah, right, sure you do.
Charley
  It's all about the ordinary people,
  and how they're starving.
Sally

                            Totally starved of fame.
  They're nobodies, you pass them on the street,
  no one cares about them, they're all dying
  to be famous, but do *we* care?
Charley
  So this man's come along.
Sally

                      He's like, a hero,
  a what's the word —

Charley

A saviour.

Sally

Like a saviour . . .

Charley
And if you pay some money you can stand there
with all the spotlights on you, I think ten pounds
gets you half a second.

Sally

Half a second
like totally being famous!

Charley

You can dine out
on that for ever!

Sally

And all the cash he raises
goes to help the stars, you know, with things like
outfits, stuff they need, like, big houses,
swimming pools, or else who cares about them?

Charley
Everybody wins.

Sally

It's a no-brainer.
That's why we're in business. When I've sold
this crap I'll have enough for nine seconds,
and I'm going to do a handstand.

Charley

I'll get twelve,
and I'm just going to stand there
just slowly being famous.

Sally

Let's go then,
look at the queue already!

Sally and Charley go.

Norman

> Remember I said it was my initiative,
> you know, with the black remote?
> Well, it wasn't my remote, it was your remote
> technically, so yes, there've been some changes,
> and the town's not quite as wonderful as it was,
> in terms of, well, free rides –

Polly

>   Two pounds forty,
> how many seconds of fame . . .

Norman

>   Polly, come on,
> I told you, it's all shallow, it's that creature,
> we let him out, or in fact *you* let him out,
> and everyone's out for himself, haven't you noticed,
> I noticed *you* were, did you notice that?
> The town's turned selfish and it's down to us,
> and it's up to us to do something!

Polly

>   It's nought-
> point-one second of fame. I'm going to be famous!

Norman

> Polly, listen, you shouldn't have let him out.
> You have to use that nought-point-one-second
> of fame to put it right,
> tell the people this man is the whole reason
> everything costs money! Understand?
> We have to undo the damage!

Polly

>   I understand!
> They'll listen to me, they'll even think they know me,
> those parasites, but I'm a star, an artist!

Norman

> Use your time and tell them! Then find him
> and take him back to your house. I'll go there now.

You let the wrong one out. That other creature,
the well-dressed one, he's the answer.

Norman goes.

Polly

Where will I meet you?

Meet me by this statue!
Right now I'm off to make a name for myself!

Polly goes. The Statue follows, the fair goes with him.
Quiet. Then Nono faintly singing. The house, dark.

Norman
What's that noise from somewhere?
Sir, it's me, Norman. Is that you singing?

Nono singing. His wings have grown again.

Leach
That awful racket, no. It's *that* up there.
Norman
It's bigger than it was.
Leach

It's an infection.

It spreads if you do nothing.
Enough! Enough!

Singing stops.

No place in the world for that.

Norman
I didn't see you there.
Leach

I wasn't there.

I was here and still I am, a prisoner.
Norman
I'll put a stop to that! My friend, Polly,
she let that creature out, the wrong one, him

with the sunglasses, we didn't realise,
he's changing everything.
Leach

What a surprise.
Norman
She fell for it.
Leach

You wouldn't have done that,
presumably.
Norman

I would not.
Leach   You're a sharp one.
Norman
Though I do say so myself!
Leach

But you don't say it,
you're modest, aren't you? I'm the one who says it,
I see it in you.
Norman

Really? The whole town's
changed and things cost money.
Leach

The whole town's changed?
You don't have to tell me that. Chocolate cigar?
Norman
Yes please, how much?
Leach

How much? To a special friend?
Norman
Well, thank you.
Leach

You and me, we think alike,
and that's rare, you know, two fine minds combining.
Norman
Two fine minds combining . . .

Leach

Times have changed.
I'm a Lakesider myself. Time was, Norman –
do you mind if I call you Norman?

Norman shakes his head with his mouth full.

Time was,
Norman,
you could circumnavigate the entire lake
in an afternoon and never see a soul,
see only nature, sky, meadows, water,
bluebells by the waterside, it was heaven.

Norman
Heaven . . .

Leach

Picture it now.
Filth, garbage, litter, rubbish.

Norman

I know,
it's everywhere.

Leach

They are,
they're everywhere. And they're not the same as we are.
They've come from somewhere else with all their
baggage,
the way they talk, can you understand a word?
There's a reason we are here.

Norman

What's – the reason?

Leach
Picture it in the old days.

Norman

The old days . . .

Leach
Not a soul in sight. Just starlings.

Norman

Starlings . . .

Leach

The air pure, the sky blue, the water . . .
you could see clear to the deeps: or you could see
your face on the surface smiling back at you.

Norman

Smiling . . .

Leach

That's our country,
Norman, that's our heritage.

Norman

Heritage . . .

Leach

And they took it from us.

Norman

Them . . .

Leach

They're not our kind.

Norman

Not our kind . . .

Leach

I respect their right to live
in whatever way they choose, but not here.
In fact I don't respect it, but that's it,
they exist, alas, too late at the end of the day.

Norman

Is it too late, do you think,
to have all those things again, I mean blue sky,
starlings, the deeps, the –

Leach

Purity.

Norman

Heritage.

Is it gone for ever?

Leach
> Perhaps. And perhaps not.
Come with me now, Norman – chocolate cigar? –
and I'll walk you through the ruins of a once great
culture.

Norman
> What about him?

Leach
What about who?

Norman
> The little one.

Leach
> That creature?
That thing is part of the problem. You and I,
Norman my man, are part of the solution.

Leach and Norman go. Nono starts to sing again.
Bright. The Moving Statue comes. The fair comes
with him, then Polly.

Polly
Stop, I want to talk to you! I know
you're made of stone and you can't hear a word
but no one else will listen – the whole town's
forgotten me! I was famous,
for nought-point-one seconds
the lights were shining on me, and I gave it
everything I had and I told them
everything I knew about that creature,
and how he'd spoiled the town, but by that time
the lights had all gone out and some other girl
was doing this mental dance, she was bathed in light
all with a cloud of moths, then it went black
on her and she just stood there, like you,
backstage in the dark.
She couldn't be consoled.

Norman.

Norman
Polly, I lost the gentleman!
Polly
                              What gentleman?
Norman
The creature in the suit and tie, he told me
everything so everything's been explained,
and we shared a cigar or two, he said I too
was a gentleman, and it's all about our country's
heritage, you see, he's my guide,
there were starlings, but I've lost him in the crowd.
Polly
You lost your guide in the crowd?
What kind of a guide is *he*?
Norman
                              He has the answers,
he's going to sort things out.
Polly
                              Look, it's my sisters!

Sally and Charley with clipboards, earphones, smart.

Did you see when I was famous?
Sally
                              That was then.
Charley
That was *so* then.
Sally
                    There are more important things
than fame, Polly.
Charley
                    There's quality of life.
Did you know that there's an area near here
of outstanding natural beauty?
Or there used to be.

Norman
>   That's right, in the old days,
> yes, the town was beautiful in the old days!

Charley
> Not now. It's been polluted, it's been spoiled
> by miles and miles of houses.

Sally
>   Ugly houses,
> cheap houses, dirty houses . . .

Charley
>   And all those houses
> mean people.

Sally
>   Ugly people . . .

Norman
>   Dirty people . . .

Charley
> We can only imagine what they do in there.

Sally
> So we do, we do imagine it and, you know,
> it's disgusting.

Charley
>   It's disgraceful we allow it.

Norman
> Ladies, you are talking my language.
> Once upon a time the air was pure,
> the sky was blue with starlings, and the water . . .
> you could see clear to the deeps: or you could see
> your face on the surface smiling back at you.
> Those days are gone.

Sally
>   We're going to bring them back.

Charley
> We're collecting signatures from citizens
> who'd like those houses moved.

Sally

Not destroyed,
just moved somewhere, away.

Charley

They've found a place
to put them all.

Sally

I suppose if they wouldn't leave
there'd have to be a different plan to make them,
but that's not up to us.

Charley

That's politics
and we leave it to the politicians.

Norman

Here,
I'll sign, I'm pro-heritage, I'm pro-beauty.

Polly

Do all those people know they have to leave?
Perhaps someone could tell them in their language.

Sally

They'll know in a minute, the army's on its way,
that's breaking news I'm hearing.

Polly

The army?
But somebody might get hurt!

Charley

Polly . . . Polly . . .
Outstanding natural beauty, Polly, *beauty*.
Is it not worth fighting for?

Norman

Of course it is!

Sally

Or is she *anti*-beauty?

Polly

Anti-beauty?
Er . . . no . . . of course not . . .

Charley

Sign the petition.
Sign it for beauty, Polly, sign it for nature.

She does.

Sally
A thousand signatures!

Charley

That's all we needed!

Polly
But the army's on its way already, you said,
to make the people leave the ugly houses.
Why did you need our signatures?

Charley

Research,
you could call it, so we know where we all stand
on major issues.

Sally

A thousand points of light!

Polly
It's a thousand men with torches.

Sally

Same thing!
Beauty is on the march!

Norman

There! I've found him!
Projected on that mountain! My guide!

Polly
What mountain? There never was a mountain.

Charley
There *always* was a mountain.

Norman

It's his mountain!
His dream is coming true!

Marching music. Sally, Charley and Norman join the throng.

Polly

His dream is coming true . . .
But his dream was down to us. We let that creature
out, and Norman thinks it's the right creature,
not the wrong creature . . . I don't know what to think.
I'm talking to a Statue, so it's clear
I don't know what to think!

Sound of the army going by.

Vehicles are moving, they have guns
on top of them, swinging this way and that.
Crowds are following, men with flames and sticks . . .
Can that be the right creature?
But they're doing it all for beauty. I suppose
if they tell the people living in the houses
it's being done for beauty, that might work,
those people would understand and say *alright,*
it's being done for beauty, we'll move off.
We'll go and live in a place you want us to.
Then there won't be any fighting.
They only have to say it, the army:
we're doing this for beauty,
and the people will collect their pots and pans,
their souvenirs and satchels,
and go while there's still time.
They only have to say it.

Sound of fighting.

I think they didn't say it. I think they didn't
say it in any language.

Statue

THIS.

Polly

What did you say?

Statue

THIS.

Polly

This? This what?

Statue

THIS WILL NOT STAND.

Polly

What? 'This will not stand'?

What will not stand?

Statue

THIS. THIS WILL NOT.

Polly

Who are you?

Statue

I AM STATUE, I AM SILENT
NO MORE. THIS WILL NOT STAND.

*The Statue beckons, and, one by one, more Statues
come, stiffly, slowly, who haven't moved for years.*

WE STOOD TOO LONG
STONE.
MEANING ONE THING
ALONE.
NIGHT AND DAY
BY WIND AND STARS.
TO PASSERS-BY
BYSTANDERS.

WE STOOD TOO LONG
STONE.
MEANING ONE THING
ALONE.
IT WILL NOT PASS.
YOU FLESH AND BLOOD

ARE STONE AS US
      LONG-STANDING DEAD.

WE STOOD TOO LONG
      STONE.
MEANING ONE THING
      ALONE.
WE WILL NOT STAND
      IF THAT DAWN BREAKS.
WHEN MAN IS IRON
      STATUE WALKS.

The Statues move towards the fighting.

Polly
    Now everything is alive
and everything is fighting, and it's me,
I let it happen – Norman, the black remote –
when they said I was not to touch it,
I did and I let it happen. I let the wrong
creature out and he let the right one out
but now it's wrong and stone men came to life
and all in all I wish my mum and dad
would find themselves and bring themselves home
where *I* am, because, because – no one's found me.

Nono – what about him? Is he the answer?
But he just hangs there singing, he does nothing,
he doesn't mind, he's easy. How could *he* matter?

And how could the answer to anything be in an attic?
It's all the things that are over,
things sitting there for ever,
things that are sad and dusty and pathetic –
poor Nono, stuck in there.

Home again. Singing.

Now there's no one else the singing could be.
Nono? Your wings . . . they look too big to fly with.

The singing stops. Nono's wings are huge.

Now it's quiet and he's listening but now
I've nothing to say to him.
Except I do keep thinking:
in every story I read when I read stories,
it was the third thing that mattered. The young one,
or the ugly one or the poor one got the treasure.
Things went in threes, and these three, they were Things,
weren't they? Two have gone, and . . . Nono?

Nono
  Yes.
Polly
      Do you – I don't know what to say –
  do you miss the others?
Nono
                  No.
Polly
  Is it dark up there?
Nono
                Yes.
Polly
  Do you want to come down?
Nono
                  Don't know.
Polly
  Come down then.
Nono
             Okay.

Nono comes into the light, blinking.

Polly
  Do you want to hear the news?
  We let them out, those others, and between them,

Nono, they ruined everything. It's our fault.
We used the black remote.
What do you think of that?

I've never seen somebody shrug with wings.
We let two bad Things out. They were bad Things,
weren't they, Nono?

Nono

Don't know.

Polly

Now the whole town
is fighting. Everyone's fighting for himself,
or they were, now they're just fighting to hurt others.
That's bad, isn't it, Nono?

Nono

I'm hungry.

Polly

Er, right . . . of course. There's nothing in the kitchen.
My sister kept it all until it rotted.
I've got – I've got these sachets,
tomato ketchup, Nono.
But nothing to go with it.

Nono takes them and eats.

The army went to move the Lakeside people
over the hills, they can't be the Lakeside people
now, I mean – 'Lakeside' can be their *name*,
to remember who they were. There were all these statues
came to life and fought against the army,
it was incredible, Nono!

Nono

I'm bored.

Polly

Er, yes . . . alright. But the television's broken,
and you can't play with the blinds, the remote is broken,
and we don't have any books.

My sister sold them for a ride in Splashworld.
She got soaked! She got a photo.
I've got – I've got this booklet,
Insects of Antarctica.
It isn't very long.

Nono snatches it.

Talking about my sisters, now I'm worried,
they went towards the Lakeside and there's fires
and bombs and rockets there, can you hear them, Nono?
I can hear them. I don't much like my sisters
except that they're my sisters
so I think I ought to look for them, my mum and dad
would look for them or would if they found themselves.
Do you mind if I leave you here?

Nono

                    No no, no no.

Polly

You have your book, and you – well, you *had* your
   ketchup.
I would have got you mustard but it's rare now.

Norman.

Norman, what happened?

Norman

               Beauty . . . heritage . . .
starlings . . . they're just words.
It's a war zone, Polly. Mud and blood and ashes.
Anyway, you wouldn't want to live there.

Polly

What about the Lakeside people?

Norman

                  They fought,
Their houses were burned down but still they fought.
I do believe they're naturally violent people.

Polly
And the statues?
Norman
They fought too,
but *everyone* looked like statues, mud-splattered.
And the water looked like chocolate-flavour Nesquik.
Polly
What have we done to the town?
Norman
Us?
Polly
I mean . . . I mean me.
Norman
What have you done to the town?
You let the monsters out.
Polly
I've been thinking . . .
Norman
You let the monsters out and you've been thinking.
Very nineteen-nineties.
Polly
It's a story,
Norman, what this is, it's a breaking story,
this whole night, and stories go in threes,
and *I* let one monster out,
and *you* let one monster out –
Norman
Yes out of *your* house.
Polly
And there's still one creature left. See? Nono.
Norman
What is he now, a vampire?
Polly
It's ketchup.
It's all I have for him, but he doesn't mind.
I only had one book, but he doesn't mind

reading that. I don't believe he minds
anything. How could *he* be the answer?

Norman

Polly. That – *thing* – is why I'm here.
I've been thinking too, and now I understand.
It's not that he doesn't mind.
It's that *he doesn't care.*

Polly

What's the difference?

Norman

The difference? *In*difference.
What's missing from the town we used to know?
People always fought, people were greedy,
thought about themselves, thought they were better
than other people . . . That all went away,
just for a while it did, when there were fireworks,
free things, good things,
but it all came back again when we let those creatures
out. There's only one thing
different now. *Everybody cares.*
This is a town where even statues care
what happens, don't you see?
Already the army's started to pull out,
and let the Lakeside people have what's left
of where they lived, and everybody wounded
is being cared for. As I was turning back,
I saw the two sides sitting face to face
at an endless table on the no man's land
between them. They were talking.
It looked like a good start.
And if you let him out . . .

Polly

If I let him out . . .

Norman

It'll be a town where no one cares again
for anything, it'll be like any town.

137

Polly
So I won't let him out. I'll keep him here,
he doesn't mind.
Norman
     He doesn't care.
Polly
         I'll hide him
somewhere –
Norman
      Where? Your parents will come back,
they'll let him out –
Polly
      I'll keep him in the attic,
he was safe in the dark, in the attic –
Norman
          Look at him, Polly.
He's growing.
Polly
    He can't help it.
Norman
        So what?
The roof of your house will pop like a champagne cork,
and a vast bat-winged cloud will blacken all the sky
and they'll all know it was you.
Polly
       So I can't keep him . . .
and I can't let him out . . . What am I meant to do?
Norman
In the course of all this thinking,
I referred to this – the List of What Not To Do –
where I find the following: Third Thing Not To Do:
DO NOT TAKE MORE THAN TWO OF THE YELLOW
 TABLETS
ON YOUR MOTHER'S BEDSIDE TABLE. IT WILL
 KILL YOU.

This is a drink I made from forty-nine of them.
   Two sugars as well, for taste.
Polly
                              He might not take
   sugar.
Norman
             Take sugar, Nono?
Nono
                           Don't mind.
   Don't want to be no trouble.
Norman
                           Sugar it is.
I'm leaving now, Polly, for a while,
I'm going back into town to tell the people
what you did, and why all this has happened,
and how you're putting it right. I'm going to tell them
my best friend is a hero. While I'm gone,
you can *become* that hero. One sip,
and the thing is done. Our town will be the town
where people care. Be our hero.
One day *you'll* be a statue.

He gives her the cup.

Here's a little rhyme, from the old days,
when they used to talk in rhyme so they'd remember:
Don't Care was made to care
Don't Care was hung
Don't Care was put in a pot
And boiled till he was done.
Just say it to yourself and you'll be fine.
You'll know what you have to do.

He goes.

Polly
   Don't Care was made to care . . .

Don't Care was hung . . .
Don't Care –
Nono

I'm bored.

Polly
Don't Care was made to care . . .
Don't Care was hung . . .
Don't Care –
Nono

Not many.

Polly
Don't Care was – what?
Nono
Not many.
Polly

Not many what?

Nono
Insects in Antarctica.
Polly
You read the book?
Nono

Not many in the book.

Insects.
Polly

Good.

Nono

I'm thirsty.

Polly
I have a drink for you, Nono.
Nono

I'm thirsty.

Polly
Did you say you do take sugar?
Nono

I don't mind.

Polly
You might not like the taste.

Nono
No, I don't mind.

Polly
It's a very peculiar colour.

Nono
I don't mind.

Polly
Why don't you mind, Nono? Why don't you mind?
Why don't you care?

Nono
Don't know.

Polly
Why don't you know?

Nono
Don't know. It's just – I don't.

Far off a Crowd has been raised. Faintly we hear:

Crowd
DON'T CARE WAS MADE TO CARE
DON'T CARE WAS HUNG
DON'T CARE WAS PUT IN A POT
AND BOILED TILL HE WAS DONE.

Polly
I'm supposed to give you this drink.

Nono
Good. I'm thirsty.

Polly
You just have to take one sip, and you'll feel good.

Nono
I won't feel any different.

Polly
Don't you want to?
Don't you want to feel something, Nono?

Nono

No, don't mind.

Don't want to be no trouble.

Crowd nearer.

Crowd

DON'T CARE WAS MADE TO CARE
DON'T CARE WAS HUNG
DON'T CARE WAS PUT IN A POT
AND BOILED TILL HE WAS DONE.

Nono

I want my drink.

Polly

Is there anything in the world
you care about?

Nono

Don't want to be no trouble.

Polly

But you *are* the trouble, Nono! If someone came
and wanted to kill you, Nono, would you want
to be no trouble?

Nono

I'm hungry.

Polly

If someone came
and wanted to kill *me*, Nono, would you want
to be no trouble?

Nono

I'm bored.

Polly

If the whole world
was about to end, would you want to be no trouble?

Crowd

DON'T CARE WAS MADE TO CARE
DON'T CARE WAS HUNG

DON'T CARE WAS PUT IN A POT
AND BOILED TILL HE WAS DONE.

Polly
You don't care, do you, Nono?

Nono
I'm thirsty.

Polly
Fine. You can drink this drink.

Nono
It'd be lonely.

Nono is about to drink.

Polly
What would be lonely?

Nono
There. Be pretty lonely.

Polly
Who would be lonely – where?

Nono
A fly would be.

Polly
What?

Nono
A fly would be, in Antarctica.
Not many. If there was one, there was one fly,
that'd be pretty lonely.

Polly stops him before he drinks.

Polly
Don't drink that.
Drink this instead – it's water.

Nono
Not thirsty now.

Polly
That's good,
Nono, drink.

Nono

        Don't want to be no trouble.

The Crowd reaches the house, led by Norman, Sally and Charley.

Crowd

    DON'T CARE WAS MADE TO CARE
    DON'T CARE WAS HUNG
    DON'T CARE WAS PUT IN A POT
    AND BOILED TILL HE WAS DONE.

Norman

    Polly, what have you done?

Polly

                I've done nothing.

Norman

    Exactly! Kill the creature!

Crowd

            KILL THE CREATURE!

Polly

    Nono, you have wings. There's a window.

Nono

    Window.

Crowd

    KILL IT!

Norman

           This girl has lost her mind!
    That's the creature everything's the fault of!
    It cares about nothing! It cares about nobody!
    It has to be killed!

Charley

          Our sister's new best friend!

Polly

    Go to the window, Nono.

Sally

          Ugh it's so ugly,

    kill it, please!

Charley

        Do something right for once.

Nono has gone to the window.

Polly

  Fly, Nono, fly.

Nono

        Be pretty lonely,
  that insect, pretty lonely.

Polly

            Fly, fly, Nono!

Norman

  Polly, no! *Noooooo!*

Nono flies away. The Crowd speaks in indifferent unison.

Crowd

  DON'T CARE WAS MADE TO CARE,
  DON'T CARE WAS . . . I DON'T KNOW, WAS WHAT . . .
  I'VE ABSOLUTELY NO IDEA. YOU KNOW,
  IT'S FINE BY ME. WHAT ARE WE DOING HERE?
  NICE GARDEN, POLLY. ANYONE KNOW THE SCORE
  IN THE ENGLAND GAME? ANYONE FANCY A PINT?

*The unison disintegrates to ad lib and the Crowd
disperses, leaving Norman, Sally and Charley, and the
Moving Statues, who have stopped moving.*

Norman

  You are looking at the girl who had the chance
  to make this town a better place. You are looking
  at the girl who missed that chance.

Sally

  What is he on about?

Charley

           It's nobody,
  it's Polly's little friend. I got to go,
  we're hanging on the Level Krossing.

Sally

                                      Losers.
I'm going down the Kaves, I haven't danced
for ages, so I'm gonna dance for ages.

Sally and Charley go.

Norman

   See that, hear that, Polly?
You are looking at the girl who had the chance
to change this town.

Polly

                         No one's looking at me.
Only statues are,
and now they're going home.

The Statues are leaving, except the original one.

Norman

                         Exactly! Right!
They're returning to their plinths and pedestals,
to be ignored for ever – because of you!
But I, I am Norman W. W. Jones,
I used the black remote and I tried my best
to change the town, but I got overruled.
So now, when there are wars,
injustices and ignorance and suffering,
and spite and greed and poverty and no one
does a thing about it – blame this girl!
The girl who wouldn't kill one single creature.
One single creature. That was all it took.
And you wouldn't do it. If that's the kind of town
you want to live in, well,
you're welcome to it.

Norman goes. Polly is alone with the Statue.
   We hear, far away, the beating of wings.

Polly
  Nobody cares again,
  and you're stone again, and somewhere my parents
  maybe are thinking of me, maybe not.
  It's light. I've been up all night.
  I'm not allowed to do that and I'm tired,
  I'm going to sleep till when,
  till my dreams are finished. Nothing's been written down,
  nothing's been remembered.
  Did you see all this?

  The Statue nods.

  Will you remember it for me?

  The Statue nods.

  One day could you describe it?

  The Statue nods.

  Then I'll go to sleep till then.

  Polly finds a place to lie down.
    Light only on the Statue.
    Light only on the Statue's face.
    Light out.

Production Notes

God, Freedom, Nation, Justice – how far are people prepared to go for abstract principles? There are an infinite number of things not to do. When a child goes to sleep at night, it's a sort of abandonment, being deserted in some way. The world is a series of things you can't do.

The Lakesiders could be any group that has arrived later than the natives. They are the outsiders, the despised – asylum-seekers perhaps. You could explore this by looking at where your actors come from.

Actors can be derailed by looking too much for stuff outside the text. For an actor, it is *all* in the text. It's in the vocabulary of the characters, their syntax.

Why do the statues come to life?

At the heart of the play is a question: if you've been told a person is responsible for inflicting woe, and you have the option to destroy them, do you do so?

There appears to have been a chance to make the world a better place, but the window closed. Only hope is left. The hope is that there are people who are ultimately merciful. It's an idea found in many religions. The need for Polly to kill Nono is false hope: it wouldn't be a better world if she'd killed someone. She wants to wake up with the world as it was. Her parents have deserted her. The only thing she's left with is a big blank TV screen. The world is what's she's been shown by her parents.

Charley is intelligent, thinks of herself as an intellectual, a bit nihilistic. Sally likes going out. Everything's pointless to both of them, but they have two ways of saying it. Polly comes face to face with Nono, but how they connect is up to you. Maybe Polly is a mirror image of Nono: she does care, he doesn't. The number three comes up a lot. There's the box, then the house around it, then the world.

Norman is a bit geeky, intelligent at school. He's morally thin, and won't take responsibility for anything – are these masculine traits? He represents the arrogance of a scientific approach which refuses responsibility. Polly goes along with what he says because he's got all the words. They've known each other since childhood and they've got a habitual relationship. He's quite knowledgeable, but is still led into believing unpleasant doctrines. He's dangerous. His grasp of history is distorted. He postures and aspires to intellectual superiority based on inadequate knowledge.

STEPS FOR DIRECTORS

STEP 1

Read the play. We all have slightly different experiences that we bring to reading. Get rid of as many affinities as possible.

STEP 2

Work out the logic of this imagined world, approaching it as if you've never been there before. On your own, look first at the title, then the cast list, then every page of script, noting a list of ingredients. Write every ingredient down (see below). By creating this list, you become objective, and then it will be easier to find agreement with actors. This is a better way to start rehearsals, to get everyone inside the world of the play.

Title: The Black Remote   There is the colour black •
There is a remote.

Cast   There is Polly • There is the idea of youth •
There is Sally • There is the idea of elders (realms of
authority) • There is Charley • There is Norman •
There is the idea of the middle • There is friendship •
There are winged creatures • There are statues • There
are statues that can move • There is the general public
(by now we see there is something bizarre in this world).

First line   There is the idea of leaving • There is the
idea of 'finding yourself' (something that Polly is
interested in: she's at that stage in her life) • There is the
idea of meaning and things having meaning • There is
the idea of 'here' • There is the idea of 'there' • There
is the idea of 'waking up' (the play frequently refers to
going to sleep) • There is the idea of meaninglessness.

*Through this approach we learn from the first pages of
the play*   There's technology, darkness and light, winged
creatures • What's important in this world • That the
play is interested in nothingness, the idea of abandonment,
of things not being there any more • To split your
interpretation from the objective reality of the text •
Patterns start to emerge to give an imaginative picture
of the world.

When you have created the list, go back over it to see what
picture is built of the world.

STEP 3 – TIME

Two fundamentals in creating a production and an
imaginative world are time and place. Every play benefits
from locating these and deciding when and where it is
taking place. It doesn't have to be somewhere realistic; it
can be a dream world. But there needs to be logic.

Establish what the rules are.

EXERCISE   *Split into groups. Go through the play together to make a list of any reference to time – implied time as well as real time. Note anything that relates to time. Find quotes. Ask questions rather than making statements, because statements need not necessarily be true. From this the whole group will construct a timeline.*

Some references and questions relating to time:

It's nowadays • How old are the girls? • What do the statues represent? How old are they? • How does Polly's time differ from others? • References to 'big bang', 'broken time', 'end of time', 'time of money' • The importance of time changes through the play • Milestones in Polly's life: birthdays, Christmas • The idea of using time wisely, time as a commodity, something that can be harnessed • References to different time scales: cost of time • The difference between adult and childrens' experience of time • Random playing, fast forward, rewinding – controlling time • Leach's wish to rewind time: 'time was you could circumnavigate the lake and not see a soul' • How people experience differently the same length of time • References to clocks • The idea of doing something too long (how long have the statues been standing?) • Real time versus stage time – what's the relationship? 'It's show time!' • 'Times have changed' • 'Those days are gone' • The title: is *Black* – night-time? • Is the remote a time-saving device? • Can you save time? Is time something you can save? • Is time something you can never reach – is it always beyond? • What's the relationship between the telly and the big bang? (The white crackle on the TV is created by the big bang. Static has been travelling through time) • Are statues representative of time? •

References to history: 'once upon a time', 'Victorian'
'we won the war', 'what is this olden times?' • Parallel
time scales • Using biros as permanent ink • DVDs as
recorded time. Prequels, sequels: time before, time
after • Real time – rolling news. (They tune in to BBC
News 24) • What's the relationship between the TV
stations and time? • How long does it take for Nono's
wings to grow? • How do time and pressure change
through the play? • How does time create pressure? •
How does pace of time change through the play? •
How old are the creatures? • Is there a parallel
universe? Is their time scale the same as ours? • Birth
and death • Mention of technology places it in time –
but it's not in our time. It's cutting-edge. It's brand new
• What is dream time? Can you measure it? • What
is the relationship between the language people use
and time? • 'Words have served their purpose', which
assigns them into history • References to 1990s and
1960s • 'Got this product before the summer' – is it
early in the summer? This may vary between different
characters • Stage directions: everything going by
faster, more busily • The time of your life • What
has happened in the theatre in this time? When did it
die out? Some time ago? According to Norman – he
has been taught it in history – it has died out, but it
might not be true. A type of theatre has died out.
People had to practise it. They could be old stories.
People sat in silence. They went into big rooms •
They're going clubbing – how late is it? • It is night –
Norman has crept out at night? • There's a reference
to a midnight feast • Is this play a debate between
evolution and creationism? In the house things
develop. Outside, things appear quickly, which make
no sense. What is the relationship between what
happens in the house and what happens outside? •
How long did it take to write the list in biro? • If

Polly kills Nono, what will happen? Will she become a statue: how do statues evolve? • Why is everything so vague – why is there nothing deliberate about time?

The objective of this exercise is to give the actors as much imaginative material as possible. When they step into the world of the play, they really need to be *in* that world, no matter how strange it might be. If a character says they have just come from outside, the audience should believe they really have. If they're watching TV on stage, the audience has to believe it – which is not to do with intimate naturalism, but about being totally immersed in the world you've created.

Although time shifts a lot, you need to create a version that is actable, that an actor can relate to. Rather than directing actors to change their energy, give them the imaginative material to effect that. If you are telling them how to act, they will always think about what the director wants rather than thinking about the backstage life. Look for the simplest answer that will get the actor to where you want them to be. You don't have to discuss what the play's about to get them where you want to be. Keep discussions about meaning short.

The list of questions above shows that time is not typical in this place. A useful framework for the play is the world of dreams, where time can be compressed or go backwards. It takes place overnight. Get the actors thinking about it by staging a dream. The rules of the dream world have a relationship to this play. The concept of dream doesn't have to be obvious to the audience – it's a way of getting the actors into the way the world works, how it feels, justifying it.

Create rules for each section of the play. Worlds can switch. You want the ideas to be enacted. Try and boil a play down to three or four themes. Find ways of them relating what the play is concerned with to their own lives so they act with conviction.

The next stage would be to split the play up into scenes. Perhaps scenes begin and end when the winged creatures are released. When the market is in town there is a different atmosphere. The war is different. Scene changes could be gradual or sudden shifts between atmospheres: e.g., it's 4.00 p.m., three minutes later it's 7.00 p.m. How did that happen? Well, it happens in dreams . . .

You have to judge whether or not people are lying in the text. If they seem to be telling the truth, is that helpful? Experiment with ideas of time in their imaginations, with the speed of time going on outside. Find out what solipsism means. Theatre means nothing to Norman, so to him it doesn't exist.

Has Polly come home at the beginning of the play or has she been upstairs? The answer depends on the energy you want to bring into the scene.

The sisters know their parents have left: decide what happened before this moment. Decide also how they all will relate to what the winged creatures are about. For Glimmer, celebrity is recognisable. Leach has a vision and is determined to realise it. Your design will tell a lot about the winged-creature world.

Dreams can be about prediction, the sorting of ideas in your head, making sense of the world. There's a cyclical pattern in dreams: the creatures go over the same ground. The idea of dream comes with incoherence rather than fate. It might be helpful to think about Polly being in a story.

STEP 4 – PLACE

Now create a list of places. Create a map. What is in the rooms? Where are things?

The house is symbolic of the self – the rooms you haven't been in are the parts of yourself you haven't discovered.

Ask where the winged creatures leave from. Which window does Norman come through?

Draw a map of the town, of the lake – how far are they from the house? Is it relevant?

STEP 5 – CHARACTER

Group work. Assign a character to each group: Polly, Norman, Nono, Glimmer, Leach.

1 Write a list of absolute, non-negotiable facts about each character. Polly has two sisters, those sisters have parents. Plus factual questions – how old is Polly?

2 List everything that the character says about themselves (I think, I feel). These aren't facts: they're about how the characters express themselves.

3 List what everyone else says about them.

4 Finally, look at relationships. List what Polly says about Norman. What Sally says about Charley.

POLLY
She's the youngest of three • She's a girl • She's friends with Norman • She lives with her sisters • She has parents, but they're not there • She feels abandoned • She has to make a decision at the end • She lives near a lake • She's not famous • She is more obedient than normal • Is Polly well-behaved? • Is she always obedient?

(What are the rules and who set them?) • Is she local?
Does she watch a lot of TV? • Does she feel abandoned?
• Is she close to her sisters? • Is she tomboyish? • She
mostly follows rules?

NORMAN
He lives next door • His full name is Norman W. W.
Jones • He is Polly's friend • He knows Polly's family
• He comes round every night, through the window •
He has a personalised playlist • He knows about
technology • He mixes up the stories • He tries to get
his parents to notice him when he leaves the house •
His parents never leave the house • He talks in statements
• He gets things wrongs • He believes his culture to be a
desert • He's a rationalist • He doesn't take responsibility
• He directs people into action • What are his values?
What is important to him? • How complete or assumed
is his knowledge? • Does he think he knows more than
he does about history?

The purpose of this exercise is to build a backstory for
Norman. When he comes onstage, he brings that past with
him, but he doesn't know what the future will be. It's easier
to give actors facts to work from rather than concepts.

LEACH
One of three winged creatures • He's a purist • He has
broken wings • He wears a suit and tie • He was born
at the Lakeside • He walked in the hills as a boy • He's
changed for the worst • Feels native community is better
• He wants grace, purity and love • He believes he has
found an oasis • He believes others are not the same as
we are • Believes the others took it from us • He believes
he is a prisoner • Thinks Nono is a problem, he and
Norman are the solutions • What criteria do they use
for doing nothing? What does 'nothing' mean? • Think
about Leach as a human, as well as winged creature.

GLIMMER

He has wings • He is one of three creatures • He comes
out of the TV and lands on the carpet • He wears
sunglasses • He was in a police drama, medical drama,
and saved the earth in a film • He carries around a
generic contract • He can speak English • He's
everything Polly wants him to be • He is outwardly
dismissive of his own work • Did he have his wings in
the police drama? On the TV the creatures are normal,
but through the supernatural act of jumping out of the
TV they have metaphorical wings • When Leach is
released, Glimmer's influence disappears • The world
changes when he is released • What he wants: respect,
privacy and dignity • He was safe inside the TV • He
wants to be left alone • He wishes he was nobody •
He is dismissive of his own work • He dislikes the other
creatures • His face is projected onto a cloud • He is
selling stage time for money • What happens to him?

NONO

It has wings • It gets hungry • It gets bored • It can
sing • It gets hungry • Its wings grow • It drinks •
What trouble does it think it will cause? • What is its
gender? • Nono is not its name – it was given to him •
He goes on a journey more than the others.

Ask what's ghastly about him. Glyn wanted him to be
without care. The only thing he seems to care for are the
insects in Antarctica – which perhaps makes Polly merciful
to him. Regardless of what you feel, what's heaped on
him is that the world is shit because of him. If he were
dead, things would get better. He's not meant to be evil –
he's indifferent, uncaring about good or evil. He's singing
an unearthly song. But it's for you to decide what it is.
When Glyn writes stage directions he wants them to be
open. Find something maddening, ugly, tuneless.

In the play the evils of the world are boiled down to three elements:

1 Caring only about oneself (include superficiality, celebrity). Greed. Selfishness.

2 Caring only about one's kind and despising other kinds. Pride in the worst sense. Hatred. Xenophobia.

3 Not caring about anything. Indifference. Apathy.

Nono grows wings because, symbolically speaking, indifference spreads. If you don't do anything about it, it gets worse.

To imagine that indifference would be gone from the world after Polly's act would be fantasy. The fact that everyone could save another's life is *not* a fantasy. Because Nono shows a glimmer of life, Polly saves him. What your deeds are to other human beings, is important, a global concern.

The creatures are there to test the other characters and the way that they behave. They are fallen, not flying. The first two are visually pleasing, Nono is less so – it's darker. Perhaps you could use bat's wings?

THE VERSE

A note on the script: the dots are a drift-off – not an interruption in the script, but an energy lull.

The verse in this play adheres to the same rules as Shakespeare's. Verse could have different effects – it could frighten the actors off – so avoid the words poetry and poetic. The play is written in lines – there's a reason why they start and end as they do. These are contemporary pentameters. You don't have to break them up, but they are mostly five-beat lines. Honour the fact of the line and you'll get the result you want. You can do that by exaggerating the lightness of it in rehearsal.

SHARED LINES

Polly
What do you mean they've gone?

Sally
I mean they went

Here, Polly and Sally are sharing a line – Polly takes the first half, Sally the second. With Sally you can sense tempo, which shows a lack of patience with Polly. DON'T LEAVE GAPS WITHIN THE SHARED LINES, or the piece will tail off. The actors have got to be good on cueing and accurate in their delivery. Honour the line, and you'll be okay!

THE PENTAMETER   Think of pentameters as breaths, not as time being marked. Hear time pass in the strokes of the line. Metre measures out time and space. Think of the lines like a violin – there are pauses as the bow returns. Verse can play a sense of containment and mortality much better than prose can.

DESIGN AND STAGING

Once you've decided what the play's about, go and look at art, architecture, see which artists are exploring these ideas. It's helpful to see when an artist has been working at the same time as a writer. Look at Rothko. Look at Gormley – particularly the men standing in the sea, moving statues.

If your cast is large, you could use many actors to play the three winged creatures.

Trust yourself that you'll be able to work out the logistics of: How will Norman fly? Does the TV stay there all the time? The fair, the market – do they stay or go?

Have freedom with music, colour, movement.

There could be colour when there is talk of fireworks.

Crowd lines could be parallel to the other lines, not necessarily sequential. Lines can blend.

Moving into rhyme indicates a rapid change of atmosphere, and an elevation showing how peculiar the world has become.

Workshop facilitated by Bijan Sheibani
with notes taken by Emma Gosden

A BRIDGE TO THE STARS

Henning Mankell
adapted for the stage by John Retallack
from the translation of the original novel
by Laurie Thompson

Born in Stockholm in 1948, Henning Mankell
was raised in a village in northern Sweden and
now divides his time between Sweden and
Maputo, Mozambique, where he works as the
director of Teatro Avenida. He gained bestseller
stardom with his series of crime novels featur-
ing Inspector Kurt Wallander, which have been
published in thirty-three countries and have
consistently topped bestseller lists in Europe,
receiving major literary prizes and generating
numerous international film and television adaptations. His novels *The Dog That Ran Towards
a Star*, *The Shadows Grow in the Dawn* and
The Boy Who Slept with Snow in His Bed tell
the story of the boy Joel on his way to adulthood. *A Bridge to the Stars* is the fourth and
final book in the series about Joel. He has also
written a novel about Joel as an adult, *The Eye
of the Leopard*, which takes place in Africa and
tells the story of Joel's first traumatic encounter
with the continent.

John Retallack is the founder and director of Company of Angels, which produces new and experimental work for young audiences. He has written and directed a number of plays in recent years, including *Virgins*, *Risk*, *Sweetpeter*, *Club Asylum*, *The Wild Girl* and *Hannah and Hanna*, which has toured widely and been translated into several languages. He was a director at Performing Arts Labs, where he ran the Playwrights Labs, and is a former director of Oxford Stage Company, where his adaptation of Melvyn Burgess's *Junk* won the TMA Young People's Award in 1998. He was the founding director of Actors Touring Company. He has toured and worked in many countries including Europe, India, Japan and America.

Adapter's Note

I love the visual quality of Henning Mankell's book, the dynamic image of a boy in the night in a white country, on the hunt for a black dog.

In this adaptation, I have tried to illuminate the book, not illustrate it – to give the novel a new life on the stage.

The story is about a boy who's unhappy. He lives with his dad and, although they get on, they don't have a real father and son relationship. They need one another, but they do not know it. The play is partly about the way in which they discover and communicate this need.

It is also about taking risks and making choices. Joel initiates Rolf into his secret society. The central conflict of the story begins here. Rolf wants the society to 'create fear'. Joel wants the society to find the dog that will lead the way to the stars.

It is really cold in this little town in the far north of Sweden. It is a coldness that we can barely understand. 'Inside' has a very different relationship to 'outside' than it does in England. The citizens of this town have, literally, to *insulate* themselves. They make their interiors as safe, warm and secure as possible. They survive most of the winter indoors. No one goes out for a stroll with the dog in the evening as they might in England. It's far too cold.

Joel's choice to go outside into that world at night is more than just a boy going out of his front door. It could almost be likened to self-harm. He is trying to take control of his own destiny, and it is a hard choice.

Joel is the leading character in the play and, as a reader
or an audience, we view the world through his eyes. For
this reason, Joel often speaks directly to the audience,
confiding in us, sharing entries in his logbook about his
secret society with us.

The other main character in the play is the town itself,
the chorus. The whole company (except Joel and Rolf)
play the chorus. The opening of the play is all bustle,
with a sense of the town and the school, and with people
introducing one another. Mankell establishes a town that
is a small community, but Joel, a child of the town, has
no one to watch over him apart from Simon Windstorm,
an eccentric insomniac who drives around at night.

Simon, like Gertrud, is someone living on the margins, an
adult who knows what it is like to feel utterly lost and
rejected. Each understands who Joel is without him having
to explain – and, given how Joel feels, he cottons on to
them pretty quickly too. It reminds us that the conventional
world rarely grasps how profoundly a child can suffer –
or how much they can see. Towards the end of the play,
Joel actually cares nothing for his life – the scene in
which his father saves him is a wonderful metaphor for
how profoundly children need parents and parents need
children.

There are a lot of stage directions in the play. This is
because there is lots of physical action without dialogue.
These visual scenes are part of the narrative. They are
as much text as the dialogue, and a great opportunity
for ensemble movement. Sometimes these sections are
speeded up, like an old black-and-white movie, to comic
effect.

The story is set fifty years ago, and the language is not
modern speech. This gives a group the opportunity to
experiment beyond their usual vocal range.

I am about the same age as Henning Mankell and, though I am not from Sweden, I can remember how much less attention adults paid to children in the early 1960s. Your family fed you and got you to school, but what you did with the rest of your time was left up to you. I was free to go outside as much as I wanted to do (not all night long, of course) and as long as I ate my greens and looked smart for school, I was pretty much left alone to get on with it. There was no TV, no mobile phone, no iPod, no PlayStation, just the radio and the local streets and park. A trip to the cinema was a huge event. Being given a bicycle gave one freedom and status all at once. It would instantly become Joel's most prized possession, nothing less. But that's what Joel has more of than a child today – freedom.

Henning Mankell brings us up abruptly against harsh truths in his Kurt Wallander crime novels. He does this also in his children's books. *A Bridge to the Stars* is the last of a quartet – the other three books have not yet been published in English. This is a story that is based on Mankell's own childhood. Mankell grew up without a mother in the north of Sweden and was himself a merchant seaman.

The play starts with citizens who are isolated and unneighbourly; it ends with the coming of spring, with Joel on his bicycle and a sense of community. The selfishness and isolation of the start relates to people's need to survive. In the end it affirms our need to look beyond ourselves, to our parent or child, to our neighbour, to our community.

JOHN RETALLACK

Notes on the Staging

The play is set in the winter of 1956 in a remote town in the north of Sweden.

Although this adaptation can be staged in different ways, the one feature that all productions should have in common is a sense of the intense cold. The contrast between interior and exterior temperatures is extreme. The emotional narrative of the play also moves from deep winter to the first thawing of spring.

The stage directions are a guide that emphasise the white winter landscape against which Henning Mankell has set his story – mostly at night.

As if in a folk museum, the characters are positioned all over the stage. Their homes could be denoted on the floor by white chalk or tape. Each home is distinguished by only one or two simple props: a chair, a table and certain objects significant to the story. Nothing is superfluous.

All the exterior spaces have a white floor. A white cloth surrounds the back and the sides of the playing area. When it is night, a single candle burns in every home. Nothing moves except the flame of the candles.

The spaces are: Samuel and Joel's flat; Mrs Westman's flat; Gertrud's house; Simon Windstorm's place; the school; Sara's café; Joel's rock; the arch/metal strip; the street. All interior spaces have a black floor.

Characters

Chorus
*As the Chorus, the people of the town also have
a collective role. In the opening pages,
led by Simon Windstorm, they introduce
each other. They create the schoolyard,
the echo in the forest, Joel's daring climb, etc.*

Simon Windstorm
The Narrator/Chorus Leader
*Key objects: a lorry (represented by a big steering
wheel or similar), two chairs nailed to make one
and a tailor's dummy for his coat*

Joel Gustafson
aged eleven, son of Samuel
*Key objects: saucepan of potatoes,
thirteen tin soldiers, his bed, shopping bag,
alarm clock, logbook, school satchel*

Samuel Gustafson
late twenties, father of Joel
*Key objects: axe, socks, his model ship, his paper,
photos, radio and sea charts, hammock*

Rolf von Swallow
aged twelve, son of district attorney
*Key objects: telescope, snowshoes,
spade, sack, shears*

Otto
aged twelve, boy at school
Key object: a bicycle

Sara
late twenties, girlfriend of Samuel:
the glamorous one, she wears a red hat
Key objects: apron, a tray,
beer in glasses, her smile

Miss Nederstrom
twenties, Joel's teacher: has a club foot;
married to a surveyor; a mother
Key objects: a Bible, mug of tea,
crossword puzzle, a pointer, spectacles on a chain.
(Also plays Jenny, Joel's mother, a silent character)

'No-Nose' Gertrud
twenties
Key objects: rocking chair, religious pamphlets,
a musical (wind) instrument, a record-player,
a globe, a red nose and cigar, her 'creepers'
(ideally, this actress plays a wind instrument)

Mrs Westman
very old, lives downstairs
Key objects: religious candles, a 'Jesus doormat',
a broom, her embroidery

It is intended that all the cast are on stage
throughout the performance.

ONE

Joel is the only character who moves.
He moves like a shadow through the white street.
He takes out a small black notebook and speaks to the
audience.

Joel
This is the ship's bible.
It tells the history of the vessel and its voyage.
T-S-F-T-D-T-H-F-A-S,
The Search for the Dog that Headed for a Star.
T-S-F-T-D-T-H-F-A-S.
'The search for the dog that headed for a star began
    on March 8th 1956.
Absolute secrecy was observed.
The weather was fine.
Clear sky, plus four degrees, colder towards evening.'

He goes into his home and hides the logbook under
a model ship.
He then lies down on his bed, as motionless as
everyone else.
As he lies down, Simon Windstorm begins to walk
through 'the town'.
When he speaks about each character, he or she
comes to life and begins to move a little in their space.

TWO

Simon Windstorm.
He wears a coat of holes and two completely different boots.
He looks as if he lives outdoors.
He walks in and amongst the characters as he speaks.

Simon
This story is about the town I love
and a boy who lives here.
His name is Joel.
He wishes he lived somewhere else,
not here, not in Sundstrom.
Sundstrom is far off in the far north,
a thousand miles from the sea.
All around us is forest.
A million trees.
Trees as far as the eye can see.

Sara
See the house by the river?
That's Samuel, off to work at five a.m. –
He's a lumberjack who works
For the Sundstrom Timber Company.
That's where most men here work.
He tiptoes out the house
So as not to wake his son.

As she speaks, Samuel does as Sara says.

Simon
It's winter now
And it's light from ten in the morning
Until three in the afternoon.
That's all the light you get in Sundstrom.

Mrs Westman
> There's Joel, Samuel's son.
> He's done the shopping and now he's boiling the
> > potatoes for their supper.
> His mother had enough of Sundstrom.
> She left her family and went south.

A young woman walks from the front of the stage to
the back with a small suitcase; she wears a green coat;
we only see her back.

> Where?
> No one knows.
> Joel can't remember her face.
> He's his own mother now.
> He brings himself up.

Simon
> Winter is like a long long night.
> Everything is frozen.
> Every lake and river.
> Our town becomes a town of ice.

Samuel
> Mrs Westman lives in the flat below us.
> She's talking to Jesus.
> The only man left in her life.
> She doesn't approve of me.

Simon
> Then spring comes and it rains for weeks.
> Spring hoses winter out.

Miss Nederstrom
> That's Gertrud,
> selling religious magazines for the Pentecostal Church.
> They call her 'No-Nose'.
> Well, it's true.
> She had a tumour
> And they cut her nose off.
> Everyone is scared of Gertrude.

Simon

And in the summer?
It's never dark.
It's light all day and night.
Extreme is not extreme in Sundstrom.
It's normal.
Some say it drives you mad, living here.

He laughs.

But that's not true.

Gertrud

Sara is cleaning up the empties.
Most of the timber company drink at her bar on
    Friday nights.
Sara's had her fill of hard luck stories;
She's got a tale of her own to tell.
But no one to listen.

Simon

We get a bit isolated sometimes, that's all,
We get set in our ways –
In the dead of winter
Even decent people freeze over.

Otto

Miss Nederstrom is setting up for her geography class.
She teaches me and Joel.
She's alright when she's in a good mood.

*Otto walks behind Miss Nederstrom, imitating her
limp.*

Miss Nederstrom

That's very good, Otto – that's exactly how I walk.

Simon

My name is Simon Windstorm.
Why is it me who's asked to tell you about
the good people of Sundstrom?
Because I never sleep.

I've given it up.
So I get into my lorry and I drive around.
I see everything.
I see things no one else sees.

He calls to Joel.

Come here. Come and give me a hand.

Joel looks around and sees him.

Come over here and hold this.

Joel takes the rope and stares at Simon Windstorm.

You're looking at my feet, are you? People have no idea
of what's best. I can slide forward using my wellington,
and use the spiked boot to dig into the ice and keep me
steady. Who says you have to have identical boots on
both feet? Does it say anything about that in the Bible?
Do the police have the right to arrest people who wear
odd boots? Of course not. No two feet are the same.
Hang on to this rope now.

*Simon Windstorm takes the rope and lays it across the
stage.*

Joel
What are you doing?
Simon
Doing? I'm laying out the rope in the snow. I think it
looks good. I only do things that look good.

Beat.

Do you think it looks good?
Joel
Of course. It looks really good.
Simon
I was ill for a long time. It was only when I started to do
things that look good that I started to be healthy again.

Joel

No normal person lays out ropes in the snow and thinks it looks good.

Simon Windstorm lies down in the snow.

Simon

The earth is round. It spins round and round. Sometimes I get dizzy and I have to lie down. The snow cools my head down. Then I can think about the past and the future. And while all that stuff's going on, I'm alive. When I'm dead I won't be alive any longer. That's the top and bottom of it really.

Simon Windstorm puts out a hand for Joel to help him up. Joel does so.

Thank you for your help. You can go now. I want to be left in peace. But come back some other time and I'll give you some soup that will make you to see into the future.

Joel

That's not possible.

Simon

Oh yes it is. Come back to see me and I'll show you.

Music.
    Simon Windstorm watches Joel go.
    Joel climbs onto his rock.

Samuel

I can see Joel on his rock.
It's by the river and no one else ever sits upon it
so it's his.

Joel is sitting on his rock.
    He has a model ship in his hands.
    Samuel, his father, puts a hand on his shoulder and talks to audience:

I don't know my son very well.
I'm always working.
And I get so tired,
I'm always sleeping.
What makes Joel happy are my sea stories.
I'm a sailor who got marooned – in a forest.
It happened because I came here to live with Jenny.
I left the sea for Jenny.
Then Jenny left me.
So I lost the sea and I lost Jenny.
Joel has never seen the sea.
When I'm at work he has too much time alone.
Once he told me his dream,
his favourite dream.
He'd like to pull up anchor,
and to sail our house all the way to the sea.

THREE

School time.
   The cast create the sound of a schoolyard with their voices.
   Otto's voice is heard loudly though the din of playtime.

Otto
   If I'd have been a mum and had a son like you, I'd
      have run away as well.

   Joel silent.

Joel
   My Mum's a figurehead.
   But I don't suppose you know what that is.

   Joel and Otto square up to each other.
      Miss Nederstrom rings the bell for class.

Joel and Otto sit down at desks. Otto puts up his hand.

Miss Nederstrom (*to Otto*)
Don't you feel well?
Otto
Miss, what is a figurehead?
Miss Nederstrom
Is there anybody in this class who knows what a
figurehead is?
Otto
Joel knows. His mum is a figurehead.
Miss Nederstrom (*to Joel*)
Where on earth did you get that from?
A figurehead is a wooden carving attached to the bows
of a ship.
Not nowadays, but in the old days when they had
sailing ships.
Nobody can have a mum made of wood.

*As if they were the rest of the class, the cast laugh
mockingly at Joel.*
Joel stares down at his desk lid and won't look up.

Joel! Joel, look at me!

Joel looks up.

You know a lot about all kinds of unusual things, but
I must say you sometimes get carried away by your
imagination!

Otto laughs at Joel.

Otto
Figurehead . . . that's funny.

FOUR

Night time. An old-fashioned alarm clock sounds.
  Music.
  We hear the dog barking again in the distance.
  Joel appears to be tracking something through the street.

Simon
  I'm driving around at night like I always do,
  I see a snow fox
  Or the odd drunk stumbling home.
  Maybe Gertrud walking solitary in the night . . .
  But who's that in the shadows?
  It's Joel.
  He's walking along the street.
  Nothing unusual in that –
  Except it's one o'clock in the morning.

  Joel comes to the front of the stage.
    He stops and speaks to audience.

Joel
  Why was the dog here?
  All alone and cold?
  Where was it going?
  Why did it stop and sniff?
  In all directions?
  A black elkhound –
  here one moment
  gone the next.

Sound and light effect of lorry coming up, passing and disappearing.
    Joel tries to hide but lights (perhaps an onstage light operated by Simon Windstorm) catch him full on for a moment and blind him.

179

Joel runs back down street to his chalked 'home'.
Joel tiptoes up past his father, sleeping in bed.
Joel slips into bed and sits up and writes his
logbook.

'On the first night
Joel Gustafson completed his reconnaissance mission
   to everyone's complete satisfaction.
The adventure has begun.
The dog will be tracked down.'

Joel goes to sleep.
   As he does so, Samuel gets up and tiptoes past him,
on his way to work.
   Mrs Westman watches him come down and stops
him.

Mrs Westman
   Good morning, Samuel.
Samuel (*gruff*)
   Morning.

Samuel exits down street.

Mrs Westman (*to audience*)
   There were no evil intentions in his wife.
   She had an itch inside her, that's all;
   You can't blame her for that.
   He should forgive her.
   I pray for him and his boy.
   And for her.
   Jesus forgives.

Mrs Westman lights a candle through following.

FIVE

Miss Nederstrom is reading aloud from the New Testament.

Miss Nederstrom
'When Jesus heard what had happened, he withdrew
by boat privately to a solitary place.
Hearing of this, the crowds followed him on foot from
the towns –'

She sees that Joel is asleep at his desk.

Joel! Joel Gustafson! How dare you sleep through
my lesson!

Joel wakes with a start

Joel
No, I wasn't asleep.

Laughter from the whole cast.

Miss Nederstrom
Don't sit there telling me barefaced lies. You were
asleep.
The whole class could see that.

Joel turns around and the whole cast is looking at him.

Leave the room at once.

Joel goes and sits outside on the floor.
He takes a pen from one of the children's jackets
hanging up.
He takes out his logbook.
He writes:

Joel
'The lookout on the mizzen mast, Joel Gustafson,
fell out of the crow's nest.

Exhaustion was the cause.
He survived without serious injury.
After resting for a couple of hours,
he was ready to climb up the mast once more.'

Music.

The following is visual action and without dialogue:
Joel goes up to Miss Nederstrom and says he is
sorry; she accepts his apology.
At the same time, Rolf, a new character, a boy aged
eleven, gets up onto Joel's rock in a pair of snowshoes,
takes out a telescope and looks through it.
As Joel turns from Miss Nederstrom, he sees Rolf
and throws himself to the ground in order not to be
seen.

Rolf (*unhurried*)
What are you lying there for? Did you think I hadn't
seen you?
Joel
Who are you?
Rolf
I moved here today. I didn't want to but I was forced to.
Joel
Where do you come from?
Rolf
That doesn't matter. I shan't be staying here anyway.
Joel
Those of us who live here don't sit down by the river
and start blubbering.
Rolf
I rubbed my face with my glove.
I am allergic to wool. That's why my eyes are red.
Joel
That's my rock. Nobody else is allowed to sit on it,
only me.

Rolf
Do you have a title deed?

Joel
What's that?

Rolf
If you own a rock, you have to have a title deed.
A certificate of ownership, with an official stamp. You have to have that.

Joel is angry. Rolf jumps down from the rock. Is a fight about to start?

Rolf
Would you like to look through my telescope?

Beat.

Joel
That rock is mine.

Rolf
It's yours. I don't want it. Are you going to try the telescope or not?

Joel
Okay.

Through the following Joel looks through the telescope.

Rolf
What else are you called, besides Joel?

Joel
Gustafson. But how do you know my name's Joel?

Rolf
It's carved into the rock. It must be you if you say the rock belongs to you.

Joel
It is. What about you? Apart from Rolf?

Rolf
Swallow. But I'm a nobleman and so I'm called von Swallow. Rolf von Swallow.

Joel

Eh? Nobody's got a name like that.

Rolf

I have.

Joel

And why don't you go to school? Why've you moved here?

Rolf

My dad's the new district judge. I'm working at home and I start school in the autumn. That's what they think anyway. I'll have run away by then. I can't live here.

Rolf takes off a glove and checks his watch.

In one week, three days, seven hours and nine minutes from now I'll run away. Just in case you're interested.

Joel (*amazed*)

Why? Why are you going to run away just then?

Rolf

Because there's a train leaves for Orsa at that time. Dad will be away at sessions. Nobody will notice me carrying my suitcase. There's a lot I need to take with me. I could really do with someone to help me to carry it. Maybe you could do that?

Joel

Of course I could.

Rolf

Thanks. Can I have my telescope now, please?

Joel returns the telescope to Rolf.

Joel

I've thought about running away as well.

Rolf

Show me something exciting.

If there is anything exciting to show round here.

Joel
I've got a secret.
But it's at night. Only at night.
Perhaps you'll be asleep then?

Rolf
I'll be there.

Joel
I'll be waiting for you under the viaduct, by the bridge.
At midnight. But I shan't wait long.

Rolf
What happens?

Joel
It's not sure that anything will happen.
But there's a Secret Society.

Rolf
I'll be there.

Joel makes a 'secret sign'.
Rolf copies it. They exit.

SIX

Music.
The following is visual action and without dialogue:
Sara's café.
Sara is putting on her red hat.
Samuel is waiting for her at the door and puts up an
umbrella for her. They speak together easily and
intimately under the umbrella.
Then they walk off down the street.
We cannot hear what they say.
Simon Windstorm turns around to see them.
Mrs Westman looks out at them as they pass her door.

Mrs Westman
Good evening, Samuel.

Samuel
> Good evening, Mrs Westman.

Samuel and Sara pause at the chalk 'door' before entering.
> *Joel is on the other side, writing his logbook.*
> *On hearing them he hides his logbook under the ship in the glass case. He is examining the potatoes when they enter.*
> *Image of Joel seeing Samuel with Sara.*
> *Joel is shocked and both Samuel and Sara know that he is.*
> *Music ends.*

Samuel
> Sara's come back with me for a cup of coffee, Joel. Sara, this is Joel.

Sara
> Hello.

Joel (*still staring at Sara*)
> There isn't any coffee.

Samuel
> What do you mean by that?

Joel
> We've run out. I didn't have time to go to the shop. There's enough for you tomorrow morning. But not for her.

Sara
> Never mind.

Sara pats his cheek.

> So you're Joel, then? Haven't I seen you in the bar selling newspapers?

Joel stares at the floor.
Samuel shakes coffee tin.

> It's a nice place you share.

Samuel (*to Joel*)
  It's annoying that we don't have any coffee.
Sara
  Oh, it doesn't matter.

  Sara pats his cheek again.

  How did it go at school today?

  Joel grunts inaudibly.

Samuel
  You're a real misery today, aren't you?

  Tricky silence.

Sara
  You can invite me to coffee another time, Samuel.
Joel
  I'm going to my room.

  Music.
      The following is visual action and without dialogue.
      As soon as Joel has gone through the chalk 'door' to his room, he goes down on bended knees and watches his father and Sara laughing and chatting intimately together.

Joel (*to audience*)
  My father will disappear.
  The red hat has started to eat him up.
  I'll kill her.

  Samuel and Sara get up. Samuel approaches Joel's door.
      Joel just gets under his bedclothes, with a book in his hand, in time.
      Music ends.

Samuel
  Sara's leaving now. Come and say goodbye.

Joel obeys.

Sara

Bye-bye, Joel. The next time you come to the bar, I'll
make sure the customers buy all your newspapers.

Sara pats his face and exits.
Music.
*Image of Samuel and Joel eating at table together in
silence. Joel feels betrayed.*

Joel

I want a bike. I'm the only one in my class who doesn't
have a bike.

Samuel is not listening, he is thinking happily of Sara.

Joel (*much louder*)

A bike!

Samuel

I beg your pardon?

Joel

I want a bike. I don't want to be the only one who
doesn't have a bike.

Samuel

When I have the money, you will have a bike, Joel.

Pause. Joel gawps.

Joel

Really?

Samuel

Why not? It was fun to have a visitor; usually it's just
you and me, sitting gawping at each other.

Joel

Are you going to get married again?

Samuel

No. I haven't got round to thinking about that. But it
does get lonely sometimes.

Joel
Tell me about my mum.

Samuel
Soon. But not just now. Not when I'm in such a good mood.

Music.
    Image of Samuel and Joel clearing table. Joel gets into bed. Samuel sits at the end of Joel's bed.

Sara. The lady who was here. She had a boy just like you once. But he died in a fire. Him and his dad. They were living a long way from here at the time. She moved here after that. It must be hard to be reminded of it all every time she sees somebody like you.

Exit Samuel. Joel sets his alarm clock.
    Light goes off.
    Music ends.

SEVEN

The alarm clock sounds under Joel's pillow.
    He stops it after one ring.
    The distant sound of a dog barking.
    Extreme cold.
    Rolf appears alone by the bridge under the viaduct. He hides.
    Joel appears. Joel waits, and while he does so he whispers to himself.
    Rolf creeps up on Joel and puts a hand on his shoulder.
    Joel yells in shock.

Rolf
Did I scare you?

Joel shakes his head. He almost peed himself.

I'm pretty good at creeping up on people. Who were
you talking to? I heard you whispering.
Joel
To myself. Could you hear me?

Rolf is amused.

Rolf
Yes.

*As before, loud sound of truck approaching, passing
and disappearing.*
    The lights briefly catch Joel and Rolf.

Who's that?
Joel
He's a madman who never sleeps. He drives around in
his lorry all night. He hasn't slept for thirty-four years.
Rolf
He'll die. If he hasn't slept for as many nights as that,
he's dead. That would mean there's a dead man driving
around in that lorry.
Joel
Maybe he is dead.
Let's go.

Music.
    *Joel now leads Rolf on as challenging a route as he
can create around the set/town. The dialogue that
follows happens as they climb, creep and pause for
breath. It is important that Joel is seen to be the leader.*

This is where an enemy lives. He's been excluded. He's
called Otto and he's a real bastard.
Rolf
Excluded from what?

Joel

You'll find out soon enough. How old are you, by the way?

Rolf

Twelve. You as well?

Joel

Nearly. Another enemy lives here. The Lady in the Red Hat. She will be eliminated.

Rolf

Why? Who is she?

Joel

She serves beer in the local bar. She's broken into my flat.

Rolf

Why don't you go to the police?

Joel

It's not that kind of break-in. Follow me. Not too much for you?

Rolf

No problem.

Joel

This is where I live.

Rolf

The whole house?

Beat. Joel wants to say yes, but he resists.

Joel

Just the top floor.
Come on.

They move across the stage for a few seconds.

See the arch?

Rolf

Some of it

Joel

High, isn't it?

Rolf

Yes. What about it?

Joel

If you betray the secret society you have to climb to the top of it and over it.

Rolf

With gloves?

Joel

As you wish.

Rolf

It's like ice.

Joel

Too much for you?

Rolf

I have no intention of evading my obligations.
What is the secret society?

Joel

I can't tell you till you're a member.

Rolf

What must I do to be one?

Joel goes on his knees and puts his tongue against a metal strip.

It appears to stick and it clearly hurts when he removes it.

Joel

You must place your tongue against ice metal and count up to fifty. And you must promise to crawl over the highest of the iron arches in the middle of the night if you betray the society.

Rolf

I promise.

Rolf goes on his knees and places his tongue full on the metal strip.

Joel counts to fifty, getting more anxious the longer it goes on.

*On the count of fifty, Rolf removes his tongue with
great difficulty and evident pain.*
Rolf is shocked but conceals it, as does Joel.
*He appears to spit blood into his hand and then
shakes Joel's hand.*
Joel then makes a secret sign that Rolf copies.

Rolf
Now what do we do?
Joel
We look for the black dog.
This is the logbook of the secret society.
This is the code:
T-S-F-T-D-T-H-F-A-S.
Rolf (*slowly*)
T-S-F-T-D-T-H-F-A-S . . .
Joel
T-S-F-T-D-T-H-F-A-S.
Rolf (*calmly*)
T-S-F-T-D-T-H-F-A-S.
Joel
The Search for the Dog that Headed for a Star.
That's what the letters stand for.
Rolf (*slickly*)
T-S-F-T-D-T-H-F-A-S.
Joel (*reads from the logbook to Rolf*)
'The search for the dog that headed for a star began
   on March 8th 1956.
Absolute secrecy was observed.
The weather was fine.
Clear sky, plus four degrees, colder towards evening.'
That's the first entry of the secret society,
Made yesterday.
Rolf
The secret society is good.

Beat.

But we can do more than just look for a dog.

Joel

But you're going to run away soon.

I thought that we could find that dog while you're still here.

Rolf

A secret society must create fear.

We have to show that we're dangerous.

Joel

How?

Rolf

I'll show you.

He whispers:

Quick! Hide! Somebody's coming.

Joel and Rolf flatten themselves against a wall.

Do you know who it is?

'No-Nose' Gertrud approaches. She carries church pamphlets.

Joel

Yes, I know her – everyone does.

Music.
Now Rolf becomes the leader as Joel follows him.
Rolf trails Gertrud as if she is prey in a hunt.
They follow her around the different chalk 'corners' of the town with great stealth.
The following conversation is in whispers:

Rolf

Why is she out in the middle of the night with her head bowed?

Joel
  She's always wandering around on her own.
Rolf
  Why?
Joel
  She hasn't got a nose.

  Rolf redoubles his concentration on his prey.

  She had an operation and they took it off. She tried to
  drown herself in the river and she put a snowchain
  round her neck to go to the bottom. But Happy Harry
  saved her in time.
Rolf
  Who's Happy Harry?
Joel
  The minister – she works for his church.
Rolf
  What's she got if she hasn't got a nose?
Joel
  It's a hole. She puts a handkerchief in it usually. Most
  people are afraid of her. Except Happy Harry.
Rolf
  I'm not afraid of her.
Joel
  Nor am I.

  They stop.

Joel
  You said you were going to show me something.
Rolf
  I will. How to create fear.

  The following is visual action and without dialogue:
    Rolf leads Joel.
    They 'jump' Gertrud with ear-splitting noise.
    Gertrud is really terrified.

She drops all the pamphlets that she is carrying.

She stands there, terrified and hyperventilating, her back to us.

Then she turns around – Rolf has disappeared.

Joel stands there terrified and Gertrud stares directly at him.

The sound and lights of Simon's lorry pass and catch them momentarily.

Rolf is laughing. Rolf exits.

Gertrud exits.

Joel is left alone.

EIGHT

The following continues as visual action and without dialogue:

Joel creeps back home and indoors, careful not to disturb Mrs Westman or his father.

He pauses outside his father's room.

Silence.

On impulse he enters his room.

He finds himself in complete darkness.

He 'feels' his way over to Samuel's hammock and then very tentatively reaches out to verify that his father is actually lying there.

He feels – and then sees – that the bed is empty

He runs all over the small house, looking for his father, shouting, 'Dad! Dad! Dad!'

Music.

The following continues as visual action and without dialogue

Lights come up in several 'windows' (squares of gauze) around the stage.

We see 'No-Nose' Gertrud, Mrs Westman, Simon Windstorm, Rolf, Miss Nederstrom, each one alone in their window, sitting or reading, or in the case of Mrs Westman praying.

Each one is alone.

In only one window are there two people: Sara and Samuel.

Joel goes out onto the street.

As he does so, Mrs Westman comes to her door and stops Joel.

Mrs Westman
It's shocking all this running up and down stairs. Has something happened?

Joel
No, nothing at all.

The following continues as visual action and without dialogue:

Mrs Westman returns to pray.

Joel runs out into the street.

He stops by each window, looks in and then moves on.

The last one he reaches is Sara's home.

Samuel and Sara are kissing.

Joel is disgusted; he retches and then spits. He is furious.

He finds a stone and he hurls it at the window.

The window smashes noisily.

Every head in every window turns to stare.

Joel runs back to his bed.

He takes out his logbook.

End of music.

Joel
'All the crew have been lost now. The last one to be swept overboard was Able Seaman Samuel Gustafson.

His son fought to the last to save him, but it was all in vain. The only one left on board now is Joel Gustafson. No other soul, only Joel Gustafson.'

Fade.

NINE

Music.
The following continues as visual action and without dialogue:
Morning routines, all simultaneous.
Samuel is on his way to work with his axe.
Miss Nederstrom is taking out her books.
Otto sits in class.
Sara is in her café, cleaning glasses.
Mrs Westman is sweeping her front doorstep.
Rolf is gouging his name onto Joel's rock.
Joel appears and walks to school with his satchel. He pauses outside the school and decides against going in.
He turns and walks away.

Miss Nederstrom
Nils Wiberg.
Christian Johansen.
Margareta Erikson.
Joel Gustafson.

Beat.

Joel Gustafson!

Beat.

Otto Lund.

Otto puts up his hand.
Joel plays truant and goes to Simon Windstorm's area.

*Simon Windstorm is reading a book and also
writing in it.*
Joel stands there until Simon Windstorm sees him.

Simon
I have some soup for you.

Joel
I'm not hungry. Thanks.

Simon
Later then.

Joel
What are you reading?

Simon
I've no idea what books are called. I read bits here and
there and if there's something I don't like, I change it.
This book has an ending I don't like, so I'm writing a
new one – as I want it to be.

Joel
Are you allowed to do that?

Simon
There are all sorts of things you're not supposed to do.
But I do them all the same. As long as I am doing no
harm to anyone. Besides, I'm mad.

Joel
Are you?

Simon
No doubt I was once. All thoughts I had caused me
so much pain. But that's all changed now. Now I only
think thoughts that I like.

Joel
You said you were going to serve me your soup. I need
to know what's going to happen this afternoon and
this evening.

Pause.

Simon

You don't look very happy. You look as if you have a
lot of thoughts in your head that you would prefer not
to be there. Is that right?

Joel

Yes.

Music.
    *The following continues as visual action and
without dialogue.*
    Joel pours his heart out to Simon Windstorm.
    Samuel comes home with his axe.

Mrs Westman

Good morning, Mr Gustafson. What are you doing
here at this time of the morning?

Samuel ignores her.
    *He enters the flat, sits and puts his head in his
hands.*
    Sara is in the café.
    Gertrud is rocking gently in her chair, reading.
    Miss Nederstrom is leaving the schoolroom.
    *Rolf sits on the rock, now sharpening the blade on a
pair of shears.*
    *Simon Windstorm and Joel stand up and walk
together to the front of the stage.*

Simon

This lake doesn't have a name on the map
The first time I came here I was very mixed up.
It was in the winter, just like now, and I stood on the
    ice,
and then I shouted out my name as loud as I possibly
    could.
'Simon, Simon', I shouted.
I don't know why. It just happened.
Then all four winds came blowing out of the forest.

One from each point of the compass.
One of the winds was cold and whispered, 'Sorrow,
  sorrow,' in my ear.
Another one whined and growled, 'Fury, fury,' in my
  ear.
The third one was warm and whispered in my ear,
  'Happiness, happiness.'
The fourth wind was both warm *and* cold,
It was telling me to choose which wind I wanted.
I turned my back on all the other winds and
I let Happiness stroke my cheek.
The sorrow I'd been feeling just melted away.
You have to be on your own if the winds are to appear.
All you need to do is to shout your name.

Joel is on his own.
  He takes in a big breath and is about to shout.
  No sound.
  He tries again.
  He says his name but it comes out very quietly:

Joel . . . Joel.

He grins a bit sheepishly on his own.
  This time he says his name clearly and firmly.

Joel.

He takes a big breath.
  He shouts his name.

Joel!

Again, he takes a breath.
  This time he shouts his name loudly:

Joel!
Chorus (*the cast echo his name at the same volume*)
  Joel!

From here, each shout and each echo become louder.

Joel
Joel!

Chorus
Joel!

Joel
Joel!!

Chorus
Joel!!

Joel
JOEL!

Chorus
JOEL!

Maximum . . .

Joel
JOEL!!

Chorus
JOEL!!

Silence.
Joel turns and Simon Windstorm joins him.

Simon
All okay?

Joel
Yes . . .
Maybe the four winds don't exist?

Simon
Maybe not. But you feel differently from the way you
felt before . . . don't you?

Joel nods.

Joel
I'd better be going home now.

Simon
You didn't have any soup.

Joel
I'll come some other time.

Simon Windstorm
Maybe . . .

TEN

Samuel sits alone at the table, his head in his hands.
Joel enters; he is visibly startled to find his father at
home.

Samuel
There's been an accident; somebody was hit by a
falling tree.
We had to take him to hospital by horse, but it was
too late.

Joel stops, looks at his father and then goes into his
customary routine in the kitchen, peeling the spuds.
Samuel looks at the table and clenches his fists.

He's dead now. This morning he got out of bed and
made coffee. He had no idea.

Joel
What happens when you die?

Samuel
If only I knew. But I don't.

Joel faces his father as he peels.

Joel
The forest is no place to be.
Why don't we move away from here?
Why don't you become a sailor again?
Next time it'll be your head a tree falls onto.

What shall I do then?
Move in with old Mrs Westman downstairs?
Or go and live with Sara?

Samuel (*fazed*)

I've thought about that, in fact, about what will
happen to you if anything happens to me, I've thought
about that –

Joel

I'm not moving in with Sara.
I'd rather live with Simon Windstorm.

Samuel

Whatever for? Isn't he mad?

Joel

He's not mad at all. I think he's very sensible.

Samuel

That's not on. But I have thought about it –

Joel

If we move away from here you don't need to think
about it. There aren't any trees at sea.

Samuel

There are other things at sea. Other things that can fall
on your head.

Beat.

Joel

I don't like Sara. Why do you keep on seeing her?

Samuel

There's nothing wrong with Sara. She's okay. She puts
me in a good mood. She laughs her way through life
even though she's endured a lot of things bad enough
to make her cry.

Joel

Don't we laugh, then?

Samuel

Don't keep comparing all the time. Sometimes I miss
her so badly, I do so miss her.

Joel

Mum? Jenny?

Samuel nods.

Samuel

Of course I miss Jenny. But she ran off. I don't want to miss her. I don't want to miss somebody who doesn't miss me.

Joel

How do you know that?

Samuel

She left me. She ran away from me and you and all the things we were going to do. We were only going to stay here for a few years, while you were little. I was a sailor, this was the only other job I could get at that time. We thought it was a good idea to live here where neither of us had been before. Only for a few years. After that I would sign up with some ship again. But then she got up one day and left.

The mother in the green coat passes; we only see her back.

Samuel smashes his fist down on the table.

Not a word for all these years. Not a single word. I don't know if she's still alive or what she's doing . . .

Joel

She had an itch. That's what Mrs Westman thinks.

Samuel

Mrs Westman? What does she know?

Samuel stands up.

I don't want any food. You can make whatever you want for yourself. I know you can. I'm going out for a bit.

Joel

Don't go to Sara. Don't go to her.

Samuel

I'll go to whoever I want to go to.

He looks hard at Joel.

Joel, somebody threw a stone through Sara's window.
It wasn't you by any chance, was it?

Music, very low.

Was it?

Joel (*to Samuel*)

No. I haven't been throwing stones.

Beat.

(*Aside to audience.*)

Now I must be careful to hold his eye and not to look
away.
If I do he will know it was me.

Joel holds Samuel's eye until Samuel looks away.

Samuel

I just wondered. But it happened in the middle of the
night so it can hardly have been you.

Joel

No, Dad.

Samuel

Come with me to Sara's. She'll make you a bite to eat.

Joel

Me?

Samuel

Why ever not?

Joel shrugs.

Let's go over there together.

Music.
    *The following continues as visual action and
without dialogue:*

*The mood is abruptly very light and the following
action is 'speeded up'.*
*During this Rolf turns up to wait for Joel, holding
a pair of shears.*
*Joel cannot believe how happy he feels all of a
sudden. Father and son put on coats and hats and
walk to Sara's place.*
Sara is surprised and pleased to see Joel.
The three sit and eat.
Joel gets up and Sara gives him a place to lie down.
Joel falls asleep instantly.
*Samuel and Sara talk, look at Joel, shrug, kiss
goodnight. Samuel lies down next to his son.*
Sara lies down alone on her bed.
All three asleep.
Light goes out on Rolf waiting for Joel.

Music ends.

Joel sits up in bed and looks at his dad's watch.

Joel
Rolf! I've missed him!

*He sits upright for a moment, his eyes close as soon as
he has spoken.*
Sara also sits bolt upright. She is still asleep too.

Sara
You're a nice boy.
Your dad can be proud of you.
Joel (*to Sara, but in his sleep*)
T-S-F-T-D-T-H-F . . .

They look at each other for a second.
Both then collapse back to sleep.

ELEVEN

Music.

A dog barks in the distance.

Rolf is again waiting for Joel. He holds the shears once more.

Joel arrives.

Rolf

Where were you last night?

Joel

We had to stay at this house of a woman that's got a dog that barks. I couldn't get out without waking everyone.

Rolf

Let's go.

Rolf presents Joel with the shears.

Now it's your turn. Last night I did what we agreed to do. I poured varnish over her window boxes. It's your turn tonight. You're going to cut the plants she has growing up her walls with these shears.

Joel

We hadn't agreed anything. I don't want to pour varnish over her window boxes. And I'm not going to cut back any of her plants.

Rolf

Just as I thought. You're a coward.

Joel

I'm not a coward.

Rolf

You don't dare.

Joel

I do. But I don't want to.

Rolf spits on the floor.

Rolf

You said if you betray the secret society you have to
crawl over the arch.

Well, you've betrayed it.

You didn't turn up last night.

I waited but you never appeared.

In a secret society, you don't come out with a series of
excuses.

You do what you've agreed to do.

Rolf points upwards.

There's the arch. I'm waiting.

Joel looks upwards slowly, sickeningly.

Joel

I couldn't come last night. That's all there is to it.

Rolf

It's the climbing plants or the bridge.

Joel

But I told you I couldn't come.

Beat.

I need a pee.

He turns away.
  Music .

Rolf

You could have a piss from the top of the bridge.

Joel

I want to look for the dog.

Rolf laughs.
  Joel zips up and faces him.
  Music ends.

I'll do it. But not because I've betrayed the secret society.

They cross to 'No-Nose' Gertrud's house.

Rolf

I'll wait here.

Joel

You can wait wherever you like.

Joel opens 'the gate' chalked on the floor.
He tiptoes to the creepers (chalked or represented by string).
He snips three branches.
'No-Nose' Gertrud appears in her chalked doorway, barefoot.

Gertrud (*calmly*)

What do you think you're doing?

Joel turns around, but Rolf is not there.

Come here.

Again, Joel does not move. Gertrud's voice is still calm.

Come here.

Joel steps into her house.

Who are you?

Joel doesn't answer.

I'm not going to hit you. Even though I'm very strong.
I just want to know why you're doing this.
One night you terrorise me in the street.
The next morning I find that somebody has killed all
    the flowers in the window.
And now you are destroying my climbing plants.
Why?

Joel

We want to create fear.

Gertrud

You create sorrow.

Beat.

Joel

I want to go home now.

Gertrud goes out and comes back with a trombone (or similar, possibly a kazoo).
A record-player plays a simple marching tune (e.g., 'Colonel Bogey').
Gertrud plays along with it, note for note. It is a real 'party-piece'.
Silence. Joel is shaken by what she has done.

Gertrud

Why do you think I did that?

Joel shakes his head. He is out of his depth.

Just because you're deformed it doesn't mean you're
    an idiot.
If I'd still have had a nose I don't suppose I'd ever
    have learnt how to play it.
Do you understand what I mean?

Joel shakes his head again.

I know what a lot of people whisper about me. I know
a lot of people think I shouldn't be allowed to walk
around in the street like other folk. Perhaps they think
I ought to be shut up in a cage and put on show as a
freak. For ten years I could not bear to look at myself
in a mirror. Now I can. And I want my flowers to
grow in peace.

Joel nods sheepishly.

What's your name?

Joel

Joel Gustafson.

Gertrud

Why did you do all this?

Joel is silent. He does not know what to say.

I want to know.

Gertrud grabs him by the shoulders and gives him a good shake.
She puts her face right up close to his.
Then she shakes him much harder and drops her hands.

Go now. But come back and tell me why you did it, once you've understood why yourself.

Joel stares at her.

Don't promise me to come. Promise yourself. Go on . . .

Joel leaves and immediately looks for Rolf.
He can't see him anywhere.
Then he appears out of the shadows.

Rolf

I didn't expect that. That you'd get caught.

Joel angrily sticks the shears into Rolf's hands.

Joel

I'm glad you'll soon be running away.

Rolf

Before I run away I'll make sure you climb over that arch.

You got caught before you did what you'd promised to do.

Joel

I'll climb over the bridge. I'll climb over it now if you like.

I'm not afraid. I'll stand on the top and pee all over you.

Rolf

You wouldn't. You wouldn't dare.
You'll slither back down again.

Joel

We'll see about that. Go and stand in the middle.

The Chorus gather to 'watch' Joel as he turns to climb.
Their eyes and heads follow him as he goes ever
higher.
The Chorus speak in the first person, i.e., as Joel.
The distribution of lines may vary a little from those
proposed below. There are many ways to stage the
following: a stepladder will suffice.

Music.

Joel

I climb onto the parapet, next to where the arch begins.
If I reach both arms out I can just reach far out
    enough to cling on to the sides.
Hold tight and ease my way upward . . .

Joel *and* **Chorus** (*together*)

. . . Hand onto the iron.
Cold penetrates the glove.
Close my eyes and edge upward.
Iron rivets scraping knees.
One hand, opposite leg.
Opposite leg, other hand.
If I don't move I'll freeze.
Up, up.
Higher and higher.
I'm mad,
I'm going to kill myself.
Almost at the top . . .

Joel

I can't go any further up
And I can't come down.

I'll fall.
I'll die.
Or I'll freeze to the arch
Till spring comes . . .

Rolf

Come down, Joel! Come down!

*Simon Windstorm arrives in his lorry with Samuel.
Samuel holds the headlight and he directs it to his son.
Samuel follows the climbing route taken by his son.*

Samuel

Lie completely still. Don't move at all, Joel. Don't
move . . .

*Samuel places his hand with infinite care in the middle
of Joel's back.*

Creep backwards. Slowly. I'll hold on to you.

*Music.
Samuel saves Joel by guiding him back down to the
ground.
Simon and Samuel jointly carry Joel 'chair-style' up
to Rolf.*

Samuel (*to Rolf*)

He is my family and he is my son.
He's alive and he's coming home with me.

Rolf turns away. Samuel turns to Simon.

Thank you, sir – I don't know your name

Simon

I'm Simon Windstorm.
I just happened to be in the right place at the right time.

*They carry Joel to the chalk 'door' of his home.
Mrs Westman is waiting there.*

Samuel

All is well, Mrs Westman. No one came to any harm, I'm glad to say.

Music.

Simon and Samuel put Joel into Samuel's hammock.
Samuel rocks him gently.
Joel puts out his hand for the ship he held in the first scene on the rock.
He holds it up above him and the light catches it as it appears to bob and swell on the air.
Music fades.

TWELVE

The next day.
Joel is walking round in his father's giant dressing gown with the logbook and a pencil in his hand.

Samuel

The most important thing for you to understand is that you are not still stuck on top of that arch.

Joel

I know that, Dad. I mean that I know that I'm here at home with you.

Samuel

It's something that's over and done with.

Joel

I know.

Samuel

I'm not saying that you should forget it. You shouldn't forget it.

Joel

I won't.

Samuel

But it's in the past now.

Joel

Yes.

Samuel

You could have killed yourself, you know.
I'd never have got over that.

Joel stares at his dad.

I'll never do what your mother did.
I'll never abandon you.
What are you always writing in that notebook, Joel?

Joel

It's a logbook.

Samuel

Read it to me.

Joel

Alright.
'During yesterday's violent storm Captain Samuel
Gustafson climbed up a mast to rescue an injured
lookout. Once again Captain Samuel Gustafson
carried out yet another heroic deed . . .'

*Joel takes off his dressing gown and starts to put on
his coat and hat.*

Samuel

Where are you going?

Joel

I'm not going to climb over the arch. I'll soon be back.

Samuel

You ought to stay home tonight.

Joel

I'll soon be back.

Joel puts on his hat and scarf.

Samuel

A penny for your thoughts.

Joel

I'm thinking about a dog.

Samuel

What dog?

Joel

A stray one. I want to see he's okay.

Joel goes out past Mrs Westman.

Mrs Westman

Are you like your mother? Have you got the itch too?

Joel

No. I'm like my dad. I'm not going anywhere.

Mrs Westman

You're a good boy. He needs looking after.

Joel walks across to the rock where Rolf is sitting.
Rolf jumps down and faces Joel.
Rolf produces the shears and holds them out to Joel.

Rolf

You didn't complete the climb.

And you didn't pee on my head.

Joel (*blood up*)

I can do it again.

Rolf

If I hadn't run for help, you'd still be up there.

Joel hits Rolf hard.
Rolf drops the shears and falls over backwards.
Joel squares up for a fight but Rolf backs off.

Joel

The secret society is mine. Not yours.

And I'm not your servant. Or steward. Or slave.

Rolf gets to his feet.

Joel is ready for him to fight back.
But he doesn't.
He backs off.

You're no longer a member of my secret society.
You'll have to start a society of your own.
Alright?

Rolf shrugs. Joel has shaken him.

If we're going to be friends,
you'll have to act like a civilised human being.

Joel walks on to Gertrud's home.
Rolf watches him as he goes.
He gets to her chalk gate.
He stands there.
Gertrud appears and looks at him.

I don't know why I did it.

Gertrud
That's alright, I know you won't do it again. Let's not
speak any more about it. Take your shoes off and I'll
show you what I found in the attic of the church.

*Gertrud leads Joel to an old globe. It has a little hole
in Africa.*

I think whoever made that hole used to live there.
Maybe a missionary, a long, long time ago.

Joel runs his finger all over the globe, tracing the seas.

Joel
Samuel has been to all these places.
I'm going there as well when I grow up.
Samuel is my dad.

Gertrud
Do you know what it smells like there?

*Gertrud unhooks a little pouch of seeds from a hook
and places them under Joel's nose.*

Caraway seeds. They come from Zanzibar.
Joel
How can you smell them?
Gertrud
I can't. But I can remember the smell of caraway seeds
from when I was a child. Every time I see that pouch,
I remember the smell. You can smell things even if you
don't have a nose.
I'll show you something else.

*She turns away briefly and turns around with a red
clown's nose on her face.*
She calmly takes a cigar and strikes a match.
She then breathes smoke through the clown's nose.

The only living steam engine in the world!
Anything is possible!

Joel gets up and shakes Gertrud's hand.
They smile and he leaves her.
He walks across and sits with his father.

THIRTEEN

Joel
Where is she?
Samuel
Somewhere out there. I really don't know.
Joel
Why did she leave us?
Samuel
Maybe she was too young. I'd like to think so.
Maybe when she had you, when she had a child,
perhaps she was a child herself.
And maybe now, when she's no longer a child,
maybe she regrets having run away.

I think she doesn't dare to come back,
can't face looking her son in the eye.

Joel

Perhaps I can go and find her?

Samuel

It's up to you. If you want to meet her, you have a
right to do so.

Beat.

Joel

What about you?

Samuel

It's different for me. It was so long ago. And now
I have Sara.

Beat.

Joel

I don't want any sisters, Dad. With Sara as their
mother.

Samuel (*laughs*)

Or brothers?

Joel

No. I prefer it just you and me.

Samuel cuffs him.

Samuel

Sara likes you. A lot.

Joel

She's alright.

Samuel

She is. She's alright.

Samuel stands up.

Come on now – what do you reckon? Is spring really
on the way?

Joel
> Can we move to somewhere we don't have snow all
> the time?

Samuel
> We'll do that.
> We'll move to the sea one day.

Joel
> Yes, that's what I want.
> Sail our house all the way down the river to the sea.

Samuel
> But before we do, I've got a little present.
> Come with me – we don't need coats now.

Joel and Samuel go out.
> *Simon Windstorm is in the street outside.*
> *He has a big brown-paper parcel.*

It's for you – now you're twelve. Happy birthday!

Joel stares.

Go on – open it.

Joel tears at the paper.
> *It's an old-fashioned, drop-handlebar boy's bicycle.*
> *Joel gets on it and rides on the stage.*
> *As he does so, Samuel, Sara, Otto, Rolf, Miss*
> Nederstrom, Gertrud and Mrs Westman come out on
> the street and see him wheeling around.
> *Music.*

Simon Windstorm
> Sundstrom is far off in the far north,
> A thousand miles from the sea.
> All around us is forest.
> A million trees.
> Trees as far as your eye can see.
> Now the snow has gone and spring has arrived,
> Life begins again in Sundstrom.

Through Simon's speech, the people of the town
position themselves all over the street and outdoor
areas of the stage, as if in a folk museum.
   Joel reads his logbook to the audience.

'The search for the dog that headed for a star ended
   on May 25th 1956.
The captain and crew are confident that the dog
   reached its destination.
The weather was fine.
Clear sky, plus eighteen degrees, warmer weather in
   prospect.'

Joel is still and completes the tableau on the stage.
   Lights fade.

End.

Production Notes

Although the play stands on its own, the novel has to be worth reading to gain an even greater sense of the mental and physical landscape of the play.

John Retallack hadn't met Henning Mankell until well into the *Connections* programme. But he had been aware of his work and attracted to his knack of confronting harsh truths in whatever he's writing.

Henning lives in Sweden and Maputo, where he runs Teatro Avenida, Mozambique's national theatre. He is critical of the egocentricity of Europe and needs distance to have perspective on his two homelands. He writes about Sweden in Africa and Africa in Sweden.

A Bridge to the Stars is based on Henning's own childhood. He grew up without a mother: her absence has been a disappointment to him all his life, and he was equally disappointed with her when they finally met. He was once a seaman, and is now married to Eva Bergman, a choreographer, theatre director and daughter of Ingmar Bergman.

John has spent lots of time in Scandinavia, so his sense of the location is strong. In the far north of Sweden there is daylight in December only between eleven in the morning and three in the afternoon. Sometimes depression and extreme behaviour follow from the introspection that comes with darkness. The Swedish sensuality comes from the long summer nights, when it scarcely gets dark. The difference between the two is extreme.

The narrative starts with people who are isolated, with candles in their homes, and ends with the coming of spring, with Joel on his bicycle, and a sense of community. The selfishness and isolation of the start relate to people's need to survive, to be indoors. Spirituality is a replacement for neighbourliness.

CHARACTERS AND THEIR PROPS

The characters are seen through Joel's eyes – they are filtered through his child's view of the world. This gives everybody a slightly larger-than-life quality. Avoid making them caricatures. No-Nose, for instance, can partially be characterised by how people react to her.

The props listed in the script are the only ones that matter – it is important for the style of the piece that the production is stripped down. And each serves a function. Do not try to create a room for every character – start from a basis of the props. Perhaps you'll find you need a chair or a table later, but don't add to the set unless you have to. The chalk on the floor is as in Lars von Trier's *Dogville*, which was shot in a black studio with white tape on the floor. Take a look at this movie.

SIMON WINDSTORM'S PROP   Lorry wheel. The lorry is what he drives around in, and a big wheel is a fun way of establishing this. Perhaps it has a torch on it. It can suggest the whole lorry. He has been to hell and back, but has managed to maintain a celebratory view of life.

OTTO'S PROP   Bike. Not only has he got a bike, unlike Joel, but he has the advantage because he is part of the bright majority who loves school and fits in. Otto can bully Joel, who is caught up in his own world and not adequately parented.

SARA'S PROPS   A red hat, beer glasses and a smile. She is the opposite to Joel in that she has a job that always puts her into contact with people. She is vibrant and voluptuous – imagine seeing her through a glass that's all steamed up, chatting and laughing. Her hat should stand out as a symbol of her sexuality, eating Samuel alive (or so Joel thinks). Joel loathes the bar as much as he does school. He is both repelled by and attracted to Sara's smile – he desperately wants a mother, but he is afraid of her.

SAMUEL GUSTAFSON'S PROPS   Steaming socks, model ship, newspaper, hammock, photos. His socks are huge, heavy, steaming after having been in the snow all day. The model ship represents the life he lost – he is a sailor, marooned in the forest. The newspaper is for when he returns from work, too tired to function, unable to communicate with his son. The photos represent the past. The hammock is his home. Samuel must be an attractive man for Sara to have singled him out from all the other lumberjacks.

ROLF VON SWALLOW'S PROPS   Telescope, snowshoes, spade, sack, shears. Rolf is hi–tech. He has shiny new snowshoes, which are the equivalent of a skateboard. He also has a telescope, which is an expensive piece of kit. He is from a different class to Joel: his father is a district attorney, and he lives in a house rather than just a flat. The book describes his room as being like Hamley's toy shop. The spade, sack and shears represent his ruthlessness. Explore just how cruel he is. He is a practical person – he comes up with new plans and supplies the tools. He's not bought just any shears, but the biggest, shiniest, sharpest shears he can find. The key to Rolf's mentality is the way in which he orders Joel around, gets him to do jobs for him. Joel finally gains the confidence to say he won't be Rolf's slave any more. Rolf thinks he's better than others, more important.

JOEL GUSTAFSON'S PROPS   Saucepan of potatoes, tin soldiers, alarm clock, shopping bag (he is his own mother). Joel is a little, sleepy, lost creature – he barely functions at school, and doesn't bring anything into the room. His thirteen tin soldiers contrast with all Rolf's toys. He does the shopping even when he is tired. He relies on his alarm clock, and one day it lets him down.

MISS NEDERSTROM'S PROPS   Bible, mug of tea, crossword puzzle. She represents society's conventions. She is like Otto – she fits in (the Bible is crucial). She's cosy with her mug of tea – she's in the settled society that Joel can't be part of.

NO-NOSE'S PROPS   A rocking chair, religious pamphlets. She is the most prop-heavy character. Gertrud has been shunned so much that she has wanted to take her own life. But then she found the Church – or the Church found her. Simon, No Nose and Joel are on the margins of society. Mrs Westman, Otto and Miss Nederstrom are at the centre of accepted society. Gertrud's disability is an unsettling deformity that is hard for a child to rationalise, because it looks frightening. Rolf wants to crush her because she is frail – he wants to see her suffer.

MRS WESTMAN'S PROPS   Devotional candles, 'Jesus doormat', etc. She sees Jesus in everything. Her broom and embroidery are her activities.

JENNY   The key to her is that we don't see her face. She's like a ghost – Joel wants so much to see her that he tries to see her face in everyone. The casting has been arranged so that the same actor who plays the teacher can play her. When Joel and Samuel talk about Jenny, it marks a change – they are opening up for the first time. It is the first grown-up discussion they have had.

THE DOG   The book opens: 'It all started with the dog.'
Joel says he saw the dog trotting down a street alone.
It's probably a stray. Either Joel thinks the dog needs
protection or that it will take him somewhere happier.
By the end of the play the need to find the dog has
disappeared – it's been symbolic. Look out for the
reference to the dog at the end of the book where it's
found its way to a happy place. The dog is described as
heading for a star, and it got there. The play captures
the moment when the boy stops holding his father's
hand. He is still sexually innocent but he has started
on the road to adulthood.

SETTING

It is really cold – a coldness that is almost unbearable.
Inside is insulated, warm and secure. Joel's choice to go
outside into that world at night is more than just a boy
going out of his front door. He is trying to take control
of his own destiny, and it is a hard choice. It's surprising
he meets anyone at all.

In terms of the set, the doors in and out of the houses are
the most crucial. Establish how the characters feel when
they are indoors and outside. Even if you are only using
tape on the floor, you need to indicate the physical and
emotional change people undergo when they step from
outside to inside, and vice versa.

Make a clear stylistic choice about the scene changes, but
be consistent. The white and black is there to make the
landscape clear and to show how elemental it is, but this
is not compulsory.

MUSIC AND CHORAL WORK

Don't be over-complex. Live music is a great resource, as it can be soulful and specific to your production. Single instruments give the effect of loneliness and isolation. Isolated sound in a space such as the hollow sound of a room / a forest / outdoors at night can be very effective. At all costs avoid making this piece sentimental through your choice of music. The punctuation and layout on the page give the actors an idea of where to breathe. The poetic speech goes well with the way one imagines the piece being staged. If it works, you don't even notice that it's poetry. It is important to break it up as part of the learning process, and not to let the actors run over the lines. The rhythm is key.

Originally, John wrote the part where Joel climbs the viaduct as a Chorus in the third person. But it didn't work because this is Joel's personal experience. You could try having the whole Chorus speak it together with Joel in the first person. It has a character of its own, and could give the effect that everyone in the town is implicated.

EXERCISE

In three groups, mark out the acting space with masking tape on the floor

GROUP 1 *Map out the whole town in detail, indicating trees, Joel's rock, etc.*

GROUP 2 *Map out the whole town but in an abstract way (e.g., allow No-Nose a chair to sit on, indicating she is isolated).*

GROUP 3   *Mark out the doors with tape and define the other spaces with props.*

Play a section of the script and discover which of these approaches or combination of solutions works best for you.

Now have each group find a solution to creating another level, such as in Joel's house, without using physical objects.

Experiment with keeping all the actors on stage throughout and entering when they are required.

Workshop facilitated by Giles Croft
with notes taken by Sophie Lifschutz

DEOXYRIBONUCLEIC ACID

Dennis Kelly

Dennis Kelly's plays include *Debris* (Theatre 503, 2003, and BAC, 2004), *Osama the Hero* (Hampstead Theatre, 2005) and *After the End* (produced by Paines Plough at the Traverse, the Bush, 2005, UK and international tour, 2006). His work has been produced in Germany, Austria, Switzerland, Slovakia, Holland, the Czech Republic, Italy, Australia, Japan and the United States. Other work includes translations of Peter Karparti's *The Fourth Gate* (National Theatre Studio), Gerhard Hauptmann's *Rose Bernd* (Arcola), and *The Colony*, a radio play which won Best European Radio Drama at the Prix Europa, 2004.

Characters

Mark

Jan

Lea

Phil

Lou

John Tate

Danny

Richard

Cathy

Brian

A Boy

Adam

*Names and genders of characters
are suggestions only, and can be changed
to suit performers*

Setting

The action takes place in a street,
a field and a wood

ONE

A street. Mark and Jan.

Jan Dead?

Mark Yeah.

Jan What, dead?

Mark Yeah

Jan Like dead, dead

Mark Yes

Jan proper dead, not living dead?

Mark Not living dead, yes.

Jan Are you sure?

Mark Yes.

Jan I mean there's no

Mark No.

Jan mistake or

Mark No mistake.

Jan it's not a joke.

Mark It's not a joke.

Jan Cos it's not funny.

Mark It's not funny because it's not a joke, if it was a joke it would be funny.

Jan Not hiding?

Mark Not hiding, dead.

Jan Not

Mark dead.

Jan Oh.

Mark Yes.

Jan God.

Mark Yes.

Jan God.

Mark Exactly.

Pause.

Jan What are we going to do?

A field. Lea and Phil, Phil eating an ice cream.

Lea What are you thinking?

No answer.

No, don't tell me, sorry, that's a stupid, that's such a
stupid –
You can tell me, you know. You can talk to me. I won't
judge you, whatever it is. Whatever you're, you know,
I won't, I won't . . .
Is it me?
Not that I'm –
I mean, it wouldn't matter if you weren't or were,
actually, so –
Are you thinking about me?

No answer.

What good things? Phil? Or . . .
I mean, is it a negative, are you thinking a negative thing
about –
Not that I'm bothered. I'm not bothered, Phil, I'm not, it
doesn't, I don't care. You know. I don't . . .
What, like I talk too much? Is that it? That I talk too
much, you, sitting there in absolute silence thinking,
'Lea talks too much, I wish she'd shut up once in a
while,' is that it? Is that what you're, because don't,
you know, judge, you know, because alright, I do.
There, I'm admitting, I am admitting, I talk too much,
so shoot me. So kill me, Phil, call the police, lock me

up, rip out my teeth with a pair of rusty pliers, I talk too much, what a crime, what a sin, what an absolute catastrophe, stupid, evil, ridiculous, because you're not perfect actually, Phil. Okay? There. I've said it, you're not . . .

You're a bit . . .

You're . . .

Pause. She sits.

Do I disgust you? I do. No, I do. No don't, because, it's alright, it's fine, I'm not gonna, you know, or whatever, you know it's not the collapse of my, because I do have, I could walk out of here, there are friends, I've got, I've got friends, I mean alright, I haven't got friends, not exactly, I haven't, but I could, if I wanted, if I wanted, given the right, given the perfect, you know, circumstances. So don't, because you haven't either, I mean it's not like you're, you know, Mr, you know, Popular, you know, you haven't, you know, you haven't, you know, you haven't, but that's, that's different, isn't it? I mean it is, it is, don't say it isn't, really, don't, you'll just embarrass us both because it is different, it's different because it doesn't matter to you. Does it. Sitting there. Sitting there, all . . . all . . .

You're not scared. Nothing scares, there, I've said it; scared. Scared, Phil. I'm scared, they scare me, this place, everyone, the fear, the fear that everyone here, and I'm not the only one, I'm not the only one, Phil, I'm just the only one saying it, the fear that everyone here lives in, the brutal terror, it scares me, okay, I've said it and I am not ashamed. Yes, I am ashamed but I'm not ashamed of my shame, Phil, give me that much credit at least, thank you.

Everyone's scared.

'S not just me.

Pause.

We've got each other.
We need each other.
So don't give it all . . .
You need me as much as . . .
Don't give it all the . . .

Beat.

What are you thinking?

Jan and Mark enter.
   Pause.

Mark We need to talk to you.
Lea Oh, shit.

A wood. Lou, John Tate and Danny.

Lou It's fucked.
John Tate No, no, it's not, no, Lou, it's not
Lou We're fucked.
John Tate No, Lou, we're not . . . it's not . . . we're not . . .
    nothing's . . .
Lou It is.
John Tate No, no, no, look, there, I have to, I really have
    to, you're going to have to listen to me on this one,
    and you are going to have to believe me. Everything is,
    everything's fine.
Lou Fine?
John Tate Not Fine, no
Danny Fine?
John Tate not fine exactly, alright, fair enough, I mean
    things are bad, things are a little, alright, yes, I'm not
    trying to hide the, this is tricky, it's a tricky

Lou Tricky?

John situation, but it's not, because actually what you
are saying is very negative, and that's . . .

Look, haven't I looked after things before?

Lou This is different.

John Tate Lou, are you scared of anyone in this school?

Lou You?

John Tate Apart from me.

Lou No.

John Tate Exactly

Lou Richard, maybe

John Tate exactly, that's exactly, that's what I'm saying –
Richard, you're scared of, are you . . .? I mean, you
can walk down any corridor in this – I don't think
Richard's – any corridor in this school and you know,
no one bothers you and if you want something it's
yours and no one bothers you and everyone respects
you and everyone's scared of you and who made that,
I mean I'm not boasting, but who made that happen?

Lou You.

John Tate Thank you, so are things really that bad?

Lou Yes.

John Tate Richard? I mean are you really?

Danny I can't get mixed up in this. I gonna be a dentist.

Lou This is different, John. This is

John Tate Alright, it's a little bit

Lou This is really serious.

Danny Dentists don't get mixed up in things. I've got a
plan. I've got a plan, John, I've made plans, and this is
not . . .

John Tate It's a bit serious, but let's not, I mean come on,
let's not overplay the, the, the

Lou He's dead.

John Tate the gravity of . . . Well, yes, okay, fair enough,
but

Danny This is not part of the plan. Dental college is part of the plan, A levels are part of the plan, dead people are not part of the plan, this is not dental college.

Lou He's dead, John.

John Tate Alright, I'm not denying, am I denying? No, I'm

Lou He's dead.

John Tate Well, don't keep saying it.

Danny This is the opposite of dental college.

Lou But he is dead.

John Tate Well you just, you're saying it again, didn't I just –

Lou Because he's dead, John, he's dead, dead is what he is, so we have to use that word to –

John Tate Alright. New rule: that word is banned.

Beat.

Lou What, 'dead'?

John Tate Yes.

Danny Banned?

John Tate Yes. Banned. Sorry.

Lou You can't ban a word.

John Tate and if anyone says it I'm going to have to, you know, bite their face. Or something.

Danny How can you ban a word?

John Tate Well, just say it then.

Pause.

Say it and see what happens.

They say nothing.

Look, we have to keep together. We have to trust each other and believe in each other. I'm trying to help. I'm trying to keep things together.

Richard enters, with Cathy and Brian, Cathy grinning, Brian crying.

Pause.

Richard He's dead.

John Tate Right, that's . . . now I really am getting a little bit cross, do not use that word.

Richard What?

John Tate No one says that word, okay? No one.

Richard What word?

Cathy This is mad, eh?

John Tate You know.

Cathy Talk about mad. I mean, it's quite exciting as well, though, isn't it?

Richard What, 'dead'?

John Tate Don't say it again, Richard, or I'm gonna

Cathy Better than ordinary life.

Richard What?

John Tate I'm gonna

Richard What?

John Tate I'm gonna
I'm gonna hurt you, actually.

Beat.

Richard You're going to hurt me?

John Tate Yes.

Richard Me?

John Tate Yes. If you use that word.

Cathy I mean, I'm not saying it's a good thing, but in a way it is.

Danny Shut up, Cathy.

Cathy You shut up.

John Tate I am trying to keep everyone together. Ever since I came to this school haven't I been trying to keep everyone together? Aren't things better? For us? I mean not for them, not out there, but for us? Doesn't everyone want to be us, come here in the woods? Isn't that worth keeping hold of?

They say nothing. Richard steps forward, a little hesitantly.

Richard You shouldn't threaten me, John.

John Tate I beg your pardon?

Richard I'm just saying. I'm just saying, I've just walked in here. I've been with these two. I've walked all the way from school with these two, with him crying and with her being weird, and I've just walked in here and I've got you threatening me. You shouldn't threaten me, you shouldn't threaten me, John.

Pause.

John Tate Or what?

Richard What?

John Tate No, I mean, you know, or what?

Richard Well . . .

John Tate Because I'm interested.

Danny He's just saying, John.

John Tate Are you on his side, Danny?

Danny No, I'm just saying that he's just saying.

Cathy Shut up, Danny.

Danny You shut up.

John Tate Don't tell Cathy to shut up, Danny, that's really not . . .

Danny I'm not telling her to –

Cathy He's on Richard's side.

Danny I'm not!

John Tate Are you, Danny? Are you on Richard's side?

Danny No –

Cathy He is.

Richard What do you mean by 'my side', there is no –

John Tate Have you got a side now, Richard?

Richard No, no, there's no –

John Tate because that's a bit, is that what you've got?

Danny John, I'm not on –

John Tate Because if you've got a side that means you're not on my side and if you're not on my side that means you're setting yourself up against me and I thought we'd got over all that silliness.

Richard We have, we –

John Tate I thought we were mates now.

Richard We are, we are mates now, we –

John Tate So if me and Richard are mates now, which we are and all that silliness is over, which it is, and you're on someone's side, Danny, then you're on your own side, which is very, well, to be honest, very silly and dangerous.

Danny No, you've got it wrong, that's not –

John Tate Are you on my side?

Danny Yes, I'm on your side!

John Tate Which means you want . . . ?

Danny I want to keep calm, I want to say nothing, just like you, you're right, you're right, John.

John Tate So what the fuck are you on about, Cathy?

Cathy I'm –

John Tate Are you on my side? With Richard and Danny? Are you on our side, Cathy?

Cathy Yes.

John Tate Good. Lou?

Lou Yes.

John Tate You're on our side, Lou?

Lou Yes, John.

John Tate You sure?

Lou Yeah, I'm –

John Tate That just leaves you, Brian. You crying little piece of filth.

Beat. Brian stops crying. Looks up.

Brian I think we should tell someone.

John Tate begins to walk towards Brian.

Mark and Jan enter with Lea and Phil, Phil drinking a Coke. John Tate stops. Goes back to where he was.

John Tate I'm finding this all quite stressful. You know that? I'm under a lot of stress. You lot shouldn't put me under so much stress.

Lea walks forward.

Lea Can I just say, John, that we haven't done anything. First I want to say that, but if we have, John, but if we have done a thing, which we haven't, but if we have then we did it together. Whatever we did, we did, me and Phil, it wasn't just Phil, if that's what you're thinking, if you're thinking it might just have been him, on his own, without me, well that's not, we are completely, I am responsible as much as he, as much as Phil, but we didn't because –

John Tate places a finger on her lips. She is silent.

John Tate Have you told them?
Mark No.
John Tate Brilliant. Is there one thing that I do not have to do?

Beat.

Jan So you want us to tell them?
John Tate Yes! Please.

He takes his finger away from Lea's lips.

Mark It's Adam. He's . . .
I mean we were just having a laugh, weren't we, we were all, you know . . .
You know Adam, you know what he's like, so we were sort of, well, alright, taking the piss, sort of. You know what he's like, he was, sort of hanging around
Jan Trying to be part of

Mark Yeah, trying to be part of, yeah, yeah, so we're
having a laugh

Jan with him

Mark yeah, with him, I mean he's laughing as well, see
how far he'll go . . . We got him to eat some leaves.

Jan Great big ones, dirty leaves off the floor, he ate them,
just like that

Mark Just like that, we were all

Jan stitches

Mark We were in stitches, weren't we

Jan Adam too, he was

Mark Oh yeah, Adam was, he was laughing harder than
anyone.

Jan Nutter.

Mark Nutter.

Jan complete

Mark complete nutter

Jan Big fistfuls of leaves, eh John

Mark laughing his head off, eh John

Jan He burnt his own socks!

Mark Yeah, yeah, he did, that's right he, he set them
alight

Jan anything, he'd do, just a laugh

Mark we got him to nick some vodka

Jan you could tell he was scared

Mark oh, he was terrified, he was completely, but like
you know, pretending, you know, pretending he's done
it before, big man, pretending he's

Jan You know what he's like, he's

Mark Do anything. And you're thinking 'Will he do
anything? What won't he do?'

Jan Let us punch him.

Mark he was laughing

Jan In the face.

Ma He was laughing.

Jan at first

Mark Yeah, at first he was, I mean we took it a bit far, alright, half-hour, forty minutes

Jan I mean, he was still joking all the way, but

Mark you could tell

Jan He weren't really

Mark fear

Jan well

Mark you don't want to admit, you know what he's like, Phil . . .

Jan Stubbed out cigarettes on him.

Mark joking, we were

Jan Arms, hands, face

Mark having a laugh, really, he was laughing

Jan and crying, soles of his feet

Mark or crying, sort of, a bit of both

Jan Made him run across the motorway

Mark you're thinking, what is this nutter, and with the vodka making you feel a bit, you know, you're having a laugh, together, what is this nutter gonna do next, we can make him do, we can make him do

Jan That's when I went home

Mark anything, yeah, only because you had to

Jan I wasn't there when –

Mark Only because you had to, you would've been there otherwise, you did all the . . .

Beat.

We went up the grille. You know, that shaft up there on the hill. Just a big hole really, hole with a grille over it, covering, just to see if he'd climb the fence, really, and he did, and we thought, you know, he's climbed the fence, which we didn't think he'd do, so walk, you know, walk on the grille, Adam, walk on the, and he did, he's walked on, you know, wobbling and that but he's walking on the grille and we're all laughing and

he's scared because if you slip, I mean it's just blackness
under you, I mean it's only about fifteen foot wide so,
but it might be hundreds of feet into blackness, I dunno,
but he's doing it, he's walked on the grille. He's on the
grille. He is.
And someone's pegged a stone at him.
Not to hit him, just for the laugh.
And you shoulda seen his face, I mean the fear, the, it
was so, you had to laugh, the expression, the fear . . .
So we're all peggin' them. Laughing. And his face,
it's just making you laugh harder and harder, and
they're getting nearer and nearer. And one hits his
head. And the shock on his face is so . . . funny. And
we're all just . . .
just . . .
really chucking these stones into him, really hard and
laughing and he slips.
And he drops.
Into . . .
Into the er . . .
So he's . . .
So he's . . .
So he's –
John Tate Dead. He's dead.
Cathy says you're clever.
So. What do we do?

> *Pause. They all stare at Lea and Phil.*
> *Lea goes to say something, but nothing comes out.*
> *Silence.*
> *More silence.*
> *Phil puts his Coke carefully on the ground.*
> *They all stare at him.*

Phil Cathy, Danny, Mark, you go to Adam's house, you
wait until his mum's out, you break in

Danny What?

Phil through an upstairs window so it's out of the way, make sure no one sees you. Get in, go to his bedroom, find a pair of his shoes and an item of his clothing, a jumper or something, don't touch the jumper, that's very important, do not touch the jumper, but you have to get it in the plastic bag without touching it

Cathy What plastic bag?

Phil The refuse sacks that you are going to buy on the way. Do not use the first one on the roll, use the third or forth, do not be tempted to use a bin liner you have knocking around the house as that will be a DNA nightmare.

Richard, you take Brian to the Head, tell him that you found Brian crying in the toilets, asked him what was wrong and when he told you, you brought him here.

Richard Me? But I hate him!

Phil Brian, you cry

Richard Me with Brian?

Phil and you tell them a man showed you his willy in the woods.

Brian Wha . . . what?

Phil By the bridge, last week, a fat Caucasian male, five foot nine inches, say, with thinning hair and a postman's uniform, sad eyes, softly spoken.

Danny Who's that?

Phil The man who showed Brian his willy in the woods, please keep up, I'm making this up as I go along

Danny What were his teeth like?

Phil Bad, very bad.

Danny Thought so.

Phil Cathy, Mark and Jan, you take the shoes, Cathy, you put them on, and you enter the woods from the south entrance

Cathy Which one's south?

Mark By the Asda.

Phil Mark, you enter from the east entrance with Jan on your back.

Mark Is he taking the piss?

Phil the two of you combined should equal that of a fat postman with bad teeth, you make your way into the woods, do not put her down unless it's on concrete or a tree trunk, never when you're walking on mud. You meet Cathy near the bridge, you move around a bit, you exit from the south,

Mark By the Asda.

Phil Lou and Danny, you meet them there, but on the way you find a quiet street, you wait until it's just you and a man, you walk ahead of him and when you're far ahead you drop the jumper. The man picks it up, runs after you covering it in DNA and then gives it back, make sure you let him drop it in the bag, say you're taking it to a charity shop. Take it to the south entrance, tear it a little, chuck it in a hedge, all go home and wait a day or two until Adam's declared missing, and then John Tate comes forward and says he thinks he saw Adam with a fat man in a uniform by Asda's but he can't be sure. They'll think he's been abducted, there'll be inquiries, police, mourning, a service and if everyone keeps their mouths shut we should be fine. Any questions?

> *They stare at him open-mouthed.*
> *He bends down. Picks up his Coke.*
> *Starts to drink his Coke.*

A Field. Lea and Phil sitting.
Pause.

Lea Apparently bonobos are our nearest relative. For years people thought they were chimpanzees, but they're not, they are completely different. Chimps are evil. They murder each other, did you know that? They kill and sometimes torture each other to find a better position within the social structure. A chimp'll just find itself on the outside of a group and before he knows what's happening it's being hounded to death by the others, sometimes for months. For years we've thought that chimps were our closest living relative, but now they saying it's the bonobos. Bonobos are the complete opposite of chimps. When a stranger bonobo approaches the pack, the other bonobos all come out and go, 'Hello, mate. What you doing round here? Come and meet the family, we can eat some ants.' And if a bonobo damages its hand, whereas the chimps'll probably cast it out or bite its hand off, the bonobos will come over and look after it, and they'll all look sad because there's a bonobo feeling pain. I saw it on a programme. Such sadness in those intelligent eyes. Empathy. That's what bonobos have. Amazing really, I mean they're exactly like chimps, but the tiniest change in their DNA . . . The woman was saying that if we'd discovered bonobos before chimps our understanding of ourselves would be very different.

Pause. Phil pulls out a bag of crisps.

You don't care, do you. I could be talking Chinese for all you care. How do you do it? You're amazing. You're unreal. I sometimes think you're not human. I sometimes think I wonder what you would do if I killed myself, right here in front of you. What would you do? What you do, Phil?

No answer.

Phil, what would you do? Phil?

Still no answer.
Suddenly Lea grabs her own throat.

I'm gonna do it!

She squeezes.

I mean it! I'm gonna do it . . .

No answer. She strangles herself, her face turning red.
She falls to her knees with the exertion.
Phil looks on.
Lea is in considerable pain. Grits her teeth and
squeezes.
She strangles until she is lying prone on the floor.

(*Gasping.*) Phil! This is it . . .

She stops.
Lies there, panting.
Phil opens his crisps and begins to eat them.
Lea gets up, sits next to Phil.
Phil eats on.

Course, they fuck a lot. Bonobos. Always at it. Sex mad.
Sex, sex, sex, sex, sex, sex, sex, sex, sex, constant sex,
randy, in the bonobo world having it off is like saying I
like your shoes. Partner-swapping, men and women,
women and men, women and women, men on men,
fathers, mothers, children, oral sex, group
masturbation, sub-dom, interracial, bestiality, the lot,
it was like an orgy, when bonobos get going, it was
fairly disgusting, actually.

Pause.

But that's bonobos for you.

Pause.

We're in trouble now.

We're in trouble now, Phil. Don't know how this'll pan
out.
Trouble now.

TWO

A street. Jan and Mark.
  Pause.

Jan What?
Mark He's not going.
Jan What do you mean, he's not going?
Mark He's not going.
Jan He's not going?
Mark Yes.
Jan That's what he said?
Mark Yes.
Jan He said he's not going?
Mark Yeah, he said he's not, he's not . . .
Jan What?
Mark Going.

  Beat.

Jan Is he off his head?
Mark I know.
Jan Is he insane?
Mark I know.
Jan Is he joking?
Mark I know, I know.
Jan No, that's a question.
Mark He's not joking, he's not going, he's said he's not
  going, I said you've gotta go, he said he's not going,
  'I'm not going,' he said.
Jan That's what he said?
Mark That's what he said, I'm saying that's what he said.

Jan Fuck.
Mark Exactly.

Beat.

Jan What are we going to do?

A field. Phil and Lea, Phil slowly eating a pack of Starburst.
  Lea has a Tupperware container on her lap.

Lea Are you happy?
No, don't answer that, Jesus, sorry, what's wrong with me, sorry –
Are you?
No, I'm just wondering. I mean what is happy, what's happy all about, who says you're supposed to be happy? Like we're all supposed to be happy, happy is our natural, and any deviation from that state is seen as a failure, which in itself makes you more unhappy so you have to pretend to be even happier which doesn't work because people can see that you're pretending which makes them awkward and you can see that they can see that you're pretending to be happy and their awkwardness is making you even more unhappy so you have to pretend to be even happier, it's a nightmare. It's like nuclear waste or global warming.

Beat.

Isn't it, Phil? Phil? Isn't it, like nuclear . . .

Phil doesn't answer.

Yeah, you know, you know it is, you know more than I do, I can't tell you any, you know. People getting all upset about polluting the natural order? When this planet is churning molten lava with a thin layer of crust on top with a few kilometres of atmosphere clinging to it? I mean, please, don't gimme all that, carbon dioxide? Carbon dioxide, Phil? And look at the rest of the universe. Venus, Phil, there's a, look at Venus, what about Venus, hot enough to melt lead or Titan with oceans of liquid nitrogen, I mean stars, Phil, a billion nuclear reactions a second, I mean to be honest it's all either red hot or ice cold, so, so, so . . . No. It's life that upsets the natural order. It's us that's the anomaly.

But that's the beauty, isn't it, Phil? I couldn't say this to anyone else, they'd say, 'That's a pretty fucking grim view of the world, Lea,' but you can see the beauty, which is why I can talk to you, because you can see the incredibly precious beauty and fragility of reality, and it's the same for happiness, you can apply the same theory to happiness, so don't start, Phil, don't come here giving it all the, you know, all the, all the . . .

Beat.

Can you remember the happiest moment in your life?

Beat. Phil eats another Starburst.

I know mine. I know my happiest moment. Week last Tuesday. That sunset. You remember that sunset? Do you? You don't, do you? Oh my God, you don't.

He says nothing.
She opens the Tupperware container.
Shows it to Phil.

It's Jerry. I killed him. I took him out of his cage, I put the point of a screwdriver on his head and I hit it with a hammer. Why do you think I did that?

Phil shrugs.

No. No, me neither.

She closes the lid.

Everything's much better, though. I mean really, it is.
Everyone's working together. They're a lot happier.
Remember last month, Dan threatened to kill Cathy?
Well, yesterday I saw him showing her his phone, like
they were old friends. Last week Richard invited Mark
to his party, bring a friend, anyone you like, can you
believe that? Richard and Mark? Yep. Everyone's
happier. It's pouring into the school, grief, grief is
making them happy.

They say John Tate's lost it though, won't come out of his
room. Bit odd. Maybe that's what's making people
happier. Maybe it's just having something to work
towards. Together. Do you think that's what it is? Are
we really that simple?

Where will it stop? Only been four days but everything's
changed.

Pause.

Adam's parents were on the telly again last night.

Phil looks up.

Yeah. Another appeal.
To the fat postman with bad teeth.
What have we done, Phil?

Mark and Jan enter.

Jan We need to talk.

Woods. Phil and Lea, Lou and Danny. Phil has a muffin.
Pause.

Lea What?

Danny They've found . . .
They . . .
Well they've found –

Lou The man.

Danny Yeah, they've found the man.

Lea They've found the man?

Danny Yeah.

Lea They've found the man?

Danny Yes.

Lea Oh my God.

Lou Exactly.

Lea Oh my God.

Lou That's what we thought, we thought that, didn't we, Danny?

Danny Yeah, we did.

Lea Are you sure? I mean are you . . .

Danny Definitely. He's in custody now. They're questioning him.

Lea But how, I mean who, how, who, who is, who is, how?

Lou Dunno.

Lea Who is he?

Lou He's the man who kidnapped Adam.

Lea Right. No.

Lou Yes.

Lea No.

Danny Yes.

Lea No, no, yeah, no, actually, because that man, the man who, he doesn't actually, I mean I'm not being fussy or anything, but the man who kidnapped Adam doesn't actually exist, does he? Well, does he?

Lou No. But they've got him.

Danny I heard his teeth are awful.

Lea You know, I mean he doesn't, he doesn't . . . Phil?
Any . . . any thoughts? Any words, any comments,
any . . . ideas, any, any, any . . . thing? At all?

I mean this is, this is, isn't it, this is, is it?

Shit. Oh shit.

Danny He answers the description. Fat postman,
thinning hair, his teeth are terrible, apparently.

Lea But that's just

Lou Yeah. That's what we thought.

Lea we just, didn't we, Phil, we just, we just, I mean you
just . . .

Danny What are we gonna do?

Lou We're fucked.

Lea We're not . . .

Lou We're –

Lea No, no, sorry, no we're not, are we, Phil? I mean
we're, no we're alright.

Danny They're looking for Brian.

Lea Why?

Danny Because he can identify him.

Lea No he can't.

Lou Because he saw him in the woods.

Lea He didn't

Lou He did, he –

Lea No he didn't, because that wasn't the man in the
woods because there wasn't a man in the woods.
Where's Brian?

Danny Hiding. Jan and Mark have gone to find him.

Lou He's shitting it.

Lea I mean what, they just picked this bloke up, they just
saw him and said, 'You look dodgy, you're a murderer
because you've got a postman's uniform'?

Danny Well, there's the teeth as well.

Lea You can't go to prison for bad teeth.

Lou What if he goes to prison?

Lea He won't go to prison.

Lou You just said –

Lea He won't get done for it because he hasn't . . .

Danny This sort of stuff sticks, you know.

Lea Look, everyone, everyone calm, okay? Isn't that right, Phil? Phil, isn't that, I mean things are, everything is, well, better and isn't everyone more, you know, and cheerful and stuff, so let's, please, let's –

Danny How am I gonna get references?

Lou We're fucked.

Lea We are not –

Danny You need three references for dental college, how am I gonna get references?

Richard enters with Cathy.

Richard We just came from the police station. It's full of reporters.

Cathy It was great.

Richard It was shit. Phil, have you heard?

Lea We heard.

Cathy They wanted to interview me.

Richard You've heard? You know?

Cathy Didn't have time, but I'm gonna go back.

Richard So you know they've caught him?

Cathy get on the telly

Lea How can they have caught someone who doesn't exist?

Richard I don't know, Lea.

Lea Because that's impossible.

Richard Why don't you tell them that? Why don't you pop down the station and say, 'Excuse me, but that fat postman with the bad teeth doesn't actually exist, so why don't you let him go'?

Lea sarcasm, that's the lowest

Cathy they might even give me money for it, do you think I should ask for money?

Lou He's gonna go to prison.

Lea Lou, they are not going to send him to prison because he answers a description, they need more than that, they need fibres, they need samples, they need evidence.

Richard DNA evidence.

Lea Exactly, they need DNA –

Richard No, they've got DNA evidence.

Beat.

Lea What?

Richard He answers the description, but they've got DNA evidence linking him to the crime.

Lea DN . . . What are you talking about?

Richard We spoke to a reporter. They matched up the DNA evidence they found on the jumper to a police database and they came up with this man, this man who answers the description perfectly.

Lea That's impossible.

Richard Well, it's what happened.

Lea No, because, we made that description up and they got DNA from a random –

Beat. She turns to Cathy.

Cathy?

Pause. They all stare at Cathy.

Cathy You told us to get DNA evidence. We got DNA evidence. We did what you said.

Lea Right.

Okay.

Hang on.

Where did you get the DNA evidence?

Cathy From a man, like you said.

Beat.

A man down at the sorting office.

They stare at her.

Lea What?

Cathy Well, we thought, you know, I mean, you'd given a description so we thought, well, I thought, you know, show initiative, we'll look for a fat balding postman with bad teeth.

They stare at her.

There were quite a few.

Danny Oh my God.

Cathy What?

Lou Oh my God.

Cathy We showed . . . initiative, we –

Lea And who asked you to do that?

Cathy Richard, we showed initiative.

Richard That is the most stupid –

Danny Oh, Jesus.

Cathy Why?

Lea Why? Because there is now a man in prison who is linked to a non-existent crime, answering a description that Brian gave.

Lou Oh, Jesus Christ.

Cathy But isn't that . . .

Lea No, Cathy, it is not what we wanted.

Richard What we wanted was to cover up what had happened, not to frame someone else.

Lou We're fucked.

Lea Yes. We might actually be . . . This is a nightmare.

Danny We can't let them think it's him. I mean, I really can't be mixed up in something like that, it wouldn't be right.

Lou What if he goes to prison?

Richard What if we go to prison?

Lea Yes, I think now, we might just actually be a little bit, well, fucked.

Jan and Mark enter with Brian. Brian is crying.

Brian I'm not going in.

Richard You dick, Mark.

Mark It was her idea!

Lou Mark, you dick.

Brian I'm not going to the police station.

Jan He has to. They're looking for him.

Brian I can't go in. It was bad enough talking to them before, saying what I said, but I can't do it again.

Jan They're searching everywhere for him. They want him to identify the man.

Brian I can't identify him, I can't go in there, don't make me go in there, I'm not going in there.

Danny This is terrible.

Brian I can't face it. They look at me. They look at me like I'm lying and it makes me cry. I can't stand the way they look at me. And then, because I cry, they think I'm telling the truth, but I'm crying because I'm lying and I feel terrible inside.

Lou We're going to have to tell them.

Lea Maybe we could do nothing?

Danny We can't do nothing, they want Brian.

Brian I'm not going in.

Lea Phil?

No answer.

Phil?

Pause. Phil walks over to Brian and lays a hand on his shoulder.

Phil This is a bad situation. We didn't want this situation. But we've got this situation. It wasn't supposed to be like this. But it is like this.

Beat.

You're going in.

Brian No.

Phil Yes.

Brian No, Phil –

Phil Yes, yes, shhhh, yes. Sorry. You have to go in. Or we'll take you up the grille.

Pause.

We'll throw you in.

Richard Er, Phil.

Danny Is he serious?

Lea He's always serious.

Phil We'll take you up the grille now. We'll get you by the arms. By the legs. And we'll swing you onto the grille. We'll throw rocks at you until you drop through. You'll drop through. You'll fall into the cold. Into the dark. You'll land on Adam's corpse and you'll rot together.

Beat.

We're in trouble now. We need your help. If you don't help us we'll kill you. Are you going to help us?

Pause.
 Brian nods.

Okay. You go in there. Richard'll take you

Richard Not me again.

Phil Richard'll take you. You take a look at that man and you say it's him. You say it's the man in the woods. That's what you do. Okay?

Slowly, Brian nods.

Everyone else stays calm. Keep your mouths shut. Tell no one or we'll all go to prison. Just get on with things.

He starts to eat his pie. They stare at him.

A field. Phil and Lea, Phil picking his teeth.
Silence.
Suddenly Lea jumps up, shocked.

Lea Woah! Woah, woah, woah . . .

No reaction from Phil.

I just had déjà vu, but really strong, I just . . .
    and you were . . .
I was . . .
I mean we were just here and, and . . .
I was sitting like that and . . .
Woah. I've been here before, Phil. Phil?

Phil carries on picking his teeth.
Lea watches, then explodes.

That's exactly what you did when I said 'Phil'! I knew
    you were going to do that, I said 'Phil' and you picked
    your teeth, Phil, you just carried on picking your teeth!
    Oh my God. This might be the real thing. Maybe I
    have been here before. Maybe this has all happened
    before. Phil? Do you think this has happened before?
    I know what you're gonna do next. I can see, I know,
    I know, you're gonna . . . you're gonna . . . you're
    gonna . . . do nothing!

Phil does nothing.

Yes! Yes, yes, yes, yes, yes! You see? This is amazing, this
    is, the world has just changed, reality is not what we
    think, Phil maybe, this isn't real, maybe we're caught
    in some sort of . . . hang on, hang on, a bird is going
    to . . . a starling, a starling is going to land by that
    stone . . . now!

Nothing happens.

Now!

Still nothing happens.

Any minute . . . now!

Again, nothing happens.
Lea sags. She sits back with Phil.

Look at that sky.

Have you ever seen a sky like that? I've never seen a sky
  quite like that. Strange time we've been born in. No
  other time quite like this one.

Pause.

Do you think it's possible to change things? I know, I know,
  but I feel like this time . . . I dunno, this time . . . I feel
  like this is an important time. Do you think people
  always feel like that? D'you think we're doomed to
  behave like people before us did?

Phil?

No answer.

Phil?
Phil?
Phil?
Phil?
Phil?
Phil?
Phil?
Phil?
Phil?

Pause.

PHIL!

Slowly Phil turns to her.

If you change one thing, you can change the world. Do
  you believe that?

Phil No.
Lea Right.
  Well I do.
  I do, Phil.

  Beat.

Phil?

THREE

A street. Jan and Mark.

Jan Okay. Okay. Okay.

  Beat.

  Okay.
  No.
Mark Yes.
Jan No, no
Mark yes
Jan no. No way, that's
Mark I know
Jan that's
Mark I know, I know
Jan And are you . . . is this . . .
  I mean are you . . . there's no mistake or . . .
Mark No.
Jan Because this is
Mark That's what I'm saying
Jan this is really
Mark Yeah, yes, yeah.
Jan really, really
Mark Exactly.
Jan Are you sure?
Mark Yes.

Jan Where?
Mark In the woods.
Jan In the woods?
Mark In the woods, Cathy found him in the woods
Jan Cathy?
Mark Yes.
Jan Cathy found him . . .?
Mark Yes, she
Jan in the woods?
Mark Yes.

Beat.

Jan Cathy found him in the woods?
Mark Yes.
Jan Oh.
Mark I know.
Jan I don't . . .
Mark I know, I know.
Jan This is . . .
Mark Yeah.
Jan Does anyone know?
Mark You and me. And Cathy. For the moment.
Jan Right.
Right.

Pause.

Right.

A field. Phil sits with a bag.
Takes out a paper plate.
Places a waffle on it.
Takes out a pack of butter and a jar of jam.
Takes out a knife.

Lea turns up. She is carrying a suitcase.
He stares at her.

Lea I'm going. I'm out of here, I'm gone, I'm, I'm, this is it. I'm running away, Phil.

Phil says nothing.

Where'm I going? I dunno. Wherever the universe decides that I should be. It's a big world, Phil, a lot bigger than you, it's a lot bigger than you and me, a lot bigger than all this, these people, sitting here, a lot bigger, a lot lot bigger.

Pause. Phil starts to butter his waffle.

Don't. No words. There's no point, so . . . What's the point? 'Why are you going? Is it me, is it us, is it what we've done, is it what we're becoming, why, Lea, why, is it me, is it the impossibility of ever saying exactly what you mean?' There's no point, Phil. So don't even try. I'm outta here. I'm gone. I am part of history, I'm on a jet plane, I'm moving, I'm discovering, I'm, I'm, sayonara baby, sayonara Phil and hello discovery and, yeah, don't try and stop me, because, because, exit stage left Lea, right now. Right now.

Phil stops buttering the waffle.
Opens the jam.
Starts putting a thin layer of jam on the waffle.

Right now. Right now, Phil, right, fucking . . . I mean it! I really, really . . .

Pause. Phil continues with his waffle.

You're not going to stop me, are you? You're not even thinking of stopping me. You're not even thinking of thinking of stopping me. The only thing in your brain at the moment is that waffle. Your brain is entirely waffle, single-mindedly waffle and maybe a bit of jam, I don't know how you do it. I admire you so much.

Phil decides that the waffle needs more jam.
Lea sags. She drops her suitcase and sits with Phil.

Did you see Jan at Adam's memorial? Floods of tears. It was wonderful, everyone felt wonderful, I felt terrible of course, but everyone felt wonderful. It's incredible. The change. This place. You're a miracle-worker. Everyone's happy. You know that? You notice that? Cathy was on the telly. Used that clip on every channel. She's like a celebrity, there are second years asking for her autograph. Suddenly Adam's everyone's best friend. Richard's named his dog Adam. Mark's mum says if her baby's a boy she's going to call him Adam. Funny thing is they're all actually behaving better as well. I saw Jan helping a new kid find the gym. Mark's been doing charity work, for Christ's sake. Maybe being seen as heroes is making them behave like heroes.

Phil considers his waffle. Decides it needs more jam.

Yeah, everyone happy. Well, it's not all roses, you know. Brian's on medication, did you know that? John Tate hasn't been seen in weeks, and the postman's facing the rest of his life in prison, but, you know, omelettes and eggs, as long as you've your waffle, who cares? How do you feel?

Phil turns to her.
Considers . . .
For a long time.
Opens his mouth to answer . . .
Stops.
Shrugs and goes back to his waffle.
Lea stares at him.

I admire you so much.

The waffle is ready. Phil looks pleased.
Jan and Mark enter.

Jan You better come with us.
Mark You really better come with us.
Lea What is it?

Beat.

Jan You really, really better come with us.

Lea goes with Jan and Mark.
Phil looks at his waffle, looks after Jan, Mark and
Lea, then back at the waffle. Irritated, he puts it
carefully away.

A wood. Cathy, Brian, Lea, Mark and Jan.
They stand around a boy who looks like a tramp. His
clothes are torn and dirty and his hair is matted with
dried blood from an old gash on his forehead that has
not been cleaned up. He stands there, twitchily, staring
at them as though they were aliens, and it looks as
though he might run off at any moment.
Finally Phil speaks.

Phil Hello, Adam.
Adam Alright.

Pause.

Cathy We found him up there, up the hill
Brian I found him
Cathy living in a hedge
Brian a hedge, I found him, I found him, I found Adam
living in a hedge, I found him

Cathy It's like this hedge complex he's made, you have to crawl to get in

Brian I crawled, I love crawling, I love crawling, Lea

Cathy Like a warren in this hedge and he's dragged bits of cardboard and rags to make it better, more waterproof

Brian I loved it, Lea, it was like a hideout.

Cathy He's been living in there.

Brian Living, she was shouting at me to get off the ground, but I love the ground, don't you like the ground?

Cathy He was hiding away at the back.

Brian D'you ever feel like the trees are watching you?

Cathy Terrified.

Adam No I wasn't.

Brian D'you ever want to rub your face against the earth?

Jan No.

Brian He wouldn't speak to us. I don't think he knew his name.

Adam Adam, my name's, I've got a name, it's . . .

Brian Shall we do that? Shall we rub our faces against the earth? What do you think, shall we rub our faces against the earth?

Cathy I think his head's hurt.

Mark Who, Brian's or Adam's?

Brian Don't they eat earth somewhere? Shall we eat the earth? I wonder what earth tastes like? What do you think it, do you think it tastes earthy, or, or . . .

He bends down to eat a handful of earth.

Cathy I think he's been up there for weeks. Hiding. I don't think he's very well.

Brian (*spitting the earth out*) That's disgusting!

He suddenly starts giggling as he scrapes the earth from his mouth.

Cathy I dunno how he's survived, what he's eaten.
Brian (*like it's hilarious*) He's probably been eating earth!

He bursts into laughter.

Cathy It took me half an hour to get him to come out.
Brian D'you feel how wonderful this day is?
Cathy I used violence.
Brian She did.
Cathy I threatened to gouge one of his eyes out.
Brian She was gonna do it. She loves violence now. Can
  you feel the day licking our skin?
Cathy He's a mess.
Mark Which one?
Brian Shall we hold hands? Come on, let's hold, let's
  hold, let's hold hands, come on, let's –

Suddenly Cathy slaps him.
  For a second he looks as if he might cry, but instead
he just giggles.

Lea Okay. Right. Okay.
  Adam.
Adam Huh?
Lea Hello, Adam. How are you?
Adam . . .
Lea Yeah. Great. Phil?

Phil says nothing.

Because this is a bit . . . isn't it? I mean this is really, talk
  about a bolt from the, yeah, shit. No, not shit, I mean
  it's good
Jan How is it good?
Lea it's, it's good, Adam, that we found, but I mean yes,
  it does make things a bit
Lou Fucked?
Lea tricky, no, not . . . don't say
Jan What are we gonna do?

Lea Don't panic.
Mark What are we gonna do?
Lea I said don't panic.
Mark We're not panicking.
Lea Good, because that's the one thing that's . . . So.
   Adam. How's . . . how's . . . how's things?
Adam I know my name.
Lea Yes, you do.
Adam Adam, it's Adam, my name's Adam.
Lea Good. Well that's . . .

   Brian starts giggling.

   No, no, no, Brian, that's, that's not gonna, so shut up.
   Please.
Cathy What are we going to do?
Lea Phil?
What are we gonna . . .?
Phil?
Phil?
Say something, Phil!

   Pause. But Phil says nothing.

Lea What happened?

   Adam doesn't answer.
      Lea goes to him.

What happened?
Adam I . . .
I was in a
dark
walking, crawling in this dark, when you're moving but
   with your hands and knees, crawl, crawling in this
dark
place and I don't remember
things
I fell, I fell into, I fell into

wake, woke, wake up, I woke up with liquid on my head,
   leaves, dead and rotting, I remember leaves, but just
   dark maybe a light high, high, high, high, high . . .
above and, I drank the liquid it was blood, there was, it
   was mine, so I, it's not wrong because it was my
crawling for a long time, I thought, but that was hard to
   tell, tunnels, scared. I felt like the dark was my fear, do
   you know what I mean? I was wrapped in it. Like a
   soft blanket.
And then I came out.
I saw
this
light, this daylight light, I saw this light and went that
   way, towards, and I thought I died because that's what
   people
go to the light, you
and there was such a pain in my
head
I thought the light would make it go, but it didn't because
   the
light was this.

   Beat.

I was confused.

   Beat.

Outside.
I was sad, crushed.
I came outside.
I couldn't remember things.
I couldn't remember anything.
I was new.
A new
a new
a new me. And I felt
happy.

Laughed. It hurt to laugh, but I laughed because I was
  new and I'd got rid of the old and I laughed until night
  came and then I was
panicked, because dark, again
I ran
scratching there was lots of, scratching my skin
and I found my place where I live, and that's where I live
  now, I live there.
And I do know my name so you can shut, you can . . .
I live there. It's
mine, I
live
there.
Adam.
I'm not coming back.

> *Beat.*

It's Adam.
Lea How've you been living?
Adam In the hedge.
Lea No, how?
What have you been eating?
Adam You can eat anything. I eat things.
Nothing dead, I don't
insects, grass, leaves, all good, but nothing, I caught a
  rabbit once and ate that, it's fur was soft, warm, but
  nothing, I found a dead bird and ate some of that but
  it made me sick so nothing, nothing dead, that's the
  rule, nothing

> *Beat.*

What?
Jan Jesus Christ.
Mark He's lost it.
Jan He's off his –

Lea Okay. Now things are strange. Things are really, really strange, Phil. I mean with the greatest of respect, Adam, you are supposed to be dead.

Adam Dead?

Lea And I mean, there's been a service, there's been appeals, there's been weeping . . . They're naming the science lab after you, for God's sake.

Adam I'm . . . dead?

Brian starts giggling.

Cathy Shut up.

Adam Am I dead?

Lea I mean now we really have, I don't know how we're gonna get out of this one because now we really have,

Adam I thought I was dead.

Lou You're not dead.

Cathy (*to Brian*) If you don't shut up you'll be dead.

Brian I love this! This is great! Mates!

Jan What are we going to do?

Mark Yeah, what are we going to do?

Lea We're gonna, right, we're gonna . . . What are we gonna do?

Phil Adam?

Adam Yes?

Phil Do you want to come back?

Adam What?

Phil With us.

Adam I

Phil Or do you want to stay? Are you happy? Here?

Lea Phil –

Phil Shut up. Do you want to stay?

Pause. Adam thinks. Looks at Phil.
Phil smiles, kindly. Nods.

Brian? Take Adam back to his hedge. Then come back to us.

Brian This is great!

Brian takes Adam off. They all stare at Phil.

Lea What's going on?

Phil (*to Mark and Jan*) Go back home. Don't say anything to anybody about this.

Lea Phil . . .?

Jan Are we going to be in trouble?

Phil If you go now and you say nothing to no one about this, you won't be in trouble.

She thinks. Nods to Mark. They go.

Lea Phil, what are you doing?
What? But he's . . .

Beat.

Phil, he's off his head. He's injured, he's been living off insects for weeks, he's insane, Phil, he needs help.

Phil He's happy.

Lea He's not happy, he's mad.

Phil He doesn't want to come back.

Lea Because he's mad! We can't leave him here, I mean that's not, are you serious? Are you seriously –
Alright, yes, there'll be –
Phil, this is insane. I mean I've never, but this, because, alright, whatever, but this is actually insane. We can't just leave him up here.

Phil I'm in charge. Everyone is happier. What's more important; one person or everyone?

She stares at him.

Lea It's Adam, Phil, Adam! We used to go to birthday parties, he used to have that cheap ice cream and we used to take the piss, remember?

Phil If he comes back our lives are ruined. He can't come back, Cathy.

Lea Oh, great, now you're talking to Cathy, like I'm not, I'm not, because you don't like what I say and now it's Cathy, you sit there and you say nothing for years and suddenly now you're chatting with Cathy.

Phil Cathy?

Lea Let's, come on, lets, it won't be that bad, it'll be, we can explain. We can talk. We can go through the whole thing and make them understand –

Phil (*to Cathy*) Do you understand?

Lea Understand what?

Cathy Yeah. I do.

Lea Oh great, now you're at it.

Brian comes back, giggling.

(*Pointing at Brian.*) I mean, I might as well talk to him for all the sense I'm getting. Phil, we can't do this, I mean, what if he comes down next week, next year, in ten years, even?

Phil Take Brian.

Cathy Okay.

Brian We going somewhere?

Lea No, no, wait, you can't, no, this is . . . Cathy?

Phil Make a game of it.

Brian We gonna play a game?

Phil You and Cathy are going to play a game. With Adam.

Brian Brilliant!

Cathy How?

Lea How what? What are you, will you please talk to me as if

Phil Brian?

Brian Who?

Phil Come here.

Brian goes to Phil.

I'm gonna do an experiment with this plastic bag. I want you to stay still while I do this experiment.

Brian I love experiments! Will there be fire?
Phil (*emptying his carrier bag*) No. No fire.
Stay still.

Phil places the bag over Brian's head.

Brian It's all gone dark.

He pulls the handles back around his neck and to opposite corners, making it airtight.
Brian is giggling inside, looking around and breathing the plastic in and out of his mouth.

Bit stuffy.

Phil looks to Cathy. She nods.

This is great!
Lea Phi . . . Phil?

Phil takes the bag off.

Brian That was great!
Phil You just do what Cathy says.
Brian I am brilliant at doing what people say.
Lea No! Stop, don't, don't, Phil, don't, what are you doing, what are you . . . ?
Phil He's dead. everyone thinks he's dead. What difference will it make?

She stares at him.

Lea But he's not dead. He's alive.
Cathy Come on, Brian.
Brian This is brilliant.
Lea No, Cathy, don't, stop, Cathy . . . ?

But she goes, taking Brian with her. Lea turns to Phil.

Phil?
Phil?

Please!
Please, Phil!

But Phil just walks away.

A field. Phil and Lea, sitting.
Complete silence.
Phil takes out a pack of Starburst.
Opens it.
Has one.
Chews. Thinks.
He offers one to Lea.
She takes it.
She begins to cry quietly.
Crying, she puts the sweet in her mouth and begins to chew.
Phil puts his arm around her.
Suddenly she stops chewing and spits the sweet out.
Gets up, stares at Phil.
Storms off.

Phil Lea?
Lea?

FOUR

A street. Jan and Mark.

Jan Gone?
Mark Yeah.
Jan Gone?
Mark Yeah.
Jan What, she's gone?
Mark Yes.

Beat.

Jan When?

Mark Last week.

Jan Where?

Mark Dunno. No one knows.

Jan No one knows?

Mark Well, not no one, I mean someone must, but no one I know knows.

Jan I mean, she must've gone somewhere.

Mark Moved schools. That's what people are saying.

Jan Moved schools?

Mark Yeah.

Jan Just like that?

Mark Just like that.

Jan Without saying anything?

Mark Without saying a thing

Pause.

Jan Oh.

Mark Yeah.

Jan Oh.

Mark Yeah.

Jan Oh.

Mark I know.

Jan Does Phil know?

A field. Richard sits with Phil.

Phil is not eating. He stares into the distance.
Silence.
Suddenly Richard gets up.

Richard Phil, Phil, watch this! Phil, watch me, watch me, Phil!

He walks on his hands.

See? See what I'm doing? Can you see, Phil?

He collapses. Phil doesn't even look at him.

Richard gets up, brushes himself down, and sits with Phil.
Silence.

When are you going to come back?

No answer.

Come on, Phil. Come back to us. What do you want to sit up here for? In this field? Don't you get bored? Don't you get bored sitting here, every day, doing nothing?

No answer.

Everyone's asking after you. You know that? Everyone's saying, 'Where's Phil?' 'What's Phil up to?' 'When's Phil going to come down from that stupid field?' 'Wasn't it good when Phil was running the show?' What do you think about that? What do you think about everyone asking after you?

No answer.

Aren't you interested? Aren't you interested in what's going on?

No answer.

John Tate's found God. Yeah, Yeah, I know. He's joined the Jesus Army, he runs round the shopping centre singing and trying to give people leaflets. Danny's doing work experience at a dentist's. He hates it. Can't stand the cavities, he says when they open their mouths sometimes it feels like you're going to fall in.

Pause.

Brian's on stronger and stronger medication. They caught
  him staring at a wall and drooling last week. It's either
  drooling or giggling. Keeps talking about earth. I think
  they're going to section him. Cathy doesn't care. She's
  too busy running things. You wouldn't believe how
  thing's have got, Phil. She's insane. She cut some kid's
  finger off, that's what they say anyway.
Doesn't that bother you? Aren't you even bothered?

No answer.

Lou's her best friend, now. Dangerous game. I feel sorry
  for Lou. And Jan and Mark have taken up shoplifting,
  they're really good at it, get you anything you want.
Phil?
Phil!

*He shakes Phil by the shoulders. Slowly Phil looks at
him.*

You can't stay here for ever. When are you going to come
  down?

Phil says nothing. Richard lets go.
  Phil goes back to staring at nothing.
  Pause.

Nice up here.
As I was coming up here there was this big wind of fluff.
  You know, this big wind of fluff, like dandelions, but
  smaller, and tons of them, like fluffs of wool or cotton,
  it was really weird, I mean it just came out of nowhere,
  this big wind of fluff, and for a minute I thought I was
  in a cloud, Phil. Imagine that. Imagine being inside a
  cloud, but with space inside it as well, for a second,
  as I was coming up here I felt like I was an alien in
  a cloud. But really felt it. And in that second, Phil,

I knew that there was life on other planets. I knew we weren't alone in the universe, I didn't just think it or feel it, I knew it, I know it, it was as if the universe was suddenly shifting and giving me a glimpse, this vision that could see everything, just for a fraction of a heartbeat of a second. But I couldn't see who they were or what they were doing or how they were living.
How do you think they're living, Phil?
How do you think they're living?

No answer.

There are more stars in the universe that grains of sand on Brighton beach.

Pause.

Come back, Phil.
Phil?

No answer. They sit in silence.

End.

Production Notes

Part of the inspiration for this play came from Dennis Kelly's own schooldays, when he and all his peers went to great lengths to stay in with the in-crowd. In one extreme instance this led to Dennis actually fighting a close friend who had become the victim of the group. The pack instinct is a very strong one. Dennis feels that he could be capable of doing great wrong if conditions seemed to demand it.

The play raises very many considerations – for instance, can morality be taught or must it be learned through experience? Is it right to do a bad thing for (what you believe to be) a good purpose? Can you start to change the world by changing yourself?

Be careful not to demonise Phil. Look at what he does within the context of the play. He makes a decision which he thinks is the easiest way out. He makes a decision for the greater good of everyone – only Adam will suffer. Put yourself in Phil's position. The play looks at the consequences of actions and how the stakes go up. It is about solving one problem but, in doing so, creating another.

The themes and situations are universal. Set the play in whichever part of the country feels right. And you don't have to stick to the suggested gender mix. Concentrate on the similarities in people, not the differences.

Don't play the characters as too ironic or knowing, or the comedy too hard. Humour is very important in this play, but the more truthful and real the characters are played, the funnier it will be.

A *beat* is intended to be a very short break, often used to indicate a change of thought, gear shift or change of strategy. Often it is more about giving the actors a clue that there is something about the line.

A *pause* is a longer gap between lines, and is often used to indicate a thought or thoughtfulness. A *silence* is temporally the longest, and often happens when nothing can be said.

Dennis Kelly uses very few stage directions in his text because he doesn't want to impose too much upon the director and actors and in doing so close doors.

ONE

At the start of the scene Mark is making Jan understand that Adam is actually dead, and in doing so informing the audience and setting up the key dilemma of the play. Lea's speech sets up a climate of fear and uncertainty. It also establishes Phil's higher status, though this might actually be projection on Lea's part.

Then comes a lengthy section of exposition, revealing the situation, the states of mind of the characters and, finally, Phil's plan, which takes the action to a new level.

Finally back to Lea and Phil. Lea is desperate to get Phil's attention. She tries to kill herself and, in the moment, she might well believe that she is actually going to do it. Dennis believes our motives are not always as clear as we think they are at the time. Often they imbue the scene with a sense of 'stakes' when things are played as if they are meant.

An atmosphere of fear and uncertainty is set up in this scene. The question, 'What can we do to get out of this mess?' is posed. A plan of action is suggested. But a current of desperation and fear churns beneath.

TWO

The uncertainty and vagueness of information passed between Mark and Jan will tease the audience and cause them to keep listening and be engaged. The precise information is disseminated at a later stage. The rhythm and the structure of the play is becoming apparent.

When Lea asks Phil if he can remember 'the happiest moment of your life', Phil appears not to remember the sunset which Lea identifies as her 'happiest moment'. This is important to Lea, but Phil can't even remember it.

When Lea produces the dead Jerry, there are two moments to be considered. These are when she killed Jerry and when she showed the body to Phil. Her motives might have been very different for both. The killing of Jerry wasn't necessarily done for effect, but the showing of the body might well have been.

When Lea says, 'What have we done, Phil?' she becomes the moral conscience of the play.

The stakes are cranked up still further with the realisation that the plan has gone awry and a man may be convicted because Cathy showed initiative. This escalation presents the characters with a further dilemma to resolve, while attitudes are hardening and fears are being compounded. The realisation of what Cathy has done is a key moment.

Lea continues to try to engage Phil and to make sense of the situation they now find themselves in. Lea still appears to be the moral voice and also seems to glimpse some hope.

The scene concludes with another key moment, when Lea asks Phil, 'If you change one thing, you can change the world. Do you believe that?' Phil replies, simply, 'No,' to which Lea responds, 'Well I do. I do, Phil.' Dennis believes this moment might well be the heart of the play.

THREE

Jan and Mark again – and again very limited information, another audience tease. It is important to keep up the pace of this opening section (see the 'Marking the Line End' exercise later). Also, Mark's observation, 'For the moment,' could be a bit of a bell-toll moment. The scene marks a further rise in Cathy's perceived status.

'I admire you so much.' There are two considerations here: firstly the word 'admire' is used, not 'love' – what implications does this have on Lea's actions/attitude? Decide if Lea is trying to get Phil's attention again.

Back in the wood, it is revealed that Adam is still alive, escalating the action and suspense still further. Brian is behaving strangely because he is on medication. The situation is growing more difficult and the characters becoming more desperate.

Cathy's violent streak is now more overt, and her status rises as a result. When Phil formulates his new and violent plan to deal with the situation, she is the obvious choice to carry it out.

There is a key moment inherent in the realisation of what is being suggested here. Try out various options to judge where the moment of realisation is best placed.

There is desperation in Lea as she realises exactly what Phil is proposing. She speaks out against the madness, but nobody, least of all Phil, listens. She is left alone, defeated, yet she doesn't actually take action to stop it herself, perhaps making her culpable.

Finally, Phil and Lea are sitting as we have seen them so many times before, but this time the ritual is reversed. It is Phil who is pro-active towards Lea. He gives her a Starburst, puts his arm around her and calls her name. But though she tries, she cannot eat the sweet, spitting it out through her tears.

FOUR

Again Mark and Jan are employed as audience 'teasers', discussing Lea's disappearance. Pacing their contribution is very important.

Richard appears to have replaced Lea. Phil is no longer eating. Richard's speech appears as an epilogue, tying up the loose ends of the story.

It seems nothing has changed, yet everything has changed. Richard's final speech hints at the fact that there is hope, there are different possibilities and different directions to go in. Phil seems unable to accept this and, in the end, doesn't move or acknowledge this philosophy. The close of the play has a very Beckett-like feel to it. A sort of inertia appears to have gripped them: no one moves.

EXERCISES

RELEASING THE SUBTEXT 1   Ask actors to say their lines and accompany every line/phrase with a physical action. The actions may reflect an idea or feeling in the subtext. This is not a staging exercise, but it may be that some of the results may influence staging.

RELEASING THE SUBTEXT 2   Ask the actors to say a line, then say what the characters are really thinking as an aside. Beware of over-analysing and over-performing. Alternatively, ask another group to provide the spoken subtext.

Ask one person to read out the text in a very neutral fashion; the actor playing the part must then repeat it, acting it out in the context of the scene. The point of this exercise is to free up actors from the script, break the speeches up and help them to learn the lines.

Ask the actors to stand palm to palm as they say their lines, and to push against one another in a physical manifestation of the control they are trying to exert. The more control being to exerted, the harder the push. The antagonist should resist when spoken to if it feels appropriate. This exercise engages the voice with the body. Make sure the actors really push and resist – don't let them be too 'nice'.

MARKING THE LINE END   As the actors say a line, ask them to stamp their feet or clap their hands when they come across a punctuation mark. This is particularly important at the end of a line, because it causes the 'energy' of the line to be pushed across to the following actor. It 'throws' the line across, and this has the effect of keeping up both the pace and the energy of a section of dialogue.

SETTING EXERCISE   Try running the scenes with specific regard to the setting – in the street (create a street scene), in a field or wood. Take account of the environment: whether it is hot, cold, dark, etc.

DIFFERENT ENERGIES   Play scenes with regard to physical energies. Perhaps play a scene as though everyone is very tired, or hyperactive, or tense, or relaxed. Explore the effects of different energies on the same scene.

STATUS   Try playing the same scene changing the perceived status of each character. What effect does that have on the feel of the scene? Does it reveal anything new about any of the characters?

CARE   Try running scenes with a different intensity of caring – e.g., varying between 'we don't care very much' to 'we care a great deal' about what is happening. Consider whether that throws up any new perspectives on character or situation. Exaggerate the style when reading.

Find the *intentions* of the characters in the subtext. If in doubt, straightforward, honest performances may well get the best results.

Workshop facilitated by Roxana Silbert
with notes taken by Stephen Downs

RED SKY

Bryony Lavery

Bryony Lavery's plays include *A Wedding Story*, *Last Easter*, *Her Aching Heart*, *Two Marias*, *Smoke* and the multi-award-winning *Frozen*. Her adaptations for stage and radio include *Behind the Scenes at the Museum*, *The Magic Toyshop*, *Wuthering Heights*, *A High Wind in Jamaica* and *Lady Audley's Secret*. She has written four plays for *Connections*: *More Light*, *Illyria*, *Discontented Winter: House Remix* and *Red Sky*. Her current commissions include *Wise Children* for the National Theatre, London, *Dirt* for Manhattan Theater Club and *The Thing With Feathers* for the McCarter Theater, Princeton, USA.

Author's Note

Well, here I am, back with my *fourth* play for *Connections*, and it's ALL YOUR FAULT! Yes, *you*! You threw down this fearsome challenge of writing a companion piece for *More Light*, the *first* play I did with *Connections*.

'*More Light* tells the story of the women . . . wouldn't it be *great* to tell the *men's* story *too*?' you wheedled.

'But that might be really *hard*,' I cavilled . . . well, all right, *whined*.

'No, no, you can do it, it'll be *fun*!' you assured.

Well, Thank You Very Much Indeed! The writing of *Red Sky* has (a) given me an entirely sleepless week in New York after I ditched the very first draft and completely reworked the story *in four days* ready for a moved reading at the Provincetown Playhouse; (b) made me realise how hopeless I am at languages when Anthony Banks and I staged its rehearsed reading *in Italian* at Teatro Limonaia in Sesto Fiorentino; and (c) awoke me to the harsh reality that I am now too old to party all night at the *Connections* retreat in Scarborough.

Well, here is my revenge.

Be warned . . .

I am going to have *my* fun: my favourite moments in rehearsals are always watching the movement experts and fight directors work out the choreography of the violent bits – the hanging in *Frozen*, the stalker getting kicked in the goolies in *Smoke* – so in *Red Sky* I have set some *beezer* stage fights: a royally ordained castration ceremony involving a platoon of soldiers; a three-stage knife/wrestling/throttling one-on-one between two men who cannot kill one another because they are dead already; plus the overall concept of two sets of characters occupying the same space, without being able to see or touch one another! Okay, directors of *Red Sky*, it is *your* turn for the sleepless nights.

Who are you? You *know* who you are! You are the National Theatre *Connections* team. You are the companies who stage our plays.

You are the people who attract us writers to this enterprise. Go away!

Let me sleep!

BRYONY LAVERY

Characters

Ross

Tark

Luce

Man

Emperor

Soldiers

Gangbang

Pure Joy

Housebeautiful

Heartlistener

Cleverhands

SeesFuture

It is now.

A forward slash / in a speech indicates that the next speech cuts in at that point.

The snatches of song sung by Tark, Luce and Ross make up one song at the end. They can sound like something out of a modern song. Lyrics are in *italics*.

ONE
LIGHT AND DARK

A wide expanse of sky in a pleasant foreign landscape.
The terrain rises to a gentle hill.
There is a huge ugly hole in the summit of the hill.
Some way off, not visible, some tents.
In the space, various crates and boxes.
A trestle table, at which sit Ross and Tark, two first world archaeology interns.
They are both writing studiously, completely avoiding each other.
Both have iPods.

Ross (*singing to himself*)
    Everywhere is dark.
    Everywhere's very dark.

Tark (*singing to himself*)
    It is light.
    It is all about light!

Ross
    Shut up!

Ross gets up and goes to the very edge of the hole.
    Looks down.
    Ross walks to the very edge of the hole.
    Puts the ladder down it.
    He looks down.
    Down
    Down
    Down.

I want to be down there!
Let me go down there!
I should be down there!
That is where I belong!
Down there!
In all *that*!!
Shit!
Blood!!
Dark!!

Tark
Ross . . .
You know what Victor said . . .

(*In a 'Victor' voice.*) 'Ebsolutely no interns near the upper
excavation entrance!'

Ross flips him a 'fuck you' mime.

'Ebsolutely no interns . . . even Ross!!'

*Ross comes over to him. Stands very close to him.
Lifts one earpiece. In his ear . . .*

Ross
SHUT   UP.

Puts the earpiece back. Sits down.

You are sooo juvenile.

iPod on.

Tark
I'm *supposed* to be juvenile, I *am* a juvenile!

He goes over to the hole, rubbing his ear . . .

(*To self.*) Please don't be too juvenile today!

(*To sun.*) Sun!
Please don't be too hot today!

(*To hole.*) Weird place!
  Weird creepy place . . .
  Please don't be too weird today!

  Play nice!

  Be Gentle with Me . . .

  He sits back down.

  Both write, listening to iPods.
      *Luce, another intern, enters, carrying, carefully,
  a beautiful model of a circular structure, with three
  concentric chambers and filigree vestiges of
  gates/walls, doors.*
      It is a model of the tomb beneath them.

Ross
  That needs *two* people!

Luce
  It does NOT!!

  Careful!

Tark (*mimicking her*)
  '*Careful!*'

Ross
  Tarquin.
  If you don't stop that
  I will kill you.
  I will seriously kill you
  Tarquin

Tark
  Tark
  not Tarquin.
  It's a re-naming decision.

Ross
Really   Tarquin?

Is it   Tarquin?

Luce
Ross . . .

Ross
Stop *mummying* me!

Tark (*to Luce*)
'Careful!'

Luce (*to Tark*)
I totally absolutely completely loathe you.

She sits down and gets out her notebook, etc.

(*To Ross.*) And I'm not terribly keen on you either!

Ross (*untruthfully*)
GUT / TED!

Tark (*truthfully*)
/ Gutted.

Ross
Oooo-kaaay! Day One of
Sitting in the open air under / the hot sun –

Luce
Ross . . .

Ross
 – instead of the nice shady tents!
Victor wants everything they got yesterday
added to the inventory.

Read back what did they get . . .

Luce
They got a *lot* yesterday.

I mean   *a lot.*
Colette's ecstatic.

Luce opens her pad.

Tark
They got
the axe!
The frigging axe!

Ross
In time order of the find . . . Tarquin . . .

Tark
Right.

He points to the two big crates.

First
the mechanical archer thingies . . .

Ross
which were found . . . ?

Luce (*shows on her model*)
Here
and here.
They were mounted at either side of the entrance to
the central chamber.

Ross
Victor wants a complete description of everything.
I mean a *complete* description.

Luce
Okay.

Tark
Completesirgoodsiryessir!

Ross stares at Tark. Tark tries to look back. Stand-off.

Luce
Ross . . .

Ross
Yes, Mummy?

Luce stares Ross out.

Luce
What was next . . . ?

Tark smacks a box.

Tark
Jewelled ceremonial robe.

Ross
Which was found . . .

Luce shows him on the model.

Luce
Here.
Right in the centre of the central chamber.
On the central raised dais.
Here.

Tark
Worth a fucking fortune!
Every *single stone*!
Fucking fortune!

Luce
Folded up.
Up one end
here.

Ross
What else?

Tark (*slapping a smaller box*)
The axe!
The axe made from a human bone!

Ross
> Can you turn your giddy enthusiasm
> down to, like . . . zero?
> Next . . . ?

> *Tark jiggles a small box with his finger.*

Tark
> The paper bird.

Luce
> Careful!

Tark
> Ex*cuse* me?

Luce
> Careful. (*She spells out for the mentally challenged . . .*)
> Be
> care
> ful
> with
> it
> it
> is
> ver / ee
> frag
> ile.

Tark (*back, as somebody even more mentally challenged*)
> I
> yam
> bee
> ying   ver   ee
> caref
> ull
> wi
> thitt . . .

Luce
It's a paper / bird.

Tark
/ Exactly . . . it's [*only*] a paper bird!

Ross
Can you two just . . . ?

Luce
It's *him*.

Tark
It's *her.*

Ross
Never mind.

Bring the irritation level up to, like, maximum!
Have an idiot competition!
Who cares???'
What did they find next?

Luce
The bones.
All the bones.

The bones disconcert her . . .

Tark (*sings*)
Dem bones dem bones
    *dem dry bone*s.
The skeletons!!
All in a big pile in the central chamber . . .
one on top of the other . . .

He slightly mimes attitudes of sleep . . . curled up . . .

Ross
and this big pile were . . . ?

Tark
    female skeletons we think.

Luce
    Victor's laying them out in the big tent
    trying to assemble them / in the right . . .

Tark
    This Christmas must-have gift . . .
    three-dimensional put-it-together-yourself female-
    skeleton-pile box set!

Ross
    They are *all* female bones?

Luce
    The *complete* skeletons in the central chamber are all
    female . . .

    The ones we found in the circle of bronze helmets . . .

Tark
    The bones that Victor thinks had been *set on fire* . . .

    He loves this idea.

Luce
    Colette's doing the tests now.
    Then we might know . . .
    the gender of the   burned bones.

Ross
    But . . . human?

Luce
    Yes.

Tark (*again, a mime or two . . .*)
    Female skeletons all in a frightened pile
    cringing together in fear,
    male skeletons in their war helmets

in a noble circle
defending their women against an incendiary attack!

Luce

And of course in your pathetic reality . . .
only men know how to fight . . .

Tark

Regard the empirical evidence!
Female skeletons   cringing pile
Male skeletons   protective circle.

Luce

And that's the *only* possible interpretation . . .

Tark

It's the most *rational* interpretation . . .

Ross

Victor said 'inventory', not 'invention'.
Can we *start* please?

They all put on protective gloves.
   They open up the outer, opaque boxes.
   They take out see-through protective boxes.
   For Ross the jewelled robe.
   For Tark the bone axe.
   For Luce the paper bird.

Luce

Careful . . .

Victor said he would chop your balls
off if you weren't careful.

They settle down to work as . . .

306

TWO
A BONE AXE

Tark is singing . . .

Tark (*sings*)
> *It is light*
> > *it is all about light.*

> What is that song?
> Arctic Monkeys?

Ross
> Concentrate.

> *They all work.*

Tark
> Concentrate.
> This is . . .
> a primitive axe
> discovered . . .

> *He checks . . .*

> in the second chamber . . .
> with the male skeletons . . .

> The blade is . . .
> a scapula
> left shoulderblade?
> right shoulderblade?
> some very clever little primitive bastard's set it in a
> handle made of . . .
> Oh God
> oh great
> oh WOW . . .
> what's this bone here called . . .?

He points to his forearm.

Ross (*with contempt, points*)
Radius ulna
radius
it's the radius.

Tark
In a human radius!
the guy who made this fashioned the bones of a
human arm
into an axe!

How cool is that?

This edge is . . .

*He runs his finger along the clear box parallel with
the axe edge . . .*
    He pretends it has cut him . . .

Ouch!

He pretends to suck his fake cut finger.

Ouch!

This is all for Luce, who ignores him.

It's lashed together with . . .

omigod
omigod . . .

this binding . . .

I bet this is a strip of   human skin!!

This is human skin!!

Admiringly.

You bastard . . .
You little bastard!!

Ross and Luce come to look.

It's one long continuous piece . . .

Ross
That's terrible.

Luce
That's amazing!

Tark pretends to pick up the axe and stalk Ross and Luce.

Tark (*caveman*)
Oo oo oo
oo oo oo . . .

They refuse to play and go back to their work.

He creeps into the central chamber . . .

hunting
what is he hunting?
with his bone axe . . .?

Sometime during this we hear Man from the hole . . .

Man
More Light?
More Light?

Are you here?

Tark creeps up behind Luce.
    Raises his pretend axe over her head.

Royal Parrot?
Bitch?
Cheat!
Murderer?

Where are you hiding??
Why don't you come out and play??

Man emerges from the hole.

He is all dust and cobwebs like the earth he comes
from.
> *Grey clothes.*
> *Grey skin.*
> *He has one hand raised, as if holding an axe . . .*

He comes into the area.
> *He sees and feels the strangeness.*

No.
Oh no.
This is trouble.

Ross (*to Tark*)
Leave her alone.
Sit down.

Luce (*to Ross*)
I can actually look after myself, Ross . . .
(*To Tark.*) Leave me alone. Sit down.

They work on.
> *They see nothing.*

Man
Be invisible.
Be invisible.
I'm not here
I'm behaving myself
I'm not doing anything wrong, lords,
lady.

Don't see me
Don't cut anything off.

He stands very still, eyes down.
> *They ignore him.*

Luce shivers. Looks around. Sees nothing.

Tark
　What?

Luce
　Nothing.

　(*Sings quietly.*)
　And in it . . . joy
　 Pure joy joy joy . . .

　She does 'What the fuck am I singing . . .?'

　Man sees they are ignoring him.

Man
　Slip past
　no noise
　all will be well.

　More Light?
　More Light?

　*He backs round them, slips anonymously past them
　and exits as . . .*

THREE
A JEWELLED ROBE

Ross　(*singing*)
　Everywhere is dark . . .
　Everywhere's very dark.

Tark
　Cool song. Cool lyrics.
　Is it by Chico, Ross?

Ross
　Shut up!

　Jewelled robe
　probably silk

probably gold buttons
probably silver froggings
probably long skirts
probably wide wide sleeves
probably the jewels of enormous wealth
cover every damn surface but
how can I tell?
I am not allowed to touch it
I am not allowed to open it out
I am not allowed to do the job properly
the job I could do-very-well *thank-you-very-much* /
if interns were allowed to touch!

Tark

Are you *ever* going to let this drop?

Luce

He *did* say he was sorry!

Tark

Give me a break . . .

Ross

Why can't interns examine the artefacts? /
Why can't interns examine the artefacts?

Luce

You know why, Ross, can you just / stop this . . .

Ross

Why can't interns examine the artefacts?

Tark

Because I dropped
one of the mechanical archer thingies, alright?!

Ross

Because you dropped one of the
mechanical archer thingies!

Right.

Clanging bell, off.
  All look at their watches.
  Furious, Ross picks up his notes and exits with them as . . .

Victor! Briefing time!
Bring your notes!

If you can without dropping them!

They collect their notes as . . .

Tark
  It was a mistake!

Boy!
Are we not human?
Are we not allowed a simple mistake?

Luce
  Leave it.

This isn't about *that*.
This is about something else.

Tark
  Ah.

This is about *you* sleeping with *me*!

Luce
  Once.

She mimics him as they exit.

'Are we not human?
Are we not allowed a simple mistake?'

Luce exits, Tark follows.
  From the tomb we hear . . .

Emperor
> Soldiers?
> Guards?
>
> My ladies!
> Where are my ladies?

The Emperor climbs stiffly from the tomb.
> *He too is all grey and dusty.*
> *He wears a sheet, plus his war helmet.*
> *He is terribly offended.*

> I am cold!
> I am cold!

But no one comes to warm him.

> I must be dressed!

But no one comes to dress him. This frightens him.

> Is this Death's Dark Kingdom?
> Is this   my destination?
> Is this   the end of my journey from life?

Man returns.

Man
> I know this hill!

Emperor
> I know this hill!

Man
> This is where all my damn troubles started!

Emperor
> This is the gentle hill where I first decided
> where my tomb should be!

Man

    I was sitting here all alone
    I'd stole a chicken

    I'd liberated a flagon of wine.

Emperor

    I dismounted and said
    'Here is where my tomb shall be.'

Man

    I stopped to look at the red sunset.

    Big mistake.

Emperor

    But there was somebody sitting on my hill!

Man

    I was sitting right here.

Emperor

    This is forbidden
    for
    the Empire is mine
    the gentle hill on which I stand is mine
    the red sun which lights the hill is mine /

    Soldiers!

Man

    Then suddenly
    things went dark
    then suddenly
    the air was full of soldiers.

*Many, many grey dusty Soldiers swarm rapidly out
from the tomb and seize the man.*
    They bring him, low, before the Emperor.
    Gangbang is among them.

Soldiers
This your land?

Man
Yes.

Soldiers
This your hill?

Man
Yes.

Soldiers
This your splendid view?

Man
Yes.

Soldiers
This your wine?

Man
And yours if you / want it . . .

Soldiers
This your chicken?

Man
Never seen that chicken before / in all my life . . .

Soldiers
Trespasser.

Thief.

Poacher.

Man
Well I can't disagree with a majority vote!
Why don't we all
get off the property
cook the chicken

split it between us – (*Counts them*) – twenty
Drink perdition to the bloody Emperor?

What do you say,
Men of tin?

Soldiers
Emperor!

They fall back.
    The Emperor walks forward.

Emperor
Theft.

Remove his hand.

Soldiers get Man ready . . .

Soldiers
Right-handed or left-handed?

Right-handed or left-handed?

Man
Never learned to write
so no point taking off either, boys.

Emperor
Insolence.

'Take both,'
I said.

Man
'Haven't you got enough hands?'
I said.

Big mistake.

Emperor
And again
Insolence.

'Yes   Dirt,'
I said.

Man
And he smiles.

Emperor
'Take something more precious than his hands,'
I said.

*The Soldiers organise themselves and the Man's body
into position.*

Emperor
'For the Empire is mine
the gentle sun that lights the hill is mine,'
I said.

He snaps his fingers.
    The Soldiers hold Man as Gangbang castrates him.

Man
AAAAAAAAAAAAGHHHHHH!!

Soldiers drop the Man to the ground.
    He has fainted.
    *They part, revealing Gangbang, a slave-master,
standing with a bloodied knife.*
    Soldiers swarm towards the tomb.

Emperor
Soldiers!
Take this Dirt away!

Soldiers swarm down into the tomb.

Soldiers!
What is happening?

You!
Remove this *Dirt* from my eyes.

Gangbang
  Sire!

  All-powerful

  Yes, Sire!

  Gangbang goes to Man, turns him over . . .
    Looks at him.

  Balls and knives!
  You!!

  Man looks into Gangbang's face.

Man
  You!

  They size off. They circle. This is a competition for
  the knife.

Gangbang
  Only doing my job!

Man
  You cut my balls off!!

  He lunges for the knife. Gangbang parries.

Gangbang
  'Convict. Slightly damaged.'
  So?

  Man grabs Gangbang. They wrestle mightily for the
  knife, as . . .

  So you lost your love member . . .
  But still got your arms and legs, boy.

  In their struggle, the knife flips down the gaping hole.

  Whoops!

Emperor
Soldiers!
Bring back the knife!

*Man leaps on Gangbang again. They wrestle
throughout . . .*

Man
You put a bloody collar on me!

Gangbang
I was the bloody slave-master!
Weapons and wounds!
Be fair!

Man
On a bloody rope!

Gangbang
I was only doing my job!

Man
Oh were you?
What did you say?

Gangbang (*lying*)
Nothing.

Man
What did you say??

Gangbang (*still lying*)
Can't remember!

Man
WHAT DID YOU SAY??

Gangbang
'Good doggie
Nice doggie
Come walkies . . .'

Man gets Gangbang in doggy position.

Man
And dragged me like a mongrel cur
down the bloody hill
and pointed at the earth and said . . .
and said??

Gangbang
'Good doggie
Seek
Find
Dig for rats!
Dig for rats, doggie . . .'

Earth and shovels!
Can't you take a joke?

*They seize each other by the throat. Try to throttle the
life out of one another.*

Man
And so it was
I dig his tomb!

Gangbang
Yes, slave!

Man
I dig the tunnel.

Gangbang
Yes, slave!

He continues to say 'Yes, slave' to each of Man's lines.

Man
I dig the first chamber
I dig the second chamber
I dig the central chamber
and it is always night

for we are always underground
and it is always day
for we are always bloody digging!

Both
DIE!!

They stop. They are utterly exhausted.

Man
Why will you not *die*?

Gangbang
Why will *you* not die??

Emperor
Incompetent!

Find me an axe.
I will kill him myself!

He turns his back to remove the sheet covering him.
Stops. Turns back.

I am naked under here!

Why am I naked under here??

Ladies!
Dress me!

FOUR
A PAPER BIRD

Luce enters alone.
Luce puts a hand on the table.
Gives herself a little lecture . . .

Luce
Listen to me, stupid.
Here are your instructions.

One. Do not 'mummy' Ross.
Two. Do not get 'between' Ross and Tark.
Three. Do not acknowledge Tark *at all on any level.*
Four. Don't *sweat*!!

Okay.

Emperor
What   is   *this* ??

Luce
Er . . . is someone here??

Emperor/Man/Gangbang (*terrified*)
No.

Luce (*to herself, very strict and frightening*)
Concentrate.

*The three Tomb Men shade their eyes from her
possible gaze.*
    *Luce examines minutely the contents of the perspex
box and annotates . . .*

Paper bird.
Found to the immediate right of the jewelled robe . . .
a little way off from the pile of . . . the pile of . . .
the pile.

Sort of . . . early origami . . .
the paper's folded
two
three
four . . .
six
eight
no, nine times
the paper at this time is wafer thin.
But
must be hand-made . . .

but . . . it's extremely . . . fine quality . . .
and robust to survive this long without crumbling . . .

Who made this?
a child?

Oh
oh no . . .

Are there child's remains
among the bones?

She looks off towards the tents.
   The thought of possible children upsets her . . .

Emperor
   She talks at herself . . . Is she witch?

Gangbang
   Is she spirit?
   Is she devil?

Luce
   Found to the right of the folded-up
   jewelled robe.

   What were you doing there?
   who made you?
   was it in your pocket?
   in your sleeve?

Emperor
   Why does she talk to the *things*?
   Why does she not talk to *me*?

Gangbang
   Tarts and trouble!
   It must be a SPELL!
   Let's get out of her range!

324

Man
> If you walk carefully, keeping out of their range,
> you can get past her . . .

> *Man and Gangbang make a 'warding off the evil eye'*
> *sign . . . Start walking carefully backwards . . .*

Emperor
> Protect me!
> Between me and the she-witch!
> Keep me safe!

> *This accomplished, they exit. As each passes Luce,*
> *a slight movement from Luce.*

Luce
> Who are you?

> Are you a child?

> Why were you there?

> *Pure Joy, an Emperor's courtesan, emerges from the*
> *tomb. She is also exquisitely dressed in formal court*
> *robes, cobwebs, dust, ceremonial sash, ornate wig,*
> *bound feet on high pattens.*
> *   She carries a fan. In her other hand nothing, the*
> *palm out, flat and open.*
> *   She is quietly, politely troubled.*

Pure Joy
> It has gone.

> It was there when I fell asleep
> I put it by my pillow
> on the right
> I reached out my hand to pick it up
> it was gone.

> *She looks up.*

Ah.
Oh.
Ah.

She feels the freshness.

Is this then a dream?
Oh, how strange.
How very strange.
But how very beautiful.
How very beautiful it is here.

But this feels   real.

Light.
Air.

Oh, at last.
A nice change.
An end to boredom.
How very pleasant.
How More Light would like this!

She sees Luce.

Ah.

She looks at Luce's clothes. Then at her face.

AH!!

. . . More Light??

Ross and Tark with another box . . .

Ah.
No.

People
 . . . from a   strange culture.

Sires. Welcome.

She adopts a formal, respectful posture.
She waits.

Tark
Anybody want water?

Ross raises a hand, Luce shakes her head.

Pure Joy
Water!!

She raises her hand.

I, Sire.
Most kind.

Tark ignores Pure Joy and exits . . .

Oh!

Luce (*singing*)
And in it joy
Pure joy joy joy . . .

What *is* that song??

Ross
Probably something you listened to on Tark's iPod. . .

Luce
No. I don't think so.

After a while. Carefully . . .

Something wrong with me listening to Tark's iPod . . ?

Ross
Oh no.
It's very sweet.
Earpiece each.
Very cute.

Luce

Fuck   off.

Pure Joy waits. Then with great trepidation . . .

Pure Joy

They are quite war-like and angry . . .
Perhaps   we have been *conquered*!

Very politely.

Please, Your Eminences . . .
I am Pure Joy . . .
Emperor's Lady . . .
Please to tell me where your Eminences would like me
to be . . .

They do not answer her.
    After a while, with great trepidation . . .

Your eminences . . .?

Slightly louder voice.

Your eminences?

Quite a loud voice.

Your eminences?

This is very bold. She must hide behind her fan.
But she is not chastised.

Oh.
Ah!

But they are oblivious to her. So . . .

Your Incomparable Strangenesses . . .?

But they are oblivious to her . . .

Oh!
Ah!

I think they cannot hear me!!

Your Obliviousnesses??

Tark returns with water bottles, gives them to humans.

Tark (*sings*)
It is light
   It is all about light.

Pure Joy
Oh.

Luce (*sings*)
And in it joy . . .
   Pure joy joy joy.

Ross
Very cute.
totally
utterly
cute.

Pure Joy
Discord! Oh. At last.
Something to see.
Something to watch.
Ah.

She walks with disguised difficulty on her bound feet.
   She sees the paper bird.

Ah.
There you are!

She tries to touch her bird.
   But she cannot.

Oh. I cannot touch my paper bird!

How very interesting!

She studies everything on the table.

How very strange!

She loves this. She smiles with pure joy.
    She touches Luce on her hand. Luce cannot feel her.

Ah.

Pure Joy touches Luce's cheek. Luce cannot feel her.

Ah.

I *can* touch you.
Yet, you do not feel my touch.

Luce looks at her hand where she has been touched.
    She scratches it a bit.
    Then strokes her cheek as if she is thinking.

Or do you?

How very strange.

Your Young Obliviousnesses . . .
I will sit here
and observe . . .
if it please.

Oh, this is most pleasant!

Pure Joy settles to watch them work.

Pure Joy
    That is the Emperor's funeral robe . . .
    Obliviousnesses . . .
    Also   excuse me   my pillow . . .

Pure Joy peruses the table.

They write about our possessions!
Someone has made a small model of . . .
the Emperor's tomb!

Why?

How very interesting!
What will happen next?

*Emperor, Gangbang and Man enter, walk stealthily
backwards. They turn slowly round.*

Emperor
NO!!

Gangbang
Feet and fuck!

Man
Just like I did a few minutes ago!

You run away . . .
It always brings you   back   *here*!!

Gangbang
Got to be a way out . . .

Man
This way!

Gangbang
No. *This way!!*

*Man and Gangbang try to escape again, in separate
directions.*

Emperor
Stay!

Pure Joy
Oh
but this cannot happen!
it is
our Emperor!

She lies face down on the floor in abasement.

Pure Joy
    If I speak to my Emperor . . .
    will *he* hear me?

Emperor
    Why will *nothing* obey me??

He sees Pure Joy.

Woman?

Woman!
Here!

Pure Joy crawls on hands and knees to the Emperor.

Pure Joy
    Ruler of All.
    Sun.
    World.
    Universe.
    O my Emperor!

Emperor
    Are you person?

    Are you devil?

    Are you witch?

Pure Joy
    Oh this is interesting
    That you do not know me.

    I am Pure Joy, Ruler of All.
    One of your ladies.
    I bore you no sons.

Emperor
    Dress me.

Pure Joy (*realising*)
His Perfection does not know me.

*Slowly, she stands. Her absolute belief in her
obedience starts to leak away . . .*

But I was in your bed many times, Sire.
Many a night
I crawled from the foot of your royal bed
on hands and knees
between your soft sheets

She is now standing upright.

to where you lay . . . All-Powerful One.

Emperor
Dress me.

Pure Joy
My face has lain upon your pillow
more times than a tree has leaves.

Look upon it.

He does not. She commands him.

Look Upon It!

Emperor
I do not look into the faces of my people.
I am the Emperor.

Dress me.

*Pure Joy stares at the Emperor, quite still, for a long
time.*

Pure Joy
Dress yourself.

Emperor
You are insolent.

Pure Joy (*with pure joy*)
> Oh.
> Ah.
> Yes!
> Suddenly I am!

Emperor
> You will die!

Pure Joy laughs with pure joy.

Emperor
> This is forbidden.

Pure Joy
> No.
> This *was* forbidden.
> But . . .
>
> Omnipotence.
> Sun.
> Ruler of All.
> You died, Emperor.
>
> Oh, this is *fascinating*.

Man and Gangbang walk in backwards, from opposite directions . . .

Man/Gangbang
> Noooo!!

Pure Joy goes to the Man. Looks at his face.

> Oh, I do know this poor man!
>
> He died *too*!
>
> I know this, for More Light killed him!

Man
> More Light?

Pure Joy
　　Yes, Sir, killed you, Sir!
　　And if you are dead
　　And he is dead
　　And our Great Emperor is dead
　　then　　I too am dead!

　　She laughs with pure joy . . .

　　Oh how perfectly wonderful this is!

Emperor
　　Woman!
　　Explain!

Pure Joy
　　Sire.

　　Your last command was . . . Lord . . .?

Emperor (*remembers*)
　　'The ladies who have borne me no sons
　　will accompany me on my journey
　　into Death's Dark Kingdom.'

Pure Joy
　　And so it was.

Emperor
　　I was in my tomb!

Pure Joy
　　And so you were
　　and so were we.

Man
　　Which *I* dug for you!

Gangbang
　　Which I *supervised* the digging you dug for you.
　　Sire.

Pure Joy

We carried you to the central chamber, Lord.

They all see, feel the experience . . .

Gangbang

And we watched your funeral procession!

Man

Stuck at the outer chamber!
A convict!

Pure Joy

Our lanterns lit your watching faces!

Gangbang

The lights! bobbing . . .!

Man

And then . . . the great doors closed!
one

two
three

Gangbang

And we heard the locks turn!

one
two
three

Pure Joy

And you must then have realised

Gangbang

This wasn't just *his* funeral!

Man

Every damn person making his tomb . . .!
Locked in that dark with him!

Pure Joy
> You were
> so generously
> taking us all with you, Sire
> on your journey
> into Death's Dark Kingdom!

> We ladies carried you into the very centre of your tomb.

Gangbang/Man
> *Our* bloody tomb!

Pure Joy
> We set you down, in your beautiful jewelled robe, Sire,
> And we looked at your face
> And you were dead.

Emperor
> I *died*?

> I am   dead?

Pure Joy
> And we were alive, Sire.

Gangbang/Man
> ALIVE!!

Emperor
> I'm dead!

Pure Joy
> Dead, Sire.

Gangbang
> I'm dead?

Pure Joy
> Dead, Sir.

Gangbang
> Decay and rot! Dead!

Man
Dead . . . ?

I'm dead? / I'm really dead?

Pure Joy
Sir. Yes.

To audience.

I have often observed that men
are less excuse me quick to welcome change
than . . .

She bows graciously.

Man
I'm dead

He bursts into tears.

Pure Joy
Ah, Sir . . .
why cry?

Man
I remember fresh air!

I remember light!

I thought I *escaped*!

Emperor
No, Dirt . . .
you *died* !!

Man
As did *you*
Gold-encrusted Dirt!

Gangbang
Watch your mouth, Dirt
in front of   Gold-encrusted Dirt!

Pure Joy
    Perhaps for the moment . . .
    Enough dirt!

    The sun is hot.

    These are some fascinating oddly dressed young people.

    I believe they dug this hole here
    into the centre of us
    and it seems   we are all   emerging from it!

    Perhaps if we observe them
    we will discover why we are here.

    Let us sit,
    Sire
    Sir
    Sir

    If Death is indeed eternal . . .
    we may be here for some time.

Emperor
    I sit first!

Gangbang
    I sit second!

Man
    I stand! I *stand*!

    They sit and stand.

FIVE
TWO MECHANICAL ARCHERS

Luce and Ross move to a large crate some way away from the table and Tark. They open the crate.

Luce
    Why are you being so mean to me?
    Why are you being so cold?

Pure Joy
    Ah!
    They converse again!

    Splendid!

Ross
    Mean? Me?
    Cold? Me?
    Get your eyes tested!

He exits. She follows as . . .

Luce
    My eyes are fine.

    Get your heart checked.
    It doesn't seem to be functioning.

Emperor
    They are . . . servants?

Pure Joy
    No.
    Scribes of some sort.
    She also!
    A *girl*!

Ross and Luce return with another crate between them.

Luce (*to Tark*)
Can you go ask Victor what we should do next?

Tark (*as he is about to go*)
Missing you already!

Ross clocks this. Tark exits. Beat.

Luce
Once!
I slept with him *once*!

Pure Joy (*to Emperor*)

Sire . . . observe A Love Triangle!

Ross
Once counts!

Pure Joy
Simplest of musical instruments!

Ross
He's such a *lightweight*!

Pure Joy (*to Emperor*)
Point proved
most complex of human / behaviours.

Luce
Anyway it's not your business!
Anyway you promised to be my *friend*!!
You said

She does a nasty impersonation of Ross.

'We can continue our relationship
in a *different* form.'
'Okay we're not (*finger-quotes*) "*together*" now
but we can still be (*point-making finger*) "together".'

341

Ross
You know
you're even getting to *be* like him.

Luce
Well, I'd rather be like him than like you!
I'd rather be light and fun and

Ross
stupid

Luce
and stupid

Ross
and shallow

Luce
and *shallow,* oh God yes!
than helping you carry your big black bag of
depression
into every room, oh God yes yes YESSS!

Horrible pause.

Ross
Thanks.

Luce
Ross . . . it wasn't your fault.
What happened at home.

Ross
Right.

Luce
And it wasn't *mine.*

Ross . . .

Tark returns.

Tark
Victor says we can get the mechanical archer thingies out.

Luce
Great.

Ross
We.

Tark
We.

As long as *I* don't touch them.

Ross
Okay.
Give me the fresh gloves . . .

He holds out his hand for the gloves.

Tark
Oh no!

They all realise at the same time that Tark has forgotten the gloves.

Ross
He's forgotten the gloves!

Luce
How could you forget the gloves?
The gloves were the *one* thing / you had to remember!

Tark
I'm *juvenile*!

All exit.

SIX
THE CLEVEREST MINDS IN THE EMPIRE

Emperor
I am awoken for *this*?

For *these* pieces of Dirt?
Children!

Robbers of the Art of my tomb!
This is why I rise from my eternal sleep!
To defend my Art!
The Art I created with my artists and architects and
metalsmiths??

From the depths of the tomb we hear . . .

Housebeautiful (*horrified*)
What is this??

A hole in my structure?

Somebody has breached my geodisic dome!!

Heartlistener
Someone is rescuing us!
Oh thank you Heavens!

Cleverhands
Somebody's not rescuing us!
Somebody's robbing the place!
Somebody's pilfering our Art!!

Emperor
What voices are these?

*As they climb out . . . these grey-cobwebby dusty
artists . . .*

Pure Joy
It is Cleverhands
the inventor.

Cleverhands
  Thieves!

Pure Joy
  House Beautiful
  the architect of your tomb!

House Beautiful
  Trespassers!

Pure Joy
  Heartlistener!
  Your infallible doctor . . .
  who promised you would live for ever!

Heartlistener
  Murderers!

Man
  Oh no . . .
  Not *This* Lot!!

Gangbang
  Books and pens!
  It's the *Clever* People! (*This is not a compliment.*)

Pure Joy
   The most splendid minds in the Empire
  who produced the most splendid Art
  who you instructed to make your tomb.

Emperor
  What are they doing in *my* tomb??

Man
  You don't remember?

  To Pure Joy . . . disgusted.

  He doesn't remember!

To the Emperor.

Because you wanted no one to know where your tomb
was

Pure Joy
and so that you would be as inviolate in death
as you were in life . . .

Gangbang
You shut *them* too
within your tomb.

Pure Joy
Oh what a splendid reunion!

Man
The Clever Ones died too?

It is a little (*tries out the word*) splendid . . . Yes!

The artists warily explore the space . . .

Cleverhands
My mechanical archers!

You pilfering bastards.

Housebeautiful
Goodness!
Good Heavens!
This space is amazing!
What is that?
A tent . . . ?
Amazing!
What is it made of?
Who made this?

Heartlistener (*calls down the tomb*)
SeesFuture!

Pure Joy
  SeesFuture!
  Your astrologer!

SeesFuture (*from the very depths of the tomb*)
  I hear you!

Heartlistener
  Come and see this!

SeesFuture
  I already see it in my mind.

  There is a hole in the tomb's ceiling.

Heartlistener
  Yes!

SeesFuture
  And a great tent full of our bones.

Heartlistener
  Yes!

SeesFuture
  And all the splendid Art you made
  all in caskets?

Heartlistener
  Yes!

SeesFuture
  Crumbling.

  They nod as:

  Old
  fragile.

  SeesFuture appears from the tomb.

And our all-powerful Emperor?

The artists spot the Emperor, abase themselves.

Emperor
Dress me!

SeesFuture
It is the future . . .
Dress yourself.

He looks for . . .

And some young souls from a different people?

He looks around, but they are not there . . .

Cleverhands
And some pilfering bastards, yes!

Ross, Luce and Tark enter in their fresh gloves. They comb through all the new tomb and start carefully taking out the mechanical archers.

Do not touch my constructions!

He tries to smack their hands away.
  They feel nothing.

They cannot feel my touch!

Pure Joy
This *I* discovered too!

Cleverhands tries to clasp Ross in his arms. Ross moves about seemingly unhindered

No. Force has no effect upon them.

Housebeautiful
What are they wearing?
What materials are these?

Heartlistener
Are they spirit?

SeesFuture
>They are future.

>*He looks into each one's face . . .*

>One or two will see you
>some will sense you
>most will not know you are here.

Artists
>Ayee!

>*They watch closely. This is very interesting.*

Tark
>Is it me . . .
>or is it *weird* today?

>*They try touching . . .*

All (*variously*)
>No!
>Yes!
>Something?
>Anything?
>This is so inefficient!
>See me? See me? Yes? No? (*etc.*)

Ross
>*It* isn't weird.
>*You* are!

Heartlistener
>There is no communication . . .

Housebeautiful
>In a room together . . . but walls are *in* the room
>between us!

Luce (*shivers*)
>It's *always* weird around here!

Heartlistener
It seems something of
a waste of the accumulation of
generations of useful knowledge . . .

Ross
Can we get on with our job, please?

*The interns open up the archers. The tomb-dwellers
watch.*

Mechanical archers
two
Cleverhands
My machines!

Emperor
My machines!

Luce
mounted at the entrance to each gate of each chamber

Housebeautiful
My beautiful gates!

Emperor
My beautiful gates!

Housebeautiful
Our gates of silver and gold
which opened as gently as if they
were a lady opening her silk robe . . .

Luce
They're kneeling
hands holding their longbows . . .
The bowstrings are gone.

Cleverhands
Gone?

They were silver thread!
That shouldn't happen!

Luce
The jerkins of the models are leather
badly perished and eaten away . . .

Man
Rats . . .
place was crawling with rats . . .

Luce
The clockwork . . .

Ross
machinery . . .

Luce (*okay, then*)
machinery . . .
that should make the bodies move
is stuck
they should move
but
time has stopped them from working . . .

Tark
They are kind of . . .
they're not . . .
they're not set to shoot vertically . . .

He gets up, goes over to Luce's model. Studies it . . .
The Artists follow . . .

Cleverhands
Well, of *course* not!

Interns and artists gaze at the model . . .

Housebeautiful
Oh, *fine* model!

Tark
They were here, right?

Cleverhands
Yes.

Ross joins him, facing the doors.

Housebeautiful
Yes.

Ross
So if the doors opened . . .

Housebeautiful
Yes.

Tark
if anyone opened the doors from *outside* . . .

Cleverhands
Yes.

Ross
a mechanism between the hinges and these things . . .

Housebeautiful
Yes.

Tark
would shoot them . . . dead in the heart!!

Cleverhands
Yesss!!

Housebeautiful
Exactly!!

Tark
What we have here is a bloody *brilliant* anti-theft device!!

Cleverhands
Do you hear that, Esteemed Artist??
'Bloody brilliant'!

My archers!

Housebeautiful
I heard it, Esteemed Artist!
But I believe his praise refers to work of the *doors*
also!

Luce
Where are the arrows?
The arrows are missing.

She shivers suddenly . . .

Cleverhands
Yes . . . where are the arrows?

Tark
Stuck in the doors?

Ross
No . . .

Tark
arrow marks in the doors?

The whole thing warps . . .
they shoot into the doors . . .
they drop out . . .
they're on the floor?

Ross
Nothing on the inventory.

Tark
What happened to the arrows?

*Suddenly, both Cleverhands and SeesFuture clutch
their hearts.*

SeesFuture (*the first thing*)
Ah!

(*The next thing.*) Ah!

Ah.

Cleverhands . . .
What happened to the arrows?

Cleverhands holds his heart.
His head moves, showing his mind working it out.

I was shot!
In the heart!
With my own bloody arrow!
And you were standing next to me, talking to me
and . . .

We see his great head working it out . . .

So . . . if you were there and I was here . . .

He gets there . . .

you were shot too!
By my other arrow!

But you are SeesFuture!

SeesFuture
And I foresee all deaths

Cleverhands
Yes!

SeesFuture
but my own.

A beat.

Cleverhands
A thousand pardons, Sir.

SeesFuture
>A sudden blinding pain
>and then . . . [*nothing*]

>Not a bad end, Sir.

>*They both bow to one another.*

SEVEN
A NEW ARTISTIC CHALLENGE

Housebeautiful
>We are all finished then.
>There are no problems any more.

>Nothing to solve!

Cleverhands
>Then why are we here?

Heartlistener
>The only ones not finished . . .

Emperor
>Are these infant thieves!

>Kill them!

Pure Joy
>Clever Sirs . . .
>the Infants are not thieves.
>They are instructed in this by their elders.
>They are just unhappy.
>What can be done . . . ?

Cleverhands (*looks at the interns*)
>There's an equation here to balance . . .

Housebeautiful
>a structure to tinker with . . .

Heartlistener
a malaise to cure . . .

All Three
play with . . .

We need to work it / yes! . . . out.
Yes? and solve it / and cure it / and put right . . .
How clever we are to spot this! Well we are clever!!

This is fascinating . . .

SeesFuture
They are hungry.

Ross looks up at the sky.

Ross
Noon.

Luce
I am sooo hungry . . .

Tark
Me too!
Lunch!

Ross
I say when it's lunch.

Tark and Luce go back to their work, radiating hatred at Ross.

Okay
lunch.

They all exit.

Emperor
I am hungry.

Feed me.

Other Men
You are dead!

Nobody moves.

Emperor
Feed me!

His Subjects
We're dead.
Feed yourself!!

Housebeautiful
I was so hungry in the
tomb . . .

Heartlistener
Ravenous . . . did we eat?

Cleverhands
We sat in the dark . . . yes!

Housebeautiful
Somebody opened the doors! Who?

Heartlistener
I saw no one.
But I heard whispering from behind the doors, yes!
From the central chamber.
Who?

Cleverhands
And then
someone opened the doors from the central chamber!

Emperor
Which was where I lay . . .
dead!

They all look towards Pure Joy.

Pure Joy
And we ladies sat . . .
alive.

She decides to enjoy the delicious fun.
Very respectfully:

And
Lord

we
became peckish
and
More Light remarked that it was high time for supper.

Emperor
More Light?

The name is vaguely familiar . . .

Pure Joy
Our leader within your dark tomb
the cleverest of your ladies, Lord,
More Light said
'Our Emperor would not like us to go hungry . . .'

Man
Oh, *that's* the bitch!

Pure Joy
Your face
in death
seemed to agree

so

we undressed you, Sire

then

we ate you, Sire

we cut you into pieces
and
we ate you, Sire.

But not before we had
respectfully
cooked you.

Man
Oh that *is* the bitch!
The Royal Parrot!

Pure Joy
You were   delicious. Sire.

Emperor
This is HELL!

Pure Joy
I rather think it is
for you,
Sire

For me
it is Pure Joy!

The interns return with their lunch.

All
Oh
What are *these* going to eat?!

They reposition themselves for the best food-eating-watching vantage points.

Cleverhands
This one has chicken!

Housebeautiful
This one hasn't.
Vegetables only!

Heartlistener
Look! This one has too much bread for a healthy equilibrium
of phlegm and bile!

Ross takes out a packet of crisps.

All
Oh.
What is this?

SeesFuture
They are called . . . crisps.

All
Crisps!

Ross rips the bags, lays out the crisps.
They all watch as he crunches into one.

Heartlistener
This is *much* healthier for the phlegm and the bile than the bread!

Cleverhands
But not as healthy as eating the Emperor!

All but the Emperor find this hilarious.

Pure Joy
Actually . . . he was a little too . . . *fatty* . . . Ah!
But once *Emperor* was all gone . . .
The only thing to do was . . .
eat the most splendid artists
belonging to the Emperor!

Pure Joy is laughing with pure joy as . . .

We ate you first . . . (*Housebeautiful.*)

Then you. (*SeesFuture.*)

Then you. (*Cleverhands.*)

You were, excuse me, somewhat leaner and tougher
than His Omnipotence here . . .
We had to braise you for quite a length of time in our
cookpots!

If these three could turn green, they would . . .

Housebeautiful
You put us in *cookpots*?

We put no *cookpots* in the central chamber!

Pure Joy
In, excuse me, the war helmets we were *using* as
cookpots!

Housebeautiful
Any wine?

The interns take out cans of Coca-Cola.

All (*reading the label*)
'Coca-Cola'.

*Everyone watches intently as the interns rip off the
tabs.*

All
Ayee!

The interns drink.

Ayee!

Cleverhands
Drink machines!!

Ross ostentatiously puts on his iPod.

Housebeautiful
A deaf-making device!

*Luce opens an improving book.
They eat.*

Pure Joy
Ah!
The girl scribe reads!

Just like More Light!

Pure Joy experiences pure joy . . .
Tark, who has eaten nothing, looks for his
cigarettes. This attracts the attention of Cleverhands
and Heartlistener.

Cleverhands
What do we have here?

SeesFuture
Cigarettes.

All (*learning the name*)

'Cigarettes'.

As the cellophane crinkles:

A tiny instrument for sound!

Tark throws the cellophane to the floor. Cleverhands
gets down to look at it . . .

Some kind of magnifying glass . . .
no.

Tark opens the pack.

Heartlistener
Ah!

Cleverhands
Ah . . .
it is a tiny light-carrying chest!
The top hinges back!

Both crane to see what it is.
Tark takes out a cigarette . . .

Both Ah!

>*Tark puts it in his mouth.*

Ah!

Heartlistener
It is a little wind instrument!
He is going to play it!

>*Tark starts patting his various pockets, humming his
Human Waste tune . . .*

See . . . he sets the beat
and the melody . . .

>*Tark finds his lighter.*

Cleverhands
Look at the wheel on that!

>*Tark lights the cigarette. He inhales deeply, then blows
out smoke.*
>   *Immediately Heartlistener has conniptions.*

Heartlistener (*to Tark*)
Ayee!

>*He babbles as fast as he can . . .*

My son
you must desist from this activity!
You are equal parts of bile and phlegm
which lie in two dark quiet pools
in the pit of your stomach.

>*He demonstrates this with his pointing finger near
Tark's body . . .*

This will heat each pool
they will boil and bubble
rise

overflow their banks
and phlegm will drip forth from your orifices . . .

Indicates the nostrils.

hither
hither

Indicates the mouth.

and hither

and the bile ooze

He points.

from your love member
hither
and your waste pipe
thither!

Tark
What you listening to, Ross?
Barry Manilow?

*He establishes that Ross cannot hear him then . . .
to Luce:*

Is this why?

Luce
Why what?

Tark
Why you won't sleep with me again?
Because I smoke?

Luce
Absolutely.

I never sleep with smokers

Tark
more than once.

She reads.

Even though you stayed all night
even though you laughed
even though you cried. But in a nice way.
Even though you shouted a lot. But in a big way.

Even though it was horrible.

Luce puts down her book.

Luce
No.
Not because it was horrible.

She checks Ross.

It is because it was nice.

She goes back to her book.

You total
utter
loathsome
stupid
self-centred
idiot.

Ross (*takes one earpiece off, to Luce*)
Did you say something to me?

Luce
I was just wondering what music you were listening to.

Ross puts his earpiece back in.

Man
He's hot for her.

Cleverhands
She's hot for the skinny one.

Man
The prick always trumps the heart.

Cleverhands
Always.
Basic rule of the Love Game.

Man
Always.
But the clever pussy
always trumps the stupid prick.

Cleverhands
Always.

Ross
Okay.
Lunch break over.
Clear the table for the bones.

Tark
More bones!
Hip-hip-hip-hooray!

He exits.

Heartlistener (*rising, excited*)
Bones?

There is a collection of bones?

Man
Over there
big tent of bones . . .

Housebeautiful (*slightly misunderstanding*)
A tent of bones?

Rises.

Cleverhands
What?
Made of bones?

The two artists leave in the direction of the bone tent.

Stretched-over bones?
I must see this!

Luce (*to Ross*)

I thought Victor had sorted the bones . . .

Ross
He's sorted the skeletons,
it's the random bones.

Luce
Ross . . .
You . . . Tark and I can do the bones.

You don't have to do the bones.

You shouldn't have to do the bones.

Ross
You're not my girlfriend any more!
Don't tell me what I can and can't do!!

Luce
Ross . . .

Ross
Go away!
I am sick of the sight of you!
Why are you always in my face?

Luce exits.

Ross
Damn!
Damn!

Damn It!
Go away!
Get out of my head!
Get out!
Get out!
Get out!!

Today
is the day he does it.
Exits
Quits
Goes

to the very edge

then
jumps
and
falls
down

into the hole
the chasm
the abyss.

Nothing will stop him
nothing.

Heartlistener (*touches Ross as . . .*)
There is no light here . . . (*His head.*)

there is darkness here . . . (*His eyes.*)

this . . . is all ice . . . (*His heart.*)

this . . . all stagnation   all confusion.

It is a condition that can hit at any age male or
female . . .
but happens most often to

this age
this gender . . .

Pure Joy
  Can we not help?

Emperor
  Kill him

Gangbang
  put him out of his misery.
  Yes.
  Good idea.

  He realises who he is speaking to . . .

  Your Excellency.

Man
  Fool! Gold-encrusted fool!
  We can't kill any more.
  Let him go.

  Let him jump. Dark. Good.

Pure Joy
  SeesFuture . . . ?

SeesFuture
  We can only watch them . . .

Emperor
  Only *watch* them?

  This is terrible!

SeesFuture
  Hopeful
  that they look at our piled skeletons and die better.
  That they examine what we made
  and make better . . . Hopeful
  that their leader looks into the faces of his people . . .

EIGHT
THE BONES

Tark and Luce enter with bones.
Luce looks towards Ross, who is standing by the
tomb.

Luce
Ross . . .

Ross
No!

Tark
Luce . . .

Luce
No!

She goes off for more bones.
Tark follows her.

Gangbang
I'm getting I'm dead.
I'm getting we're all dead but the . . .

Points off . . .

but them . . .

I don't remember how I died.

Man (*with great pleasure*)
I done it.

I done it!

You was oblivious
remember my belt?

Gangbang
No. (*As if!*)

Man

I make it into a garotte . . .

I wait

I wait until you do your usual trick of
trying to spy on the Royal Parrots in the inner
chamber . . .

He starts to sneak round behind Gangbang . . .

and I sneak up, quiet as a wolf
and I . . .

He gets Gangbang in a garotte . . .

pull it
tighter
tighter . . .
you struggle for a bit
then you . . .

He mimes 'drop like a sack of potatoes'.

then . . .
I cut this off. (*Radius.*)
and this out (*Scapula.*)
and took a strip of skin . . .
from here   to here

made a mean bastard of an axe.

Pure Joy points them towards the axe on the table.

Pure Joy

which I think is here . . .!

Gangbang, Man and Pure Joy examine the axe.

Gangbang

That's a *very* fine piece of work

You bastard!

Man

You bastard!

Luce and Tark return. Sit sorting bones.
    *Ross sits with his back to them, looking down into
the tomb.*

Man

They are going to make something from our bones!

Gangbang

Perhaps an axe to kill that one!

Tark

This is another shoulderblade

Luce

this is a hand

Tark

I'd like to take your hand

Luce

I'm giving you the cold shoulder . . .

She holds up the scapula as a warding off device.
Both find this mildly funny . . . so . . .

Tark

Luce

You like me
you like me
I know you like me.
Why can't we . . .

She looks at him.
    He gives up.

Man

Choose him, woman!

Tark

>Why doesn't Ross like bones?
>
>Why did you two split up?
>
>And why don't you really split up?
>
>*Luce looks towards Ross. She decides to tell Tark.*

Luce

>We were in a car.
>In . . .
>
>*Name an area in the town in which you are
>performing.*
>
>We'd had a row.
>So we had a further row about
>who should drive.
>I let him win to . . . (*make things better*)
>and
>he hit a kid.
>
>It wasn't his fault.
>He was within the speed limit.
>The kid just . . .
>
>*She mimes a kid dashing out with her hand.*
>
>He couldn't have seen her
>and she . . . (*died*)
>instantly
>and everything changed.
>Police
>inquest
>everybody
>cleared him.
>Everybody except   Ross
>and
>he became . . . (*like he is now*)

he finished with me because it just got . . . (*awful*)
and I feel I can't
I feel I shouldn't start
anything
new . . .

Tark touches her hand. Takes it away.

Tark
It's cool.
It's fine.
(*Lying.*) You're not the only pebble on the beach.
(*Still lying.*) Not the only fish in the sea.
(*Still lying.*) It's cool.
It's fine.

It's not.

Man
Felt that once!

Pure Joy
For More Light

Man
For More Light

Pure Joy
and she for you.

Man
The Bitch.

Ran into her at the third gate
played with her
fell for her.

I asked her to come with me, too.

'We can dig *out*,' I said

Escape. I said. Air. Light. I said.
She turned me down.

Kissed me.

Then . . . (*He remembers.*) killed me.

Pure Joy
We made her kill you.

Man
Stuck an iron sword in my heart!

Pure Joy
She was our leader.
We couldn't lose her.
Not to you.

Gangbang
Clever Pussy always trumps
Daft Prick

Pure Joy
Not always.
In the Love Game between you
and More Light . . .
she lost as much as you . . .

Man
She stuck an iron sword into my heart!
Dead!
Immediately!

Pure Joy
And you stuck a love sword in hers.
Dead.
Painfully slowly.

Man
She loved me . . . ?

Cleverhands and Housebeautiful return.

Housebeautiful
There are bones and bones and bones and bones . . .

NINE
RED SKY

*Luce, Tark and Ross in their separate spaces sing their
different songs.*

Ross
Everywhere is dark.
   Everywhere is very dark.

Tark
It is light.
   It is all about light.

Luce
And in it joy.
   Pure joy joy joy.

Emperor
They have pleasing voices, the young souls.

I have always enjoyed music.

What are they singing?

Pure Joy listens.

But how strange . . .
this is the song we sang at our end!
All the ladies of the Emperor!

As the air grew thinnner
and the food, excuse me, ran out
we were too weak to mov e. . .
Scent-of-Ginger, the most musical of us ladies,

said
tell me what our story is about . . .
I will make a song . . .
and the ladies were of two minds . . .
some said . . . ours
is a story of hopelessness
it is dark
it is very dark
others said
it is light
it is all about light

it is about joy.
I said . . .

Emperor
Listen!

My ladies!

My ladies were always clever.

Always.

Pure Joy
More Light who died first
after she killed you
after we, excuse me, ate you also
she would not eat
but sat alone often in the darkest corner
saying
'I made the wrong choice,
I should have trusted him.
He would have got me out!
He would have got us all out.
Look . . . I have killed my sisters.'
She was, excuse me, a little tedious
towards the end.

I think that is why she is not here now.

She grew to love the dark.

She forgot how she was named.

More Light
in her wide reading of other tongues
also called . . .

La Luce
Lux
Luce.

Luce looks straight at Pure Joy.

You must have *more light*!

Luce looks up towards the sun.

Man
Don't turn love away!

Don't ever turn love away!

It's the only thing you can take and *keep*!

Emperor
If they know this song . . .
they must be able to hear us . . .

All
Ayee!

Emperor (*to interns*)

I command you
infants!
Listen!

To others:

I command you
my people!
Sing!

They all sing to Luce, Tark and Ross.
  Luce looks up, listening.

Pure Joy
  Go!

Man
  Do it!

Luce suddenly gets up.

Luce
  Oh . . . alright!

She goes over to Tark.

Ross watches her.
  Takes Tark's face in her hands and kisses him.
  He lets her kiss him.
  She sits back down.

Tark
  Oh . . . al*right* . . . !

Luce
  Shh.
  Don't repeat everything I say! (*But she is smiling.*)

They think no one has seen them.
  They work separately.
  Grinning. Glowing.

All
  Oh it works!
  Oh how clever we are!

Emperor
  My people are clever
  and *magnificently* ruled over by me . . .
  here in Death's Dark Kingdom!

SeesFuture watches Ross, who is standing on the edge looking down into the dark hole of the tomb.

Ross
Alright!

Pure Joy
He goes to jump . . .

Ross jumps into the air . . . but he is caught by Man and Gangbang.

Emperor
SeesFuture,
tell him his future

SeesFuture talks to Ross.

SeesFuture
Not down there.
Not today.
No.

This is not how you will end.

Other people from the tomb help to lift him high into the air as:

You are a clever young man.
You will realise that this would be a great waste of you.

You will discover your friend Luce,

A phrase he has learned recently . . .

'is not the only pebble on the beach'.

In, I think   nine years
you will forgive yourself

You will look up.

They turn him. Ross does.

380

You will see that it is the little things that save you.
You will see this bad day is almost over.
You will see that the heat lessens.

You will feel a light breeze on your skin
This will   somehow calm you

Ross's body starts to unknot. They lower him gently.

You will notice what you missed before
the change in the sky
that the fierce blue is gone
that the almighty sun has shot the sky through with red

red sky at night
a propitious omen always

your life will be a long one
and in it
many kindnesses

your heart will sing.

*Gently, the song composed by Pure Joy and the ladies
of the Emperor begins, swells, rises, ends.
Everybody watches the beautiful sunset.*

End.

Production Notes

The first impetus to write *Red Sky* came when Bryony Lavery was asked if she had ever considered a male 'reaction' to *More Light*, which she wrote for *Connections* in 1997. Its story is about the incarceration in the tomb of some of the characters who later appear in *Red Sky*.

EXERCISE   *Stand, enter the middle of the circle and say, in a ceremonious manner, a self-created name such as More Light, Love's Gift, Young Friend, Slightly Unsure, Easily Pleased, Quietly Critical, Hopeful Fumblings. This exercise is both an ice-breaker and a first entry into the world of the play.*

STAGING ISSUES

The use of the large number of soldiers at the start of the play is a conscious decision on the part of the author to have an expanding moment of males filling the stage who then disappear – as many as possible. Bryony floated the idea that four hundred and fifty might be ideal . . .

Due to the 'real time' nature of the three central characters' story, it would be good to have an offstage set for 'the tents' of these three actors, to remain in character while they're not onstage. It is important that the grey characters are from a very different world.

The flashbacks musn't slow the progression of the play. They have a narrative purpose, but they also add texture and 'crunch' to the play as a whole.

Bryony uses many exclamation marks and a particular kind of spacing on the page. Go with this, make the play sound as it looks on the page.

SOUND   The piece of music at the end has to be gorgeous, as it reaches back over five thousand years. Also it is the moment when the two worlds fully join together. Bryony mentioned how 'Vincent' by Don McLean exists in two versions – only one of which makes you tingle. The piece of music at the end should make you tingle.

Be absolutely specific about the lines sung and those not. Those that are sung are in italics.

EXERCISES

Try this exercise as a way of exploring how the two different worlds may co-exist on stage:

Walk around the space following your own journey and don't make eye-contact with others.

Get familiar with the feel of walking on this floor and the proximity of the others in the group to you.

Increase the pace. Make your journey as interesting as possible, with turns and changes of direction.

The leader of the group says, 'Stop.' There is a moment's of pause. Feel the floor and breathe deeply. Have an awareness of where you find yourself.

The leader will now stop and say nothing. Everyone should be aware through their peripheral vision. This should be repeated a few times.

The leader then squeezes the hand of someone secretly and this person takes the lead. This is repeated.

Split the group in two, give each a leader. Ask both groups to stop and start with their leader.

Moments of communication and touch between the two worlds in the play are very important. The decision of where to touch needs working out. Establish a consistent convention.

Look at the moment when Pure Joy touches Luce. Have Luce sit at a table and get Pure Joy to come and touch her. Ask:

> What can Pure Joy touch?
> What can't she?
> What is Luce's reaction, if any?

Another touch experiment.

Get an actor to take off his T-shirt and stand in front of a large sheet of paper with a pen.

Get a second to sit behind him and draw on his back. The first actor has to try and draw what he felt was being drawn on his back. This can pose questions about how much we can understand from touch, and help the actor to isolate this one specific sense that is key in the play.

The final moment in the play has a bold use of touch that ends the original contact convention. The touching starts delicately but rises to this crescendo. The reason it is there is because it is a visually dramatic key point, and catches someone at the most dangerous moment. This moment is very interesting to explore – what are the moments that stop us?

Exploring backstories through hot-seating:

Ask the three central characters (Ross, Tark and Luce) these questions:

How long ago did you split up?
How long have you known each other?
Why did you sleep with Tark?
Ross, how do you feel physically?
What's Victor like?
What's the accommodation like on a dig?

This exercise enables the entire company to have a shared imagined reality in which to contextualise the three central characters.

ROSS (EMPEROR)   *Scene Three – A Jewelled Robe.*
Place a coat in front of Ross and have him go through the speech about the robe. Get another actor to feed him his lines. Ask the actor feeding the lines to say what s/he feels about Ross in this speech.

LUCE (PURE JOY)   *Scene Four – A Paper Bird.* Another actor should feed Luce her lines. Place a paper bird in front of her. Ask:

Would you like children?
Why do you like your job?
Is this place familiar?
How do you feel about Luce?
Did the concubines have children?

Luce and Ross are held back by baggage from the past.

THE POWER OF OBJECTS

The three objects from the tomb are important and specifically chosen.

Jewelled robe – represents money spent on art, where what is spent on materials ensures that the piece lasts longer.

Paper birds – were made by the concubine More Light. They are fragile and have a shorter life than the robe. They would disintegrate, leaving dust in the shape of the bird.

Axe – made from human bones, representing art made from suffering.

These different objects pose the question – what do we value from the past?

An exercise to examine the power of objects:

Send two actors away where they can't hear.

Get the rest of the cast to form a horseshoe shape.

Ask one person to bring up a treasured object and share its significance with the group, then join the rest of the group.

Get one of the actors you've sent away to examine and describe the object in as much detail as possible and infer its possible significance.

Write down verbatim the observations and photograph the object.

Get the second person from outside to come in and look at the photo and read out the description that had been noted before seeing the real object and discovering who the owner is.

POWER AND CONSEQUENCE

Break into small groups to explore different kinds of power and its consequences in the play. These could be trivial or epic, and examples might include the following:

POWER	CONSEQUENCE
Power of laughter/joy	Insights others cannot have
Hope over despair	Space to heal
Focus enabled by location	Given time to think
Assured freedom to speak	Punishment/dismemberment
Non-democratic leadership	Depression/death
Disobedience	Revolution
Seeing future	Ignoring present
Remembrance of things past	Brighter future
Remembrance of things past	Dark future
Leader's power in life	Disrespect in death
No power	Turmoil
Patriarchical culture	Wrong assumptions
Invisible edicts	Lack of self-knowledge
Music/art	Transcend barriers
To create	To recreate/record
Objects	Insight
Arrogance	Insecurity
Care for others	Lose sight of self
The dead	The characters being alive

CHARACTER ARCS

Lay out as one long line the pages of the play to enable people to look at it in a simple, linear manner. Get six small groups to focus on one character each (Ross, Tark, Luce, Emperor, Pure Joy, Man) and try to trace the arc or journey of the character from beginning to end. See what triggered or caused any changes. Find out if there are any character traits which emerge from this investigation. Observations might include:

EMPEROR   Before he first appears there is a sense of wealth/power. However, when he emerges, everywhere he turns is disintegrating, and he feels fear. The soldiers won't carry out his will; no one will dress him. He is incapable of doing anything for himself. He moves from uncertainty to terror very quickly: 'Will *nothing* obey me?'

TARK   The first thing Tark does is sing about Light. He is bright and is possibly a more creative thinker than the others – he works out how the burglar alarm works. He triggers all the changes in this small group – it is he that upsets the equilibrium of the past. He goes with the moment – we find out very little about his past. In the end he does get the girl.

LUCE   Luce begins the play by keeping the peace and burying herself in the past. She wants to protect Ross. When she loses control she quickly psychs herself back up. Interestingly, she is the only character with a soliloquy, so we have a special relationship with her. Her revealing of herself to Tark is a pivotal moment of change for her.

PURE JOY   When she first emerges she adapts almost instantly to the new beauty, and mistakes Luce for More Light. She undergoes an extraordinary journey as she realises the change in her relationship with the Emperor. Pure Joy is the only character who addresses the audience. Being dead does not frighten her as it does others. She is the true archaeologist of the play – using her power and knowledge for the benefit of others.

MAN   He begins angry after his death. When he discovers that More Light killed him for love, he has greater closure. The moment of castration shows not only his literal loss of masculinity but the loss brought about by being a slave. Generally selfish, he finally uses his experience to help Ross.

ROSS   He is the most introverted and tortured at the beginning, but finally achieves redemption. Three arcs of increasing size can be discerned – first the arc towards suicide, secondly the arc of his professional ambition, and lastly the arc of his life.

RESEARCH

The film *Titus* (dir. Julie Taymor) could be a possible inspiration for design. Its stylised eclecticism of periods might be a good way to humanise the world of the underground. There are many different possibilities for resolving this.

The significance of foot-binding is that it was to make the feet sex-toys by curling them. Also, walking on bound feet strengthens your vaginal muscles. Good descriptions can be found in the novel *Wild Swans*. Castration as punishment in the ancient world involved the removal of all genitals. Its psychoanalytical significance lies in the removal of phallic power.

Both these are examples of disfigurement by power in a land where a leader cannot look into the faces of his people. The political significance of this is important because Bryony is also writing about contemporary leaders who cannot look into the faces of their people. The world of the tomb is both ancient and urgently modern.

The idea of many people being incarcerated together is an alien one, but there are contemporary examples in things such as the Heaven's Gate ritual mass suicide. Interestingly, some members of this cult were also castrated. In their suicide ritual they died a few at a time, like those in the Emperor's tomb. Parallels might be drawn between the leader of this cult and the Emperor.

Workshop facilitated by Anthony Banks
with notes taken by Jonathan Humphries

RUCKUS IN THE GARDEN

David Farr

David Farr is a writer and director. He took up the post of Artistic Director of the Lyric Theatre Hammersmith in June 2005. His play *The UN Inspector*, a free adaptation of Gogol's *The Government Inspector*, opened at the National Theatre (Olivier) in June 2005 in his own production. His production of *Tamburlaine* played at The Barbican main stage in autumn 2005 to rave reviews. He was Artistic Director of the Gate Theatre, London, from 1995 to 1998, and subsequently Joint Artistic Director of Bristol Old Vic from 2002 to 2005, directing seven shows including his versions of *Paradise Lost* and *The Odyssey*, and winning the TMA Best Director Award for *A Midsummer Night's Dream*. He directed *Coriolanus* (starring Greg Hicks) and *Julius Caesar* for the Royal Shakespeare Company, and has also worked for the Young Vic, Almeida Opera and the National Theatre of the Czech Republic. As a playwright, David's work includes *The Nativity* at the Young Vic, *The Danny Crowe Show* at the Bush Theatre, *Elton John's Glasses* at Watford Palace and in the West End, *Crime and Punishment in Dalston* at the Arcola, and *Night of the Soul*, which he directed for the RSC at the Pit. His short comedy *The Queen Must Die* was part of *NT Connections* in 2003.

Author's Note

My two plays for *Connections* (the other one was *The Queen Must Die*) are what I call desperate comedies. They have an almost farcical structure, but the characters are all good. They want to make the world better, but are prevented from doing so by political and social circumstance, the cruelty of fate and their own insecurity and lack of self-respect. The comedy and the pathos stem from the gap between what the characters sense might be possible (a perfect world, being loved utterly, not getting hit on a regular basis) and the reality that confronts them.

In *Ruckus in the Garden* I wanted to write about inequality between schools and how it breeds insecurity, self-loathing and tension. Most of all, I wanted to write about the joy of being 'chosen' and the despair at never being, through the prism of two schools – one 'selective', one not. But all through a deeply painful comedy.

In the play a group of young characters from two different schools enter a mysterious garden on a school trip. All they really want to do is to have a fight, but fate, in the form of Cupid, intervenes. The plot follows a series of misunderstandings and transformations that send our young heroes into increasingly absurd situations. I have stolen liberally from Shakespeare's *Midsummer Night's Dream* and Mozart's *Cosi fan Tutte* and publicly apologise to both.

To anyone acting the play I simply say that comedy is just as awful and true and meaningful as 'serious drama'. The more fully and committedly you play every situation and emotion, the more the comedy will fly. If you love, love wildly; if you hate, hate with a passion.

I loved writing this play. I hope it's as enjoyable to play.

DAVID FARR

Characters

Riverdale Comprehensive School

Stanley

Fraser

Rock

Cath

Billie

St Nectan's Grant-Maintained Secondary School

Tamsen

Maisy

Hugh

Clive

The Garden

Cupid

SCENE ONE

The Garden of Cecil Fortescue. A warm late spring day.
In the garden – Stanley and Fraser. Both in their own
clothes.

Fraser Where are we?

Stanley Read your Creative Partnerships Activity pack.

Fraser Like I'm really going to do that.

Stanley Well, if you did you would discover that we find
ourselves at the entrance to Homesleigh – one of the
great eighteenth-century English landscape gardens.

Fraser I'm going back to the coach.

Stanley (*reading*) 'Nestling in deep wooded countryside,
Cecil Fortescue created Homesleigh in 1720 as a token
of love for his French wife Amelia.'

Fraser Why didn't they take us to Alton Towers?

Stanley 'Stand at the entrance to the garden and look
before you at the artificial lakes carved out of the
landscape, Romanesque temples and statues dotted
amidst abundant flora and shrubbery and the statues
of Aphrodite, goddess of desire, and Apollo, god of
unity and harmony.'

Fraser I can't stand all this fresh air. Makes me feel sick.

Stanley 'Look closer. A hundred small stone cupids dot
the landscape like guardian angels keeping watch over
the sleeping greenery below. According to legend, when
true lovers visit the garden the Cupids come alive and
cause chaos and disarray with their mischievous
arrows of desire. In this paradise of formal flowerbeds
and sunken ha-has . . .'

Fraser Sunken what?

Stanley Ha-ha. It's like a ditch.

Fraser If it's a ditch why don't they call it a ditch?

Stanley Put a sock in it . . . 'Cecil Fortescue . . .'

Fraser Why do toffs have to invent new words for things that already have a name?

Stanley 'Cecil Fortescue brings Apollo and Aphrodite together to suggest that only through love and peace can the world achieve true harmony.'

Fraser Last night I got so wasted I ended up puking in a ha-ha by the A36.

Beat. Enter Rock.

Rock You're not going to believe it. You know the other coach in the car park? The one with air-con and head rests? It's only St Nectan's grant-maintained.

Stanley Oh no.

Fraser Okay, now we're talking.

Stanley Why does this happen every time?

Rock Stan? Is there going to be a ruckus?

Fraser You bet there is!

Rock Between us and the St Nectan's boys?

Stanley What do you think?

Rock Jackson Miller says there is. Three p.m. in the Temple of Apollo.

Fraser Now this is a day out! We're gonna lick them bastards!

Rock I don't like fights, Stan.

Stanley Nor do I, Rock.

Rock Yeah, but you disapprove for moral and political reasons. I just get really scared.

Stanley I disapprove because three hundred years after Cecil Fortescue made his garden of love and harmony we are still beating the shit out of the local selective secondary.

Fraser We always fight St Nectan's on trips. It's cool.

Stanley It's not cool. It's pathetic and degrading!

Fraser We gonna whip their moneyed arses, Stan man.

Stanley And why? Because they've got purple blazers? Why, Frase?

Fraser Cos they drive those new minis, and cos they have okra in their packed lunch – I dunno! Because we're on a school trip to a shit-boring garden and so are they and what else are we going to do? Smell the tulips?

Stanley But it's all we ever do, Frase. Fix it so we go on school trips the same day as they do, have beefs with them, get in shit, get grounded, do it again. I'm looking for a bit of evolution.

Rock When we fought them at Whipsnade Zoo this big floppy-haired guy called Moose broke Casey Martin's ankle.

Fraser That's cos they're rugby players, innit? But we got that sorted this time. We brought ammo.

Rock What ammo?

Stanley Read this, Frase. 'It was the Greek vision of love and harmony that Cecil Fortescue set out to imitate – to create an idyll where love and peace would for ever reign.' The man was a revolutionary, Fraser. And you're using his garden as a battleground!

Fraser He was a posh git who wanted to bang his wife in a temple. They didn't have Golf GTIs in them days. He had to go with a quickie behind the statue of Venus.

Stanley But don't you see, Frase, that by fighting St Nectan's we are confirming every prejudice about Riverdale. We're chavs and sluts who can only express ourselves through the fist, and they're a progressive academy who have been provoked into retaliation. It's just so depressing, man.

Rock Are you in a bad mood, Stanley?

Fraser He's just bitter cos he's been ha-ha'd by Kelly Fisher.

Stanley I have not.

Fraser Why were you seen weeping at the Megabowl?

Stanley Kelly and I came to realise we had irreconcilable differences.

Fraser You liked her, she didn't like you.

Rock Don't be down, Stan. She was wrong for you anyway.

Stanley What do you mean?

Rock I just don't think you were cut out for each other. You're an idealist. She was all cars and shoes and stuff.

Fraser Having a good time. Laughing. Enjoying life. Shallow shallow shallow.

Stanley You know we'll be blamed. It will be the same old story. The poor unwashed sink-school scum attack the future of Britain. We always come off worse! If we are ever going to change our society – we have to make the first move.

Fraser And how are we going to do that?

Stanley I'll tell you how. I'm going to walk into this garden and the first St Nectan's boy I find – I'm going to shake his hand.

Fraser Then the second thing you should do is duck.

Stanley And then I'm going to invite that St Nectan's pupil to join with me in a peace, love and harmony action here in the garden.

Rock That's suicide, Stan. Don't do it.

Stanley Someone has to. These fights are destroying us, man. Asbos, exclusion orders . . . it's doing my head in.

Rock What if you meet a girl?

Stanley If it's a girl I'll kiss her on the cheek.

Beat.

Rock You won't . . .

Stanley The olive branch of reconciliation . . .

Rock She'll think you're trying to get off with her.

Stanley No. She won't. She'll understand the nature of my approach and we'll walk in the garden hand in hand as Cecil Fortescue intended us to do.

Fraser If anyone from Riverdale sees you, you'll get belted. And that includes me.

Stanley That's a price I'm prepared to pay, Frase.

Fraser Okay, but when you've made a right prize fool of yourself, the ruckus is at three . . .

Stanley At the Temple of Apollo. Yeah yeah.

Rock I'm gonna get whacked. I always get whacked.

Fraser Don't do this, Stan.

Stanley I don't need no ruckus, Frase. I'm going into the garden.

SCENE TWO

Cath and Billie, also in their own clothes.

Billie I want a cheeky fag. Maybe we can hide in the Arch of Artemis.

Cath You saw.

Billie Saw what?

Cath When he got off the coach. I was right in front of him. He didn't even look at me.

Billie He was being given his Creative Partnerships Activity Pack by Mrs Gunnasekara.

Cath He's been chucked by Kelly Fisher. He should be desperate for a sign of affection from even the most grievous minger. Walked right past me.

Billie I don't see why you think he's so gorgeous anyway.

Cath That's because you have absolutely no taste.

Billie I have no taste? Look at your clothes, Cath.

Beat.

Cath What's wrong with my clothes?

Billie Nothing.

Cath He's always so sad. Like he's trying to reach out for something that isn't there.

Billie Where's your activity pack?

Cath I chucked it in the bin.

Billie Cath! You'll get well in trouble for that.

Cath What's the point? They only make them so they can get funding for the visit. Pick the worst school in the world and give them money to go to some 'improving experience', like we'll all come out playing the violin and painting seascapes. Makes me sick, man. (*Grabs it.*) 'Spot the Obelisk.' 'Colour in the Temple of Flora.' Like what is that about?

Billie What's wrong with you, girl?

Cath 'Describe in thirty words how visiting the garden has changed your views on the nature of love.' Like, hello?

Billie Cath? What's eating you?

Beat.

Cath Am I a minger, Bill?

Billie No, of course not . . .

Cath I wish I could change the way I looked. Wipe it all out and start again. I'd go online and buy Kelly Fisher's legs – click; buy Bryony Sturrock's arse – click; Sandra Estevez's tits. Proceed to checkout.

Billie Sandra Estevez has got the best tits in Year Ten.

Cath Her dad's Brazilian.

Billie Costa Rican.

Cath Same difference.

Beat.

Billie Are you gonna go to the ruckus?

Cath Dunno.

Billie Go on. Do you good to tear the face off some posh tart.

Cath St Nectan's girls don't fight. They just sit on the wall giggling and swishing their ponytails.

Billie So we'll knock 'em off the wall. We've got ammo.

Cath Stanley doesn't believe in fighting.

Billie Oh, for God's sake.

Cath He's a pacifist.

Billie That's one word for him.

Cath You know when you just get someone, Bill. Like
you know what ticks inside them without even talking
to them. And the only obstacle is that they don't seem
to be aware that you exist.

Billie Come on! Let's do the activity pack together. We
can present it as a joint project – they love that kind
of thing. And then we can get down to the grotto and
help prepare the ambush.

Cath I do fancy smashing the daylights out of someone.

Billie That's more like it!

Cath Go on then, what's the first question?

Billie They're not questions. They're challenges.
'Challenge One. Find ten trees and write down their
Latin names.'

Cath That is so exciting.

Billie And then we have to mark the location of thirty
Cupids on the map.

Cath You are kidding me.

Billie Listen, girl. When did you last have a day out?

Cath Three years ago. My dad took us to Thorpe Park.
I think it was by way of an early apology. Three days
later he ran off with the hairdresser.

Billie So make the most of it. Come on!

Exeunt.

SCENE THREE

Inside the garden. Tamsen and Maisy. In St Nectan's uniform.

Maisy How could they have let us come here on the same day as Riverdale! Riverdale should be doing something useful like visiting a remand centre or going on a hip-hop course.

Tamsen They don't scare me. I do *tai kwon do.*

Maisy Now instead of being able to enjoy the neoclassical landscape I'm going to spend all day hiding behind the shrubbery.

Tamsen I'm tougher than half those boys. I'll take them down.

Maisy But didn't you get the text?

Tamsen What text?

Maisy They don't want us fighting. They want the girls to be lookouts.

Tamsen Lookouts?

Maisy We're meant to hide in the rhododendra under the statue of Cupid and make an owl-call if we see anything.

Tamsen That is sexist and patronising!

Maisy Of course, what they didn't say is which Cupid. There are Cupids everywhere. I can't tell one from the other.

Tamsen I could bury my fist in one of those Riverdale boys any day!

Maisy The boys think you might be a bit of a loose cannon, Tam.

Tamsen What does that mean?

Maisy I think they're a bit scared of you. It's the way you only ever go out with any of them for a maximum of three days before ending it. They think you're unreliable.

Tamsen You never go out with any of them either.

Maisy But I'm not asked. I'm seen as a stay-at-home-and-read-Jane-Austen type. You're tall and gorgeous but you're not interested in being their girlfriend.

Tamsen Why should I be interested? And what if I am gorgeous? I'd love not to be. I'd love to blend into the crowd like you, Mais. Then I wouldn't be treated like a trophy princess the whole bloody time!

Maisy It must be hard being that beautiful.

Tamsen Damn right it is! And you know why I never go out with any of them for more than about a minute? Because they're not real men. They're loathsome, wannabee-public-schoolboys who have already planned their careers in law, what wife to marry, what Audi to buy, what coffin to be buried in. Where's the romance in that? Where's the passion? Part of me hopes they're blown to smithereens by Riverdale. They may be a bunch of chavs but at least they're in the moment.

Maisy What about Hugh Phillips? I thought you really liked him, but now you've ended that too.

Tamsen Yeah, well . . .

Maisy I really thought he might be different . . .

Tamsen Yeah, well . . .

Maisy He's sensitive, clever, and he's so good-looking.

Tamsen Yeah, alright, Maisy! If he's so bloody marvellous, why don't you go out with him!

Maisy Keep your voice down. Riverdale could be anywhere.

Tamsen If they come near me, I'll give them a fight. More than that hopeless bunch would ever do.

Maisy Riverdale could have knives, Tam. Remember – they're the desperate underclass expressing themselves in the only way they know how.

Tamsen I don't care. Bring them on. I'll tear their eyes out.

Maisy Hugh Phillips has got lovely eyes.

Tamsen Maisy you are *this* close . . .

Enter Stanley. They see him. He doesn't see them.
Beat.

Maisy Oh my sainted aunt. A prime-cut Riverdale specimen.

Tamsen Don't move.

Maisy He's terrifying.

Tamsen He hasn't spotted us. Look at him. Typical Neanderthal.

Maisy So primitive. It's almost thrilling.

Tamsen He's coming our way.

Maisy I'll make the owl-call. Then we'll run.

Tamsen Don't you dare. We're dealing with this ourselves. What do you want, Riverdale scum? You want some action? You've come to the right place.

Stanley I come in peace.

Tamsen Very likely. One more step and you're white-trash mincemeat.

Stanley Homesleigh was built to celebrate the harmony of the spheres and the love of man and woman. I come to you in that spirit. I seek a member of St Nectan's who will walk with me through the garden. To defy the warring between Riverdale and St Nectan's that blights both our houses.

Maisy Tamsen, I smell a weirdo.

Tamsen Don't be so naive. Maisy. It's a trap. He's trying to lower our guard. Look in the bushes for other eyes.

Maisy (*looking dramatically*) I can't see any.

Stanley That's because there aren't any.

He approaches her and holds out his hand.

Tamsen What do you think you are doing?

Stanley I'm offering the olive branch.

Tamsen The what?

Stanley With this kiss I pledge peace to St Nectan's.

He kisses her on the cheek. Tamsen immediately launches a martial arts attack on Stanley, who is hurled to the ground.

Tamsen What the hell do you think you're playing at? We're at war!
Stanley I don't believe in war.
Tamsen Shut up and get up and fight!
Stanley No.
Tamsen Get up!
Stanley I refuse!
Tamsen If you don't get up, I'll kick you till you do.
Stanley Then kick me. I'm a pacifist. I'll do nothing.

She kicks him. He groans.

Stanley Told you.
Tamsen Get up, will you? Be a man!
Stanley I don't want to.
Tamsen Christ, are there no real men left in this world? Come on, Mais, let's get out of here . . . Loser!

They leave. Stanley is left on the ground.

Stanley I won't be put off the path of peace! You won't put me off the path!

Enter Cath and Billie.

Cath Haven't we done enough?
Billie We've got to mark every Cupid we find on the map with a red heart.
Cath This is beyond moronic.

They see Stanley on the ground.

Cath Stanley?
Stanley Oh, hi.
Cath Stanley, are you alright?

Cath runs to him, but he gets up and walks right past her.

407

Stanley Billie, did you see anybody from St Nectan's?
Billie No. Why?
Stanley I have to find one of them. I have to keep going.
Billie Are you going to the ruckus?
Stanley What do you think?
Cath Stanley's a pacifist, Bill, I told you.
Billie Then why . . . ?
Stanley Doesn't matter.
Cath Where you going?
Stanley I said it doesn't matter!

And he runs off.

Cath He did it again. I am invisible.
Billie Forget him, he's a messed-up saddo loser.
Cath I am one-hundred-per-cent see-through.
Billie Come on. We've found twenty three Cupids. Just seven to go and then we can have a fag. Now where could they be . . . ?

But as she speaks Tamsen and Maisy return.

Cath What do you want?
Tamsen What do you think? The battle has begun.
Cath Better get out your pom-poms then, hadn't ya?
Tamsen What are you implying?
Cath/Billie (*mock-cheerleaders*) Go St Nectan's! Go St Nectan's!
Cath I heard St Nectan's girls were made of fine china porcelain. Drop them and they smash.
Tamsen Think again, bitch.
Cath What d'you call me?
Maisy Tam, I'm not sure this is a good idea . . . These people are born into physical violence . . . It's in their blood . . .
Billie Go on, Cath. I'll take out the dwarf.
Maisy I think she means me.
Tamsen Go near her, I kill you.

408

Cath What you gonna do? Beat me to death with a violin bow?

Cath and Tamsen prepare to engage in battle. Billie approaches Maisy.

Maisy Tam. She's getting closer. I can smell her rage.
Tamsen I'll keep them here. Sound the alarm.

Maisy tries to owl-call but can't.

Tamsen Oh Christ's sake, Maisy!
Maisy My lips are shaking. I can't.
Tamsen Try again!
Maisy I can't. I'm all moist!
Tamsen Run!
Cath After her!

Billie chases Maisy out.

Tamsen So it's just you and me. Let battle commence.
Cath When I got here I wasn't much up for a ruckus. You, girl, have put me right in the mood.

Tamsen and Cath launch at each other but are suddenly stopped dead as Cupid comes alive.

Cupid
Everywhere division
Misunderstanding and misprision.
Folks a-fighting and a-spitting
And a-hating and a-hitting
And no love they is a-getting
And the garden is a-crying
At this pain it is a-spying.
It is so fucking mystifying
How their lives they are wasting
With this punching and a-pasting
How their hearts they are so sore
For there ain't no love no more.

Now Cupid cast the spell
To make the sick in love be well.
And may this garden here present
The shifting of the element
Until all hate and anger gone
Love rise in glory like the sun.

Cupid casts the spell:

Now be changèd in your look
Swap the cover, keep the book.

He casts his spell. Tamsen and Cath have magically exchanged clothes. They stare at each other. Cupid has returned to being a statue.

Cath What the . . . ?

Tamsen What have you done? Give me back my uniform!

Cath I didn't do anything! You took my clothes and somehow . . .

Tamsen Somehow what?

Cath Somehow put yours on me . . .

Tamsen Oh yeah, right, that's really believable! Did you drug me? You did, didn't you? With chloroform or one of those glues you lot are always sniffing . . . and then you tied me up and stripped me . . .

Cath I did no such thing!

Tamsen Give them back, chavess!

Cath No way. Not until you give me mine!

Tamsen You think I want to wear this tat!

Cath Take them off.

Tamsen I'm not taking my clothes off here. You take them off.

Cath You first.

Tamsen No you. You!

Enter Hugh, a boy from St Nectan's. Handsome.

Tamsen Oh my God, it's Hugh Phillips. He mustn't see me. Hide me. Please.
Cath In your dreams, lady.
Tamsen I'll find you and I'll get you for this.

She exits. Hugh sees Cath.

Hugh Hi, Tamsen. Aren't you watching the barney?

Pause.

Cath Sorry?
Hugh It's starting any minute. Are you okay, Tamsen?

Cath looks behind her. No one is there.

Cath Uh . . . yeah . . .
Hugh I asked if you were going to the barney.
Cath Uh, I'm not sure I'm gonna bother.
Hugh Nor me. I've nothing against Riverdale.

Embarrassed pause.

Look. About Saturday night. I wanted to say I'm sorry. I feel like such an idiot.
Cath . . .
Hugh Can we . . . I mean, can we forget it ever happened?

Beat.

Cath Sure.
Hugh Maybe – give it another go . . .

Beat.

Cath Sure.
Hugh Thanks. I think the guys have got you all wrong. That's why I made such a fool of myself. I became convinced you were about to chuck me so I chucked you and it was stupid and . . . you were so upset . . . You were upset weren't you?
Cath Yeah.

She fakes a little upsetness.

I mean, it was hard . . .

Hugh I know. I know. You tried to hide it, to act the hard nut. But I could tell . . . I'm sorry, okay?

He moves to hold her.

They all want me to take part in this stupid fight. I hate it – just because I'm a big guy and I work out and play football for the county, everyone expects me to be some kind of monster . . .

Cath Yeah.

Hugh So we'll give it another go?

Cath If you like.

Hugh Really?

They approach to kiss. Enter Clive.

Clive Hugh. You're needed. The scabby bastards have filled their rucksacks with stones. Hi, Tamsen.

Cath Hi.

Clive I thought you two had split . . .

Hugh Who told you that?

Clive You did. You said she was a seething pit of neuroses . . .

Hugh Shut up, Clive. Where are they?

Clive Behind the grotto. It's getting out of control. I reckon we'll be chucked out if it goes on much longer. Come on, Daddio!

Hugh (*to Cath*) I'd better show my face. See you later . . . Stay out of trouble . . . Sorry, I didn't mean to tell you what to do.

Cath No, it's okay.

Hugh kisses her and leaves with Clive.

Okay, this is weird.
My clothes are different.
But he thought I was . . . he thought I was . . .

She . . . she's tall and . . .
She's a stunner.
I'm a dog.
But even the other boy blushed when he looked at me.
No one has ever looked at me like that.
No one has ever touched me liked that.
Kissed me liked that.
Who am I?
The lake!

She looks in the mirror of the water. She sees Tamsen's face mirroring hers.

I'm her.
I'm so beautiful.
My legs go on forever.
My breasts defy all natural laws.
My eyes are clear pools.
My skin is polished marble.
This is no ordinary garden.

Enter Stanley, bloodied.

Stanley? Are you okay?
Stanley Keep away from me! I've already been kicked by you once!
Cath What are you . . .?
Stanley And now one of your school friends has beaten me up by the gothic waterfall. I went to shake his hand! He twisted my arm and smashed it against the rockery. Then like a coward he took some stones and invited his mates to take popshots! So forget it, okay? My peace mission is over! Gandhi never had to suffer this!
Cath Where are you going?
Stanley I'm leaving the garden! I'm walking home. Where no one will meet me. Or talk to me. Or kick me. Or chop me. (*Beat.*) How did you know my name?

Cath Um . . . I overheard it. Listen, I'll come with you.

Stanley No way. I don't want no St Nectan's anywhere near me. I just wanted to shake your hand! To make peace!

Cath I'll shake your hand.

Stanley Don't bullshit me.

Cath I will.

Stanley You won't. You know I'm a pacifist so you'll use that as a way to crap on me.

Cath I won't. I promise.

Stanley What about before?

Cath What did I do?

Stanley Don't pretend you don't know! Kicking a man when he's down!

Cath That was me being a stupid dumb-arse posh cow. I've changed.

Stanley That's a pretty sudden turnaround.

Cath Yeah, it is.

She holds out her hand.

Stanley You serious?

Cath Try me.

Stanley You'll walk with me through the garden?

Cath Yeah.

Stanley And perform the peace, love and harmony action? You really want to?

Cath More than anything in the whole world.

Stanley You better not be having me on . . .

Cath I'm not!

Stanley tentatively takes her hand.

Stanley This could be a major moment in our lives.

Cath (*in heaven*) I do hope so.

Stanley The beginning of peace between Riverdale and St Nectan's.

Cath Yes, of course.

414

Stanley What's your name?

Cath Um . . . it's . . . it's Tam. Tamsen.

Stanley Walk with me, Tamsen. Will you?

Cath Okay.

Stanley You know we're gonna get things thrown at us, don't you?

Cath I'd walk through arrows of fire for you.

Stanley You really have changed. Shall we . . .?

Cath Yes. Let's walk in the garden.

SCENE FOUR

Tamsen alone, hiding.

Tamsen What am I going to do?
I look like a member of the underclass.
Everyone is going to laugh at me.
Jocasta Mars-Jones will piss herself.
Now she'll be the best-looking girl in Year Ten.
I can't bear it!
I've got to take this off.
But then what – run through the garden in my underwear?

A horrible thought. She checks under her top.

Aaggh! What has she done to me?
The most awful cheap bra the world has ever known.
Oh, some tropical bush come and swallow me up!
I just need to get out of here. Get home and change.

She feels her clothes.

My purse. She's got my purse!
How can I get back with no money?
I'll kill her! I'll tear her limb from limb!
I have to find her.

Enter Billie, running.

Billie I lost her.

Pause

The dwarf. She ran into some azaleas. Did you do her?

Tamsen Me?

Billie Yeah, you. Cath – did you do the posh bitch?
Hello, is there something wrong?

Tamsen You're talking to me?

Billie No, I'm talking to a tree, I'm just looking at you to
confuse it. Of course I'm talking to you!

Tamsen Who am I?

Billie Cath, I know you're really down about Strange
Stanley but I need you to pull through for me now,
okay? Did you give the St Nectan's bitch a beating?

Pause.

I need to know! There are little beefs happening all over
the place! HQ needs to know what's going on!

Tamsen Yes. I mean yeah. Yeaaahhh.

Billie You are beautiful! I mean, I know you're not
actually beautiful. But you are beautiful!

Tamsen What did you say?

Billie Nothing . . . I just . . .

Tamsen I'm not beautiful?

Billie I didn't mean you're not. I meant that to me right
now you are the most goddamned beautiful girl on the
planet!

Tamsen Have you got a mirror?

Billie Got a compact.

Tamsen That will do.

*She looks at herself in the compact. Sees Cath. Retches
slightly.*

Oh my God . . . Oh no. Oh no . . .

Billie Oh Cath – I didn't mean it like that. Get a grip, girl.

Tamsen Oh Jesus!

Billie Cath – looks are paper-thin.

Tamsen I'm hideous!

Billie You're not, man. You're sweet-looking and you're kind.

Tamsen But my skin . . .

Billie So you don't have skin like Scarlett Johansson. Your mum lives next to a bypass and smokes four hundred cigarettes a day. It's not very Clarins, is it? Cath – look at me. It's Billie. I'm your friend.

Tamsen Billie . . .

Billie That's it, babe. Look, I know what you're going through. Your brother's all fucked up, your mum's depressed. The guy you like ain't exactly responsive. But you got mates. I'm your mate.

Tamsen Are you?

Billie Course I am!

Tamsen Thanks Billie.

Billie That's my girl. Now what we need to focus on is giving out some beef to those St Nectan's tossers. Am I right?

Tamsen You're right.

Billie Hey! Welcome back to the party, Catherine. We missed you while you were away.

Tamsen Billie? The guy I like . . .

Billie Stanley . . .

Tamsen Stanley. He doesn't like me?

Billie Well, I think you know that, babe. You have been in the same class for four years and he is yet to officially acknowledge your existence.

Tamsen He doesn't notice me.

Billie You could dance naked in front of him with a feather sticking out of your arse. I don't think he'd see it.

Enter Hugh and Clive.

Hugh Stop right there.

Tamsen Oh my God.

Clive Don't move, slag.

Tamsen How dare you –

Billie Yeah, you take that back!

Hugh We're not going to hurt you.

Clive Aren't we? Why not?

Hugh Clive, please try and grow up.

Clive This barrow boy punched me. I want payback!

Hugh The fight has gone out of control up there. Someone's brought knives.

Billie That would be the ammo . . .

Hugh I'm warning you – for your own safety – keep away from the grotto.

Billie Why should we believe you?

Tamsen Um . . . Billie, wait.

Clive Let's beat them up, Hugh. Girls want equality, right? So that means we can beat the crap out of them, just like we do with boys.

Billie Just you try it!

Clive You're really getting on my tits.

Billie What you gonna do about it? (*Aside to Tamsen.*) Let's split. I'll meet you at the Bridge of Sighs. (*To Clive.*) Come on, dopey. Fight me. FIGHT ME!

Clive Oh bloody hell.

He exits. Billie chases after. Noises of fighting.

Hugh I don't want to fight, okay?

Tamsen Okay.

Hugh There are hundreds of St Nectan's round here. We need to get you somewhere safe.

Tamsen The Temple of Aphrodite is just down the hill.

Hugh Perfect. What's your name?

Tamsen My name is Cath.

Hugh Hugh. Hi.
Tamsen Hi.
Hugh Come with me, Cath.

Exeunt.

SCENE FIVE

Cath and Stanley are walking hand in hand.

Stanley This is the Grove of Apollo. From here we head
up to the grotto. That's when we will begin the peace,
love and harmony improvised action.
Cath Do we have to go straight away?
Stanley You're not getting cold feet?
Cath No, I just thought . . . if we're going to do this, we
need to know more about each other. They may try to
divide us.
Stanley No, you're right. There must be no secrets
between us. Alright, what do you want to know?
Cath I don't know . . . just a bit about you . . .
Stanley My name's Stanley. I'm in Year Ten in . . .
Cath No, I know all that. I mean, really about you. Why
are you doing this? I mean, it's great. But why?
Stanley I dunno. I just want to change something, you
know? I don't know if you'll understand.
Cath Try me.
Stanley Have you ever been to Riverdale?

Beat.

Cath No, never.
Stanley Well, it's a dump, right? Any kid whose parents
give a toss has got out to St Nectan's or Gordon High,
okay? So it's just the rest of us left here to rot. And
what do we do? We just pick fights, take drugs and
piss our lives away. So anyway, I formed a club – to get

419

people to think about how to make Riverdale better!
It was after school on Wednesdays. First meeting – no
one came.

Cath That's not true!

Stanley What?

Cath Sorry – I mean you were there.

Stanley Well, of course I was there!

Cath And was there no one else?

Stanley Well, yeah, there was this girl called Cath. But
that was it.

Cath And wasn't she worth having the club for?

Stanley She's just some messed-up girl. Just came because
she wanted some friends, I reckon. Her mum's this . . .
what's the word when she don't leave the house?

Cath Agoraphobic . . .

Stanley She just needed the company. So anyway, I
cancelled the club there and then. Decided I was better
as a lone operator.

Cath What did Cath do?

Stanley Dunno.

Cath Don't you think you might have hurt her feelings?

Stanley Maybe. Why you so obsessed with her?

Cath But was there something wrong with her? Was she
a real minger?

Stanley No. She's quite pretty.

Beat.

Cath Is she?

Stanley Yeah. But she didn't look after herself. No self-
respect. I mean, I look at you. You look after yourself.
You project an image.

Cath But I've got money.

Stanley But there are people without money who do that.
I was with this girl, okay, for a while. She was called
Kelly.

Cath Fisher.

420

Stanley You know her?

Cath Through a friend.

Stanley Well, Kelly, right, she looks after herself. She projects self-respect.

Cath My friend says she's a vain airhead.

Beat.

Stanley Yeah, she is. I hated her really. But she projected an image. But Cath, right – she might be a diamond, but it's all hidden. What can I do with that?

Cath Maybe she just needed a bit of a push. Maybe she's just like staggeringly, unbelievably unhappy and needs someone to bring her out of herself. I mean maybe.

Stanley Yeah, maybe. But I've had enough trouble doing that to myself, I ain't got time to be nobody's counsellor.

Cath Oh, Stanley . . .

Stanley No don't say you know how I feel. Cos you don't.

Cath What do you mean?

Stanley St Nectan's is selective. I mean, they say it's not, right, but it is.

Cath Yeah.

Stanley So you're chosen, right? You were selected. And that made you feel good. No one ever chose me. D'ya get it? What it feels like never to be chosen?

Cath Yeah. I mean no.

Stanley Like, what you up to at the moment? In school.

Cath Oh you know I'm getting ready for exams.

Stanley Get straight As, won't ya, I bet? Everyone at St Nectan's gets straight As.

Cath Probably.

Stanley How many you taking?

Cath Oh, sixteen.

Stanley Sixteen?

Cath Yeah. And then I'll do five A levels. Maths, Further Maths, Even Further Maths, Drama and Politics.

Stanley You into politics?

Cath Yeah. Massively.

Stanley Wow! I want to take Politics. Thing is, I reckon I'm going to fail all my GCSEs, which is a drawback.

Cath Why you gonna fail?

Stanley I don't find Riverdale a very conducive learning environment.

Cath But you're clever, Stan. You shouldn't be failing at anything!

Stanley And then you'll go to university I bet.

Cath Uni, we call it.

Stanley Which one?

Cath Well, I'm lined up for Cambridge Uni but I might choose London Uni because I like to mix my academic work with living in a thriving urban scene.

Stanley What will you study there?

Cath Politics, yeah. Specialising in the history of peaceful political protest.

Stanley They do a course in that? That's my dream course.

Cath Martin Luther King. Mahatma Gandhi. And naturally we get to meet Nelson Mandela.

Stanley He's my hero!

Cath He's going to talk to us about the problems of post-apartheid South Africa. It's going to be fascinating. And then I'm going to go into politics. Labour Party, probably, though I reckon we need to take a long, hard look at the whole party political system which is rapidly becoming a joke.

Stanley You're amazing. Everything you say . . . I believe the only way forward is through . . .

Cath Individual and collective action. Citizens joining together . . .

Stanley Spontaneous collective action –

Cath – through real and online dialogue –

Stanley – to create a better –
Cath – and more loving world.

Pause.

Stanley You're very beautiful. Your skin. It's like –
Cath – polished marble.
Stanley Your eyes are like –
Cath – clear pools.
Stanley I've never met anyone like you.

Beat.

Cath I encourage you to individually act now, Stanley.

He kisses her.

Stanley No one at Riverdale kisses like that. That was . . .
that was . . .
Cath Shut up and do it again.

They kiss again.

Let's walk.
Stanley Okay.

They take hands.

Cath Whatever happens, I will never let you go.

SCENE SIX

Maisy is crawling through the undergrowth.

Maisy I got away. Dived through a camellia and crawled
round the Temple of Flora. Two Riverdale boys were
pinning a St Nectan's ninth-year up against a statue of
Vulcan. It was horrible. I just want to find somewhere
quiet to finish *Middlemarch*.

She almost literally bumps into Rock, who is crawling in terror in the other direction. Both scream and recoil.

Aaaah!
Rock Don't kill me! Please don't kill me!

Beat. They look at each other.

Maisy Are you from Riverdale?
Rock Are you from St Nectan's?
Maisy Are you alone?

Rock nods.

Rock You?
Maisy (*nods*) Are you going to shout for help?
Rock Are you?

Beat.

Maisy What's your name?
Rock My name is Tim but everyone calls me Rock.
Maisy Why do they call you Rock?
Rock Because I'm the puniest boy in Riverdale. It's kind of a joke.
Maisy You shouldn't have told me that. I'm going to beat you up now.

Beat. Rock gets scared.

That was a joke too.
Rock Oh, right.
Maisy Nice to meet you, Rock. I'm Maisy.
Rock What are you doing in the camellias?
Maisy I was trying to find somewhere to read.
Rock Read what?
Maisy *Middlemarch*. It's a novel by George Eliot.
Rock Never heard of him.
Maisy It's a woman, silly. She writes about a nineteenth-century woman who is trapped by her society into

marrying for respectability rather than for love. George Eliot is my second favourite author.

Beat.

Aren't you going to ask who my favourite author is?

Rock Go on then.

Maisy It's Jane Austen. My favourite book is *Emma*. And my favourite character is Mr Knightley.

Rock What's he like, then?

Maisy He's quiet, unassuming and in some ways shy, but with an inner moral integrity that Emma finally finds irresistible.

Rock I don't read books much.

Maisy I blame the decline of the lending library.

Rock Just never really got into it.

Maisy I could read to you.

Rock What, now?

Maisy Neither of us want to fight. We could just stay here until it's time to go back to the coaches and I could read to you from *Middlemarch*.

Rock Suppose.

Maisy Well, I won't bother if you're not interested. God, you try to bring a bit of literature into their lives . . .

Rock No. I want to. It's just . . . if they see us . . .

Maisy I'll say you were holding me hostage. You caught me and dragged me in here and roughed me up something dreadful.

Rock Really?

Maisy deliberately roughs up her uniform so it looks like she's been pushed around. This is oddly somewhat sexy.

Maisy How's that? Vulnerable enough?

Rock It's great.

Maisy You did that. You heathen. (*Suddenly prosaic.*) Come over here then. I won't bite.

425

He approaches her cautiously.

We're nearly the same height.
Rock I hate being little.
Maisy It's good for hiding under camellias. Now I'm
  already on chapter twenty-seven, so I need to start by
  giving you a summary of the story so far . . . Dorothea,
  a passionate young woman in search of a belief system
  to match the agitation of her mind, marries the dark
  and skeletal figure of Mr Casaubon . . .

SCENE SEVEN

The Temple of Aphrodite. Hugh and Tamsen.

Hugh You should be safe in here. It's quite a way from
  the main action.
Tamsen Don't go yet.
Hugh I don't think we should be seen together.
Tamsen Five minutes.
Hugh What do you want?
Tamsen I don't know, just to spend some time together
  here in the Temple of Aphrodite . . .
Hugh No, I think I should go.
Tamsen Are you with anyone?

Beat.

Hugh Sorry?
Tamsen Are you with a girl?
Hugh Why is that of any interest to you?
Tamsen Oh. Because I'm in love with this boy at
  Riverdale, I mean this guy, and, right, I think he's well
  in love with me, man, but we keep messing it up big-
  style. So I thought, if you were with someone, you
  could maybe, I mean it would be well phat if you
  would help me out – tell me what to do.

Hugh I'm sort of with someone, yes.

Tamsen And that's just been very straightforward, has it?

Hugh No, not at all.

Tamsen Well, could you, I mean it would be well wicked, man, if you could tell me how you've tried to make it work.

Hugh It's complicated. Tamsen . . .

Tamsen Is that the girl's name?

Hugh Yeah. She's incredibly insecure.

Tamsen Is she?

Hugh Yeah, and she has no reason to be. She's beautiful and clever. But she has no faith in herself. Anyway, I asked her out and she started playing these ridiculous games. She's done it with all the boys. It was like she was testing me or something.

Tamsen I suppose when you're pretty, you might think that everyone is only interested in you physically. Innit.

Hugh Exactly! It's as if her own beauty is destroying her! And I hate that! If God or Darwin or whoever gives you something, you should celebrate that!

Tamsen But she uses it as a weapon to beat you with.

Hugh Exactly! God, you really get it.

Tamsen So what did you do?

Hugh Well, we went out on these first dates and it was just awful. It was like war. She hated everything, she didn't want to do anything. She acted appallingly, really. So I chucked her.

Tamsen And how did she take it?

Hugh She broke apart. I've never seen anyone cry like that. And it was then I knew that somewhere inside this impossible stuck-up princess there was someone I could love. Really love.

Tamsen And who could love you.

Hugh Yes. In fact we've just got back together.

Beat.

Tamsen You what?

Hugh Yes, just now at the Porch of Venus. She was wonderful.

Tamsen What do you mean?

Hugh Amazing! Quite unlike her normal abhorrent behaviour. She was clever and sweet . . .

Tamsen Did you kiss her?

Hugh Oh yeah. That's why I don't want to fight anyone. It's crazy. We're in this garden, it's a gorgeous day, Tamsen and I could be walking down a lakeside pathway or sitting under a tree . . .

Tamsen Yeah, or equally we could be sitting here, in the Temple of Aphrodite . . .

Hugh We could be spending real time with each other –

Tamsen Holding each other. Kissing each other.

Hugh Well, yes.

Tamsen Here.

Hugh Instead we're in a war zone.

Tamsen Tell me something. Does her beauty really matter to you?

Hugh Well, I like the way she looks.

Tamsen But say for a minute, say she wasn't beautiful. Say she was in the world's worst car crash and she was horribly disfigured.

Hugh I don't really want to think about that.

Tamsen But you have to. If you really love someone, you have to know whether you would love them if their legs were cut off or their . . .

Hugh I don't find that funny, Cath.

Pause.

Tamsen I don't find it funny either.

She starts to cry.

Hugh What is it?

Tamsen Nothing.

428

Hugh I'm really sorry. Were you talking about . . . about yourself?

Tamsen nods.

Hugh But you're pretty.
Tamsen I'm not! I'm disgusting!
Hugh You're not!
Tamsen I am! I've seen myself. An ogress!
Hugh Listen. Think about that boy you love. Think about him now.
Tamsen Why?
Hugh Just do it. Imagine he's right here in front of you.
Tamsen Okay.
Hugh Are you doing it?
Tamsen I'm doing it.
Hugh You see? When you think of someone you love, you're beautiful.
Tamsen Am I?
Hugh Very. You have a quality. Almost like Tamsen's.
Tamsen Really?

They are close now. A moment's confusion. Broken by Clive, who enters at a pace.

Clive What are you doing?
Hugh/Cath Nothing.
Clive I've been looking for you everywhere. I was chasing the little mouthy one along the lakeside walk. You'll never guess what I saw.
Hugh What?
Clive Tamsen Summers. Walking with a Riverdale boy. Hand in hand.

Beat.

Hugh You can't have.
Clive I swear on my life! And not just hand in hand. They . . .

429

Hugh What?
Clive Well you know, they were . . .
Hugh They were what? They were *what*, Clive?
Clive They were . . .

He mimes necking.

Hugh Say it!

Clive whispers it to Hugh.

Not possible. Not possible.
Clive Less than five minutes after you'd . . . (*Mimes necking.*)
Hugh Take me to her.
Tamsen Hugh, wait.
Hugh Please, Cath, this has nothing to do with you.
Tamsen But it does!
Hugh IT HAS NOTHING TO DO WITH YOU!

Exits with Clive. Tamsen bursts into tears.

SCENE EIGHT

Stanley and Cath are walking together, hand in hand.

Stanley Okay, I think we should perform the peace, love and harmony improvised action here.
Cath What do we have to do?
Stanley There are a series of mini-peace actions that make up the complete action. I'm going to say some words, we hold hands, and we hug and kiss.
Cath Oh good. I mean . . . I just think that words are all very well . . . but actions really get the message across. We should probably practise . . . the kissing bit . . .
Stanley I've kissed you seven times on this walk already.
Cath Just to be sure.

They kiss. Interrupted by Fraser running fast and bleeding.

Fraser Aaaaaghhhh! What the hell, man?

Stanley Frase . . .

Fraser Have you not heard? Casey Phillips has been taken hostage by the St Nectan's boys. They're holding him in the grotto. They're demanding three Nokia phones as ransom.

Pause.

You were kissing her.

Stanley Yes.

Fraser Stan, we are in a serious shit with this lot. Whose side are you on?

Stanley On the side of peace, Frase. I thought I'd made that clear.

Fraser You cannot be on that side any more! We are getting them bastards!

To Cath.

Your mates have taken my mate hostage.

Cath How d'you know they're my mates?

Fraser They're probably torturing him as we speak. So I reckon we need a hostage too!

Stanley Leave her alone, Frase.

Fraser We need a hostage, Stan, and I'm looking at one right now!

Stanley I'm not giving her to you.

Fraser I'll give you one more chance.

Stanley You're not taking her, man.

Fraser You're a twat, Stan. You're a fucking twat.

Fraser punches Stanley. He tries to grab Cath, who launches an all-out assault on Fraser.

Get off, man! Ow! Ow, get off!

431

He retreats.

Bloody hell, man. I thought posh girls were civilised!

Cath Get with the programme, dickhead. This kitten's got claws.

Fraser Alright, alright! I don't want you as a hostage anyway!

Exit.

Cath You alright?

Stanley Yeah. It's what we expected.

Cath Your ribs are bruised.

Stanley It's okay.

She kisses his ribs.

What you doing?

Cath I admire you, Stanley Arthur Peterson.

Stanley How did you know my middle name?

Cath The same reason I know that your dad's a nutter who you do everything to avoid and your brother Shaun died in a fight outside a nightclub three years ago and that in Shaun's name all you want in life is to stop the ruckus.

Stanley How did you know that?

Cath By magic.

She kisses him. Enter Hugh and Clive.

Clive There's the hussy!

Stanley What d'you want?

Hugh How dare you!

Cath Oh shit.

Hugh How long ago was it, Tamsen? Five minutes? Ten? You're sick in the head!

Cath Hugh, listen . . .

Hugh People always said you were a liability. I didn't listen. I put my faith in you! I loved you!

Stanley Who is he?

Cath I don't really know.

Hugh You don't know! YOU DON'T KNOW! I'm your
boyfriend, Tamsen!

Stanley Is he?

Cath No!

Hugh How can you say that?

Clive She's a viper, Hugh. A double-crossing anaconda!

Stanley She says she was never your girlfriend.

Hugh Then she's more evil than I thought. (*To Cath.*) We
went to see *Pride and Prejudice*! We kissed at the same
time that the guy from *Spooks* kissed Keira Knightley!
I bought you popcorn!

Cath I've never seen *Pride and* whatever . . .

Stanley You've got the wrong girl, my friend.

Hugh Don't tell me what girl I've got.

Stanley She says she's never seen it and I believe her.

Hugh Do you? And who are you, pray?

Clive Yeah, who are you, pray?

Stanley I'm a pacifist.

Clive He's a what?

Stanley Tamsen and I are performing a peace, love and
harmony action here on Apollo's mound. Hit me and
I won't respond.

Clive What did he say he was?

Hugh You won't respond?

Stanley shakes his head.

Cath No, don't, Stan, not again.

Hugh hits him.

Stanley (*in agony*) See?

Pause. Hugh leaves.

Cath Stan!

Clive (*to Stan*) That'll teach you to be a pessimist.

Clive hits him, not very hard.

Cath Get off him! I said get off, you little bully!

She forces him back. Violently.

Clive Alright! Get off! It wasn't just me, you know!
Cath Piss off, you maggot!

Clive leaves. Cath returns to Stanley.

Oh Stan.
Stanley Are you still with me, Tamsen?
Cath I'm still here.
Stanley Don't go, Tam, please. I don't think I could bear it if you went now.
Cath I'm not going. I'm not going.

She holds him.

SCENE NINE

Tamsen alone in the Temple of Apollo. Hugh enters, sits despondently apart.

Tamsen What is it?
Hugh Nothing. Nothing.

He starts to fight back the tears.

Tamsen Are you okay?
Hugh Just leave me alone, please.
Tamsen What happened?

Beat.

Hugh Do you ever think you're just not made out for having a successful relationship?
Tamsen Yes, quite often.
Hugh There are lots of girls who want to go out with me.

Tamsen I know there are.

Hugh But I don't want them! I want the lunatic! The self-destructive insane madwoman.

Tamsen You mean Tamsen . . . ?

Hugh She was kissing him. In broad daylight!

Tamsen Kissing who?

Hugh This Kevin. Utterly shameless. There's no way she can really fancy him. She's just doing it to screw us up.

Tamsen I'm sure that's not true.

Hugh You don't know her. She has a perverse evil streak. There's nothing she'd like more than to twist a dagger in my heart.

Tamsen Don't say that.

Hugh You know my problem? My parents are too sorted. I have to find someone crazy and unreliable just so I'm not like them. I'm too reliable!

Tamsen I love that about you.

Hugh You don't know me.

Tamsen No, of course. But in our time together. I think you're a wonderful person.

Hugh Do you think so?

Tamsen I know so.

Beat.

Hugh The boy you like. Is he reliable?

Tamsen Yes.

Hugh Hold on to him. Marry him immediately.

Tamsen I'm not sixteen yet.

Hugh Book it for your sixteenth birthday. The world is full of insane maniacs. A decent human being is gold dust!

Tamsen The thing is . . . I can't . . . marry him . . .

Hugh Why not?

Tamsen Because . . . because something happened. Here today. In the garden.

Hugh What?

Tamsen You'll think I'm insane. You won't believe me.
Hugh Of course I will.
Tamsen Well, what happened was . . .

Beat.

I've found someone else . . . someone even better. Even
more amazing.
Hugh Who?
Tamsen Someone here in the garden.
Hugh I don't know what you mean.
Tamsen Someone in this temple. Right here. Right now.

Pause.

Hugh You mean . . . me?
Tamsen Well, it's either you or that statue of Hercules.
Hugh But Cath – it's not possible.
Tamsen Why? Because we're from different schools?
Hugh Well, yes. I mean . . . no . . . I mean.
Tamsen You said I was pretty.
Hugh And you are . . . but . . .
Tamsen It's a class thing.
Hugh No, it's just . . .
Tamsen You wouldn't know what to say to your parents.
Hugh Cath, what are you talking about? We don't know
each other!
Tamsen But we do!

She grabs him.

Look at this temple. Look at the carvings. They're all
kissing, making love. They don't think about what
their parents will think!
Hugh But I don't love you! I love Tamsen!
Tamsen I am Tamsen!

Beat.

Hugh It's happening again. Another wacko.

436

Tamsen Sorry I . . .
Hugh Just get away from me, please.
Tamsen Don't go!
Hugh Get off me!

She tries to hold on to him. He throws her off.

Get lost!

Exit. Tamsen gets up off the ground.

Tamsen I'm not losing you. I'm not losing you!

She follows him out. A siren sounds. A voice travels through the garden.

Voice This is Garden Security. Will all Riverdale and St Nectan's pupils make their way immediately to the exit of the garden. Make your way to the exit of the garden.

SCENE TEN

Billie and Fraser meet at Cupid's Gate.

Fraser What happened?
Billie Garden Security found out about the ruckus. They're chucking us out.
Fraser Ah, man! We were only just kicking off!
Billie I've been trying to find my way to the exit. It's a nightmare – there are Cupids everywhere. It's like they're multiplying or something!
Fraser Have you seen Stanley?
Billie No, why? He's not on one of his peace binges again, is he?
Fraser Big style. He was kissing this slag from St Nectan's on the Mound of Apollo. Said it was an olive branch.
Billie He's cracked, that bloke.

Fraser I hit him, Billie. My own mate.

Billie I haven't seen Cath for half an hour. We were cornered by these two guys. I don't know if she made it. She was having a real crisis.

Fraser What about?

Billie Take a wild guess. Your pacifist friend. She's head over heels.

Fraser Beats me why.

Billie I don't get boys.

Fraser I don't get girls.

Billie I get girls.

Fraser You are a girl.

Billie But I actually get girls. Doesn't matter.

Fraser What do you mean? You mean . . . you don't mean . . . ?

Billie Give it up, Frase.

Fraser I don't get boys.

Billie It's alright, Frase, I won't tell.

Fraser I'm not gay!

Billie Your secret's safe with me.

Fraser I AM NOT GAY.

Enter Hugh followed by Tamsen.

Hugh Will you please get your friend off my back.

Tamsen I am Tamsen! I'm not letting you go.

Billie Cath?

Tamsen I'm not Cath!

Billie Oh God, she's really lost it.

Tamsen I love you, Hugh. You can do what you want with me. Beat me, use me as your spaniel, I am not letting go!

Hugh I just want to get out of here!

Billie That's what we've been trying to do. We keep coming back to the same place.

Hugh What nonsense! I've never heard such rubbish.

He makes to leave. Tamsen grabs him.

Out of my way – you spotted toad!

Exit Hugh. Tamsen starts to weep.

Billie Cath . . . please calm down . . .

Fraser She's a basket case.

Billie Cath . . . it's just all the pressure you've been under. Your mum, your brother . . . you need to go and talk to someone.

Tamsen I AM NOT CATH! My name is Tamsen Summers. I am in Year Ten at St Nectan's. I am beautiful and leggy and witty and wonderful and that prick is in love with me but he can't see it!

Pause.

Billie Frase, I think we might need to get Mrs Gunnasekara.

Tamsen I am not in your school! I am not in your class! I am not one of you!!

Enter Clive.

Clive Oh no.

Tamsen Clive, come here.

Clive How do you know my name? You're freaking me out.

Tamsen This is Clive Marshall. He's in Year Ten and he sits next to Hugh Phillips and behind Caroline Kendall because he fancies her but she thinks he's a dork. He has a far more talented brother called Giles who is a prefect at the school and who plays the oboe. Now can you see that I am not Cath? I am TAMSEN. I am ME!

Clive Get away from me, you witch!

Enter Stanley, bleeding, with Cath.

Fraser There he is! Stan!

439

Stanley Keep away from me.

Billie What happened?

Cath The siren went and the ruckus was over. The St Nectan's and Riverdale boys saw us – they thought it was us that had snitched on them. Both schools came together and turned on us. They threw Stanley in the lake. Then they dragged him out and punched him and kicked him. There were thirty of them. The cowards!

Fraser Stan, I'm sorry.

Cath So you should be!

Billie Shut it, you rich bitch. Just because money comes out of your arse . . .

Cath Money doesn't come out of my anywhere!

Stanley None of you understand. She is the only one who tried to help me! The only one! Together we stood up and defied the hatred between the schools. You despised us for that, and you took us down. Ours is the victory. Ours is the . . .

He calls out to the garden.

Gather round, all you from St Nectan's and Riverdale. Come and join us here at Cupid's Gate. Put down your arms!

The schools gather.

My name is Stanley Arthur Peterson. This is Tamsen Summers of St Nectan's. Together we tried on the Mount of Apollo to complete the peace, love and harmony action. You threw stones at us. You threw me into the Lake of Hesperus. But we are still here. Now together we will perform the action and YOU WILL LISTEN!

He turns to Cath.

You ready?

Cath Yes.

Stanley/Cath
  We met today in the garden.
  We saw beneath the clothes
  We saw deeper than skin
  We are in love
  From differing houses
  We are in love
  From warring factions
  We are in love
  Though they hurl bricks at our heads
  We are in love
  Though they cast us into pits
  We are in love
  Though they kill our bodies
  Our souls are intertwined.

  They kiss. Silence.

Stanley That's it. It's done.
Billie That was beautiful, Stan.
Clive Wow. That was actually kind of amazing.
Stanley Thanks.

  Hugh enters.

Hugh I hate this garden!
Tamsen Hugh!
Hugh GET HER AWAY FROM ME!

  He turns and sees Cath.

Hugh Just tell me. Tell me truthfully. Who do you love?
Cath I love him.
Hugh But look at him.
Clive Love knows no boundaries.
Hugh What?
Billie Their love has bridged the divide between our two
  schools.
Fraser Yeah, we don't want to fight no more.

Hugh Have you all gone mad? That's my girlfriend!
Tamsen I'm your girlfriend! I'M YOUR GIRLFRIEND!
  I'M YOUR GIRLFRIEND! I'm Tamsen Summers!

Tamsen turns to Cath.

Tell them.
Cath Tell them what?
Tamsen Tell them what happened. At the Porch of
  Venus.
Cath Nothing happened.
Tamsen You are not me! You are not from St Nectan's!
Cath That's bollocks!
Tamsen Alright. Who do you sit next to in Geography?
Cath I'm not answering your questions!
Tamsen Clare Wyatt and Tara Willoughby. What's the
  name of the Physics teacher?
Cath Get lost, will ya?
Tamsen Mr Hemment. Who won the Victor Ludorum
  for the long jump at the school sports day?
Cath . . .
Tamsen He did! Hugh Phillips. And I'm his love! I'm
  Tamsen Summers.
Billie Cath, have you been spying on St Nectan's?
Tamsen I AM NOT CATH! SHE IS!

Enter Cupid from the Gate.

Cupid
  Now maybe I should clear up the confusion.
Fraser What the . . .
Cupid
  You schools were brought here today for a reason.
  To sort your troubles and to cure your beefing.
  The police and the council were at a loss
  Pupil referral units couldn't give a toss.
  They asked the gods of love to intervene.
  Venus gave me a call and here's the scene

I took the soul of one and switched it round,
Gave Tam the form of Cath and Cath to Tam.
Now warring ceases and love rules the day
And you have seen that you are not to blame
That while St Nectan's overflows with dosh,
And thus is like a magnet to the posh
Riverdale declines and is forgot
Like a poor cousin that you wished was not.
Now Cath be Cath and Tam be Tam again
And everything will be as right as rain.

*Cupid switches them round. Tamsen is back in her
ordinary clothes. Cath too. Immediately Stanley goes
to Tamsen.*

Billie Like what the hell happened there?
Stanley Tamsen?
Tamsen No. I mean I am Tamsen. But I'm not the girl
you . . . she is.
Stanley What are you saying? I've been kissing you all
afternoon.
Tamsen No you haven't.
Stanley I know who I kissed!
Tamsen You kissed my body, but her soul.
Stanley I don't believe you!
Cupid
Kiss both and then my friend you'll know.
Who has the body and who the soul?
Hugh Why should he kiss my . . . ?
Cupid Ssshh. Stop fretting, frat boy.

*Stanley kisses Tam. He goes over and kisses Cath. This
kiss becomes longer. And longer. They stop.*

Stanley You. It was you all along.
Cath I'm sorry, Stan.
Stanley I did the peace, love and harmony action with a
girl from my own class. We did not bridge no divide.

Cath But it worked, Stanley. Everyone stopped fighting. Look around you.

Stanley A hollow gesture! It will all start again!

Billie No it won't!

Clive No way, José. We're all pessimists now.

Fraser They're right, Stan. You did it. I'm through with the ruckus.

Hugh Does that mean Cath was . . .

Tamsen Cath was me.

Hugh In the Temple of Venus . . .

Tamsen Yes.

Hugh The light in your eyes. When you thought of the boy you loved.

Tamsen It was you.

> *They hug.*

Stanley But don't you see? We're just as we were! I'm with her and she's with you! Nothing has changed at all.

Cupid
Then now one final revelation
Before I flee back to my station.

> *Cupid reveals in the camellias Maisy and Rock kissing. They do not see us.*

Maisy If we don't stop kissing I won't be able to get to the end of chapter sixty-two. And it's a corker.

Rock Sorry. Go on.

Maisy (*begins to read*) 'She sank into the chair and for a few moments sat there like a statue, while images and emotions were hurrying upon her. Joy came first – joy in the impression that it was really herself whom Will loved . . .'

Rock Just one more.

Maisy God, you working classes are insatiable . . .

> *They kiss. Everyone laughs. They turn to see the entire school.*

Maisy/Rock Aaaagh!

Tamsen What are you doing, Maisy Haggard?

Maisy Nothing. He's been holding me hostage. Honest he has. Physically keeping me against my will.

Fraser Yeah, looks like it.

Maisy Oh, I know he looks weedy. But I tell you, when he's angry – he's a brutal raging monster!

Tamsen It's okay, Maisy. No one's going to beat either of you up.

Rock You're not going to whack me?

Stanley No, Rock. You two are the legacy we need. You are the meeting of Riverdale and St Nectan's!

Rock Are we?

Stanley You have performed the peace, love and harmony action!

Rock Have we?

Stanley Kiss her.

Cath Kiss her!

All Kiss her!

Rock Really? Okay.

Maisy Oh shucks.

They kiss. Everyone claps.

Tamsen Lead us back to the coaches, Maisy.

Stanley And anyone can go on any coach they like!

Fraser I bet theirs has got a telly.

Hugh It has actually.

Tamsen And a DVD player.

Fraser I'm going in theirs.

Clive But they only play wildlife videos.

Fraser Ah man, that is so unfair.

Maisy It's the downside of privilege.

Stanley Let's go!

A moment's freeze as the lovers join hands to leave the garden.

Cupid
Lovers join hands.
Time to exit the gate
And head for the carriages
That solemnly wait.
The journey is long
There is much to discuss
So get out of the garden
And head for the bus!

The two schools parade out, hand in hand.

End.

Production Notes

David Farr's ideas for the play stemmed from tensions between two local schools. Their differences reminded him of Shakespeare's comedies and Mozartian operas. Shakespeare's *A Midsummer Night's Dream* was a major influence when it came to writing *Ruckus in the Garden*. David refers to it being a desperate comedy and not a farce in its theatrical genre. The reason for this is that he likes all the characters he's written in his play, and all the characters are trying to do good, whereas in a farce characters are often up to bad or mischievous things. The play is essentially about friendship, identity and the need to be understood.

He believes the key points to a successful production of *Ruckus in the Garden* are:

- The transformation scene and the arrival of Cupid.

- The employment of the magical garden as a deliberate choice to allow us to enjoy the magic of theatre.

Actors should play the truth and not a caricature of their part.

The Cupid sections should not be tampered with. Obey the language, keep it real and have fun.

You can change specific words if they don't relate to your own region or dialect, e.g., 'innit', 'minger'.

The play can be set for any school year; it doesn't have to be specifically Year 10.

MAKING SURE THE STORY IS CLEAR

SCENE ONE   Make sure you set up the character of Stanley well from the beginning. He's not a wimp: he's clever and unique, but he is struggling in school. His brother's death has stopped him functioning properly.

Inviting guests into a rehearsal room can be a good way of making sure the story is clear and coherent.

Don't think too literally about the play, and avoid relating it too specifically to a particular school or schools. Think theatrically and magically.

The teenagers in the play often use borrowed language to make themselves appear more intelligent than they actually are, e.g., words like 'pacifist'.

Billie and Cath's relationship in the play is one of real and loyal friendship.

Look at what all the characters say and feel about each other throughout the play.

Swap parts around to give an idea of how casting can change the characters and our perceptions of them.

The key to Cath is that she has given up projecting an image. It's more about her own issue of confidence than her actual physical appearance. She's not ugly. But she thinks she is, and she doesn't look after herself.

SCENE TWO   The speech by Cupid is employed so the girls are given time to change.

There are at least two possible types of change:

- 'The reveal change' – where the transformation comes as a surprise.

- 'The process change' – where the transformation occurs on stage in front of an audience's eyes.

It's important to continue following Cath and Tamsen's journey, so the fact they are wearing two different costumes (one uniform, one not) becomes essential.

SCENE THREE   When the play was first workshopped at the retreat, facilitating director John Tiffany asked the actors the following questions which you might also find useful:

- How scared is Maisy by the ruckus?

- What's happened with Hugh and Maisy?

- What do you think about Maisy and Tamsin's friendship?

- What's Maisy's status in the scene?

- How does Maisy think about boys?

- Why does Tamsen decide to kick Stanley?

- How confident is Stanley?

- Has Stanley rehearsed what he is going to say before he enters the scene?

- How excited is Maisy to see Stanley?

- How does Stanley's lack of confidence affect our view of him?

- How much does Cath's anger stem from Stanley's rejection of her?

- Why does Stanley ignore Cath?

- Is the song 'Go Saint Nectan's' made up in the heat of the moment?

Have the actors re-read Scene Three and give the following directions:

- Direction to actress playing Tamsen: to play nervous that Maisy knows she was dumped by Hugh.

- Direction to actress playing Maisy: to find it harder to say to Tamsen, 'You might be a bit of a loose cannon.'

- Direction to actress playing Tamsen: to play more how angry Tamsen is with Hugh,

- Direction to actress playing Maisy: to find it more painful to say to Tamsen, 'It must be hard being that beautiful.'

Ask the cast the following questions of Scene Three:

- Why does Hugh say 'Hello' to Tamsen?

- Why does Clive use the term 'Daddio'?

- Why does Cath respond in the way she does to the arrival of Hugh?

NOTES

Maisy is not a rival to Tamsen – Tamsen is like a heroine in a novel that Maisy is writing.

The more questions you ask an actor, the stronger his/her objective becomes, thereby strengthening the comedy of the scene.

Get the actors up on their feet and begin to discover the physical nature of the play. Look at how movement in a scene can intensify and highlight key moments and character relationships.

We have really to believe in Cath's predicament when she transforms into Tamsen.

The only definite kisses that need to happen are between Stanley and Cath, particularly at the end, and this can be approached in various different theatrical ways, one of which could be to have them as a frozen tableau.

Cupid must be played as one voice. That isn't to say there can't be more than one Cupid, but when Cupid or the Cupids speaks, he or she must speak saying 'I', not 'We'.

Questions you might ask yourself about Scene Twelve:

- How do you stage the ending of the play?

- Is the play a 'happy ever after' play for everyone?

- How does the play end for Stanley and Cath, Tamsen and Hugh, and Billie and Fraser?

- How could you stage the peace and reconciliation scene between Cath and Stanley?

- How would you stage the retransformation of Cath and Tamsen?

- What would be the difference between Cath and Tamsen's first and second transformations?

- How could the voice of Garden Security increase the tension of the scene?

Workshop facilitated by John Tiffany
with notes taken by Max Key

SCARY PLAY

Judith Johnson

Judith Johnson has been writing for nearly twenty years, including work for the National Theatre, Royal Court, Liverpool Playhouse, Liverpool Everyman, English Touring Theatre, Chelsea Theatre and the Arcola. She has also written for radio and television. *Scary Play* is her third *Connections* play, *Stone Moon* having been commissioned for the very first *Connections* series and *The Willow Pattern* following in 2004. She is currently working on a radio play, a musical and two new stage plays.

Author's Note

What a nightmare it was researching and writing this play! I had to spend night after night in front of the TV watching classic scary movies (and eating chocolates). I had to sit with my kids for hours telling ghost stories and asking them nosy questions about their private fears (and when they wouldn't tell me, I had to read their diaries). I had to 'borrow' my son's top-class pristine condition children's horror books and keep them all in *my* room until he begged me on his hands and knees to give them back. It was murder. But I had to do it.

It wasn't always like this. I have long been fascinated by fear, but in my younger days I tried hard to deny it. I cried when my mates told ghost stories, I sang hymns on the way upstairs to bed to ward off evil spirits, I hid *under* the sofa during *Doctor Who* and even *Scooby Doo* gave me the collywobbles. It was only in my early thirties, when I made my husband come to the loo with me after a late-night viewing of *Nightmare on Elm Street*, that I realised it had all gone too far. Time to face the fear, I thought. Time to deal with the demons.

I started with a lone viewing of *Alien*. I made myself read Edgar Allan Poe late at night. I shivered through *The Shining* and I even, oh yes, braved *The Blair Witch Project*. But it was only when my son started showing an interest in the dark side that my fascination came out from under the stairs and made itself comfortable in my front room. Previously uninterested in reading alone if he could get me to do it aloud for him (yes and that does include *all* the Harry Potters, all sixty billion pages of them), suddenly, aged nine, he developed a secretive bookworm habit. What was going on? Fascination by fear. But rather than running away like me at the same age, he had embraced it. He loved it! He *liked* being scared! And when I gingerly peeked inside his fright-soaked pages, clearly having to prove that I could take it (not that we're competitive), I found that I liked it too! Being scared is great! Your heart beats faster, your skin tingles, your eyes open wide, adrenalin courses through your blood – and all this without taking any drugs!

And so I wrote my *Scary Play*, and thank you to my kids for inspiring it. Finally I can face my fears and go boldly into fearsome territory of my own, armed with the knowledge that fear won't kill me and nightmares are only dreams. I hope you enjoy it as much as I've enjoyed writing it. As Morticia Adams knows, fear can be just fantastic: 'Gomez. Last night – you were unhinged. You were like some desperate, howling demon. You frightened me. Do it again!'

JUDITH JOHNSON

Characters

Kal
Ten years old. Clever and tough. Or so he thinks,
anyway. Prone to telling the odd porky

Mal
Also ten. Kal's best mate. Daft as a brush

Ro
Also ten. Short for Romeo. The best-looking boy
in the class. Or, at the very least, the one with
the best clothes and largest amount of hair gel

Tilly
Also ten. Very girly. Very pretty. Ro's girlfriend

Jaz
Also ten. Tilly's best friend. Smart and feisty

Boff
Also ten. Clever and not tough. Very sweet
but very anxious

Lou
Eight years old. Kal's sister. Thinks she's a boy

The Man
Could be anything from eighteen to eighty. Calm and polite
on the surface, a seething pit of bitterness underneath

Monkey
The Man's pet. Smelly and a bit mangy

**Scary Clowns, Vampires
Jaz's Dead Mum, A Night Watchman**

SCENE ONE

Night-time. Kal's bedroom. His tenth-birthday sleepover. Kal, Mal, Boff, Ro, Tilly and Jaz sit in a semicircle facing the audience. Boff, Ro, Tilly and Jaz are wearing pyjamas or nighties, as would befit each of their characters. Kal and Mal are wearing the kit of their favourite football team. The light is out but they each have a torch switched on. The beams flash about the room.

Kal Ssh!

Mal Shush!

Jaz Shut up.

Mal You shut up!

Ro He's trying to start his story.

Jaz I'm not stopping him.

Boff For goodness' sake.

Mal (*mimicking Boff*) 'For goodness' sake.'

Kal D'you wanna hear it or what?

Jaz/Tilly/Ro Yes!!

Mal (*louder*) Shut your bloody faces then!

Kal (*whispering, angry*) Mal! You'll wake me dad up.

Mal Sorry. Sorry, Kal. Go on. Go on.

Kal Okay. Torches.

They all shine a beam of torchlight up into their faces from under their chins, in order to look scary.

Kal Right. It's about the house on Beech Street.

Tilly Which house?

Mal Shush

Jaz She's just asking!

459

Kal The only one still standing on Beech Street. Next to the old car park.

Tilly Oh, I know.

Kal The only one still standing. Nothing near it but empty space. My dad says they knocked the rest of 'em down years ago, but the old lady who lived there, she wouldn't move. She wouldn't move. And she had a son who had something wrong with him.

Beat.

Tilly What was wrong with him?

Kal He wasn't a kid, he was a grown-up, a fully grown man. But he never went out. He didn't have a job or nothing. He wasn't allowed out, he was too dangerous. And he had a monkey. A pet monkey.

Boff Tut. Nobody has pet monkeys!

Kal They did in them days. Or he did, anyway. I told you, he was different.

Jaz Did he have Special Needs or something?

Kal (*impatient*) I dunno, but anyway . . .

Tilly (*teasing*) Like you, Mal . . .

Mal (*proudly*) It's 'behavioural difficulties' what I've got.

Kal D'you wanna hear this or what?

Mal Sorry.

Kal So they lived there, for years and years, and nobody ever saw them.

Jaz Nobody ever saw them?

Kal Nobody.

Ro Didn't they ever go out?

Kal They never went out and nobody ever went in.

Boff How did they eat?

Kal They had their food delivered. The delivery man, he put the food down in a box on their doorstep and nobody ever saw them take it indoors. But ten minutes later, it was always gone.

Beat.

Mal Someone probably robbed it.

Jaz Yeah, your brother.

Mal Yeah, your sister.

Jaz Yeah, your mother.

Mal Yeah, your gran.

Jaz (*with actions*) Your mum works in McDonald's, Mally.

Mal (*with actions*) Your mother's a minger, Jaz.

Boff (*to Kal*) How d'you know they were still in there? If no one ever saw them. They might have just moved out.

Kal I'll tell you how if you'll listen, Boff.

Boff Go on then. It's not me that's interrupting.

Kal Because every night the light in the son's bedroom came on at twelve midnight, and every night it went off again at one a.m. exactly.

Tilly (*gasps*) That's the Witching Hour!

Kal That's right.

Beat.

Boff How d'you know it was the son's bedroom?

Kal You could see his shadow, him and his monkey. You could see their shapes against the curtains. Moving about, strange, weird movements. As if they were doing something.

Jaz Doing what?

Kal Nobody knows. But whatever it was, it was evil.

Beat. Kal pauses.

Ro So what happened?

Kal D'you wanna know?

Ro Course we wanna know.

Kal D'you really wanna know? It's not very nice.

Tilly (*scared*) Ain't it?

Kal You might be scared.

Mal We're not scared!

Ro I'm not scared!

Kal Not you. The girls. And Boff.

Jaz I'm not scared!

Boff It's not true, anyway. It's just one of your stories.

Kal You think so?

Boff (*unsure*) Isn't it?

Kal My dad says it's true.

Boff But . . .

Kal You calling my dad a liar?

Boff Nobody would call your dad a liar.

Kal Shut up then.

Jaz Go on, Kal. What happened?

Kal He killed her.

> *Tilly gasps.*

Jaz Who did?

Kal The son. He killed the old lady.

Mal (*pleased*) Did he? Was there loads of blood?

Kal He used a knife, just like this one.

> *Kal takes a knife that he's been sitting on and*
> *brandishes it at everyone. It's an old-fashioned knife*
> *with an ornate handle and a long blade.*

Tilly (*yelps*) I'm scared.

Kal My old grandad's knife.

Boff You're not meant to have that knife! Your dad'll go
mad.

Kal Shut up, Boff. My dad says they carried the old lady
out in a black oak coffin, and they walked her son out
in a straitjacket.

> *Beat.*

Mal What's a straitjacket?

Boff Oh for goodness' sake!

Ro What happened to the monkey, Kal?

Kal Good question, Ro.

Silence. Kal does another pause. He plays with the knife.

Mal So, what happened to the bloody monkey?!
Kal Will you shush?
Mal (*quietly*) What happened to it?
Kal No one knows. But when me mum and dad were our age, kids round here used to dare each other to sneak into the house.
Ro Did they?
Kal Yeah. And one night me dad and his mate snook in there.
Mal What was it like?
Kal It was all sort of broken up inside. The floorboards were rotting, the wallpaper was peeling, it reeked of piss, there were bloodstains on the walls and the furniture was falling to pieces.
Tilly I don't like this.
Kal And upstairs, in the son's bedroom, lying on his dirty old bed . . .

Kal does another pause.

Tilly What? What was there?
Kal Right there in the middle of the rotten, stinking old bed . . . (*Pause.*) There was a dead monkey, with a knife in its heart.

As he says this, Kal stabs the knife down as if stabbing the Monkey. Tilly gasps. Suddenly the door swings open with a bang. Kal drops the knife. Everybody jumps, gasps, screeches.

Kal Who's that?

No answer.

Who is it?
Lou (*putting on a scary voice*) It's me, the ghost of the monkey, come back to haunt you.

Tilly screams.

Kal Tilly, shut up, it's not the monkey, you dick.

Kal makes a dash for the lights and switches them on. Standing in the doorway is Lou, wearing boy's pyjamas and cuddling a fluffy old soft-toy dog (Richard). She looks very cute. Standing behind her is Kal, his hand on the light switch.

Lou Oh. Hello, everybody!

She does a sheepish little wave. Kal grabs her arm suddenly and pulls it behind her back, threatening to break it.

Lou Ow!

Kal I warned you if you came in here during my sleepover I'd break your arm.

Lou But I can't sleep! You're all talking!

Kal I warned you. Now I'm going to break your arm.

He bends Lou's arm right back to near breaking point. Lou wails. Jaz and Boff run to her aid.

Jaz Don't do that!

Boff Bloody hell, Kal, she's your sister!

Lou (*wailing*) I'll tell Daddy!

Kal drops Lou. She falls to the floor, whimpering, rubbing her arm, laying it on a bit thick. Jaz and Boff tend to her.

Kal I'm only letting you off because I don't want you to wake anyone up with your fake crying. Fucking little baby.

Boff Calm down, Kal!

Kal Shut your mouth, Boff – you haven't got a sister, you don't know what I have to go through.

Lou (*playing up to Boff and Jaz*) He's always beating me up.

Kal And you're always chatting shit – now go back to bed. It's my birthday, not yours.

Beat. Lou looks sad.

Lou But . . .
Kal I'm ten, you're eight. You're a baby. Now piss off.
Lou I . . .
Kal Now! Or I'll tell everyone that thing.
Lou What thing?
Kal The thing you're scared of.
Lou (*beat*) I hate you.

Lou gets up slowly and slopes sadly offstage. She leaves the door open.

Kal And close the door.

Lou comes back and closes the door, gently and sadly. Jaz smiles at her. She smiles sadly back. She goes. Almost immediately she comes back, sits on the other side of the door and eavesdrops.

Kal Little cow.
Tilly My sister's like that, always butting in.
Mal (*proudly*) That's what my big brother says about me! And me big sister.
Kal She thinks she's old enough to do what we do, but she's not.
Mal Yeah!
Kal She nicks my things, she winds me up on purpose, she's always following me around everywhere and if I do anything about it she tells on me and I get a bollocking off me dad!
Jaz I think she's cute.
Boff So do I.
Kal Shut up, Boff.
Mal Yeah, shut up.

Awkward pause. Kal sulks. Mal puts his arm round him.

Tilly What we gonna do now then?

Kal shrugs, still sulking

Ro Any sweets left?
Mal We've eaten them all.
Boff You've eaten them all, you mean.
Mal I only had four packets, Tilly had more than me.
Tilly (*proudly*) I had six!
Boff You're gonna lose all your teeth.
Mal (*mimicking*) 'You're gonna lose all your teeth.'
Ro Shall we have another round of spin-the-bottle?
Jaz Not again.
Ro Why not?
Jaz You've already snogged Tilly five times, Ro.
Mal

> Tilly and Ro,
> Sitting in a tree,
> Ro stood up and had a wee.

Tilly giggles, Ro smirks, kicks Mal.

Boff Maybe, actually, it's time we went to sleep.

They all look at him aghast.

Boff (*petering out*) If we can't, you know, think of
anything else to do. It is late.
Mal What? No way! It's not even midnight! Let's have
another go on Fifa Street, Kal.

Tilly and Jaz groan.

Tilly Not again!
Boff This sleepover's getting really lame.

Kal looks vexed.

Kal Least I'm allowed a sleepover.
Ro How about some more stories, Kal? Tell us another
story.

Tilly Yeah, Kal, tell us another story, you're really good at stories.

Jaz Yeah, go on, Kal.

Kal I'm not going to tell you another story.

Ro Aw!

Kal But I have got an idea.

Mal Fabaluccio!

Boff Fabaluccio?

Mal Yeah, it's Italian for 'fab'.

Boff Fab what?

Mal You know, 'fab . . .' er, 'tastic'?

Boff It's 'fabulous', you idiot.

Kal Do you want to know what my idea is or what?

Ro Yeah. /

Tilly Yeah tell us Kal. /

Mal Yeah, man.

Kal I think we should sneak into the old house on Beech Street.

Silence.

Boff You've got to be kidding.

Kal Why not? You scared, Boff?

Boff No, I'm not scared, I'm worried. It's a stupid and dangerous idea.

Mal (*excited*) I think it's a fabaluccio idea.

Kal Ro?

Ro Er, yeah. Great. Let's do it.

Kal Girls?

Tilly I'm too scared, Kally.

Ro (*manly*) I'll look after you.

Tilly (*girly*) Aw! Thank you.

Jaz I'm not scared. I think it'll be brilliant. Who knows what we'll find in there?

Boff A health-and-safety nightmare, that's what. The floorboards were rotting even in your dad's time, one of us is gonna put our foot right through and fall and break our legs.

Kal You can stay here if you're worried, Boff.

He goes to the door, puts his hand on the handle.
Lou jumps up and runs offstage.

Or is it too lame for you?

Boff That's not . . .

Kal (*cutting in, with actions*) Loser, loser, double loser – take a picture, look at the minger.

Boff Piss off.

Kal Anyone who's got the guts to do it, follow me.

Kal goes out, leaving the door open. Mal follows
immediately. Ro takes Tilly's hand.

Tilly Shall we go?

Ro Well . . . I suppose so. If Kal says.

They exit. Jaz goes to follow.

Boff You're all mad.

Jaz Why don't you come? You don't have to actually go in there. You could be, like, lookout.

Boff I . . . dunno.

Jaz It's either that or face Kal's dad if he finds us gone.

Jaz exits. Boff hesitates a moment then follows. After
a few seconds Lou comes back on stage. She is now
wearing the same full football kit as her brother and
Mal, possibly the previous season's version, handed
down from Kal. She's carrying a Batman backpack.
She also has a climbing rope over her shoulder, a
Winnie the Pooh torch, a compass on a string round
her neck, a map book tucked under her arm along
with her doggy (Richard) and a balaclava rolled up on
her head. She looks around, sees the knife that Kal had
lying on the floor. She takes it. She puts everything in

the Batman backpack. She rolls the balaclava down,
switches Kal's light off and switches her torch on. She
follows the others, sidling along the wall as if she's on
a special mission for MI5.

SCENE TWO

Bushes outside the haunted house. We see the house
looming large in the background: it looks very run down
and scary. The front door and front upstairs window are
visible. Kal, Mal, Ro, Tilly, Jaz and Boff are crouched
behind the bushes. They have coats on over their nightwear
and are wearing shoes. Kal, Boff and Ro have torches.
Kal is carrying an axe. Pause. They watch the house.

Tilly (*nervous*) It looks very dark.

Kal (*irritable*) That's why we've got torches.

Ro The front door's all locked up. How we gonna get
in?

Kal That's why we've brought the axe!

Boff You're not going to chop it down!

Kal Why not?

Boff Someone'll hear. The police will come. We'll be in
trouble!

Kal We're nowhere near any other houses. How's anyone
gonna hear?

Mal Can I do the chopping, Kal?

Kal We'll take it in turns.

Mal Fabaluccio! Can I go first?

Jaz Can I go second?

Boff If we get caught, what's your dad gonna do?

Kal Skin us alive. That's why we won't be getting
caught. (*To Mal and Jaz.*) Come on, you two, we'll
chop the door down. You lot stay here, we'll give
youse a shout when we're ready.

Mal, Kal and Jaz go to move off

Boff (*trying to stop them*) If this was a scary film you'd
be screaming at the screen, 'Don't go in, don't go in!'

Kal Oh yeah? When have you seen any scary films? Your
mum won't even let you watch a PG. Your favourite
film's *The Wizard of Oz*! (*Sarcastic.*) 'Lions and tigers
and bears, oh my!'

Boff (*it is*) No it's not. And I have seen scary films. And
this is what always happens. Stupid people go into
dangerous and frightening places even though its
completely clear to everyone else in the world that
they shouldn't.

Kal You're bricking it, ain't you, Boff?

Boff Yeah. I'm bricking it. Anyone in their right mind
would be bricking it.

Kal Loser.

Mal I've seen loads of scary films. Me brother gets them
out when he's babysitting. You name it, I've seen it.
And I always scream at the screen 'Do go in, do go in!'
Cos if they didn't go in there wouldn't be a film,
would there?

Beat. Kal is pleased.

Kal That's right, Mally! Put it there, son.

He 'high fives' with Mal, or does a special handshake.

Let's go.

*Jaz, Mal and Kal go towards the house. Kal throws
Boff a triumphant glance as they go. Kal, Mal and Jaz
reach the front door. Kal gets his axe and gives it to Mal.*

There you go, Mal. Give it a big swing.

*Mal lifts the axe up behind his head and swings down
hard on the door. As he does so, the door swings open
with a creak. Mal stumbles forwards.*

Mal Shit!

Pause.

Jaz Who did that?
Kal No one. The door's probably just loose or something.
Jaz You think so?
Kal Yeah.

Pause. They look at the open door.

Jaz (*a challenge*) Right. Better go in then, Kally. Check if it's safe.

Beat. Kal, equal to the challenge, takes a step forwards. He peers inside the door. He comes out again.

Kal (*cocky*) Look's fine to me.

Kal goes in. Mal scoots after him, leaving the axe behind. Jaz hesitates a moment, then goes in. The door creaks closed behind them with a bang.

Tilly (*gasps, jumps*) They've gone in! I thought they were going to call us!
Ro They were.
Tilly The door looked like it opened by itself. Did it look like it opened by itself to you?
Ro (*scared*) Yeah.

A light in the upstairs window suddenly comes on. They all freeze. Tilly gasps.

Tilly (*whispers*) What time is it?
Ro It's midnight!
Tilly Oh my God!

A shadow passes over the window.

Oh. My. God! It's him!
Ro (*scared, puts his arm round Tilly*) Don't be scared.
Tilly He's going to kill them!

Boff Tilly, calm down. It's probably torchlight. From Kal and them.

Tilly What about the shadow?!

Boff It's probably them, isn't it, Ro?

Ro (*unconvincing*) Er, yeah. It's probably them.

Pause. The light in the window goes out.

Tilly What are we gonna do?

Boff You can do what you like. I'm staying here. I'm keeping watch.

Ro and Tilly look at each other.

Tilly Jaz is in there.

Ro She'll be alright, she's with Kal.

Tilly But Kal's on one of his things, isn't he?

Ro What things?

Tilly You know, when he gets an idea in his head and he won't back down. And Mal, he just does what Kal wants him to do. They'll end up doing something stupid.

Boff Exactly.

Tilly We'll have to go after them.

Ro (*gulp*) Will we?

Tilly Yeah. I can't go in there by myself, can I, Ro?

Ro No.

Tilly You said you'd look after me.

Ro Yeah. (*Regretful.*) I did, didn't I?

Tilly I know you can do it, babe. There's more to you than hair gel, ain't there?

Ro Er. (*Doubtful.*) Probably.

Tilly (*getting up*) Come on.

She holds her hand out to Ro. He takes it and they go towards the house, hand in hand. As they reach it the door swings open again. Tilly and Ro freeze for a sec, then Tilly turns to Boff.

Tilly (*to Boff*) If you never see us again, tell me sister she can have me yellow poncho (*or other currently desirable girly fashion item*), okay?
Boff Okay.

Tilly and Ro go in. The door creaks shut behind them. Boff paces by the bushes. He looks scared. After a moment he hears a noise: a rustle, then something dropping. Boff jumps. Beat.

Hello? Hello? Is someone there?

No answer. Lights fade.

SCENE THREE

We are in the downstairs hall of the dark, ramshackle old house. Wallpaper peeling, floorboards broken. A very precarious-looking staircase leads upstairs. If possible, rats scuttle across the floor. Ro and Tilly enter, shining their torches around.

Tilly (*calling*) Jaz!
Ro Kal! Kally!

The children's names echo as they call. No answer. they come to a halt in front of the staircase.

Tilly They're not down here.
Ro They must've gone . . . upstairs.

He shines his torch up the creepy staircase. They both look at it.

Tilly We'll have to go up.
Ro I thought you might say that.
Tilly I wish we hadn't come here.
Ro So do I.
Tilly Why do we always do what Kally says?

Ro He has good ideas. Usually.

Tilly This wasn't a good idea though, was it?

Ro No.

Pause. They look at the staircase.

Tilly Jaz says we don't have to do what Kal says all the time. She reckons Kal's a bullshitter.

Ro That's cos he said no when she asked him to go out with her in Year Four.

Tilly (*sighs*) No it ain't! She never asked him to . . .

Ro She definitely liked him.

Tilly He's lying. She doesn't like Kal, she likes Boff.

Beat. Tilly claps her hand over her mouth.

Ro She likes Boff!

Tilly Please don't tell him, Ro!

Ro She can't like Boff – he's gay.

Tilly He's not gay.

Ro He is. He likes books and that, don't he? He can't play football. He hasn't even got any trainers!

Tilly There's nothing wrong with books. Kal likes books.

Ro Yeah, but Kal likes football too. And he's got a Nintendo DS (*or other current technological wonder*).

Tilly So how comes Kal's mates with Boff, then, if Boff's so gay?

Ro Cos Kal's mum makes him be, doesn't she? Cos she's mates with Boff's mum.

Tilly Well, I like Boff. He's nice. And so does Jaz.

Ro I can't believe Jaz fancies Boff.

Tilly You can talk to Boff. He doesn't take the piss all the time.

Ro I don't take the piss all the time.

Tilly (*linking Ro's arm*) Yeah. Jaz reckons I only like you because you're good-looking and you wear nice clean fashionable clothes. But I think you've got quite a good personality too.

Ro looks embarrassed/pleased. Suddenly there's a noise – an eery, echoey sound. They jump, cling on to each other.

Ro What was that?
Tilly I dunno!

The noise again. They cling on to each other.

Ro (*panicking*) Do we have to go up them stairs?
Tilly (*trying not to panic*) Whenever I'm scared my dad always says to me, 'Imagine you're invincible.'
Ro Invisible?
Tilly Invincible. Like, no one can beat you.
Ro Like Batman or something?
Tilly Yeah, like Batman or Superman or something like that.
Ro I've never been any good at nothing like that.
Tilly Like what?
Ro Like being invincible. Kally and Mal always look after me.
Tilly Yeah. Same with me and Jaz. But we got to help them this time, innit?
Ro I'm scared, Tilly.
Tilly So am I. But we gotta show 'em we can be brave too. Yeah?

Beat.

Ro Yeah. We gotta show 'em.

They look up the staircase. The echoey noise happens again. Ro starts crying.

I wish we could just go home.
Tilly (*also crying*) Yeah. So do I.

Lights fade.

SCENE FOUR

Outside the house. Boff is still standing next to the bushes looking nervous. He hears another noise. He jumps.

Boff Look! Whoever you are, you better show yourself! I've got a mobile in my anorak pocket. I will call the police!

There is a lot of activity in the bushes as someone tries to extricate themselves. After a bit, Lou emerges. She's all togged up and carrying her equipment.

Lou I thought your mum said you weren't allowed to have a mobile.

Boff What are you doing here?!

Lou I want to sneak in the house too!

Boff What? You're as crazy as your brother.

Lou My brother's not crazy. Don't say that about him!

She goes to thump Boff. He steps out of the way.

Boff I don't understand you. Why do you always stick up for him? He's horrible to you.

Lou He's not.

Boff He bloody is, Lou. He nearly broke your arm before.

Lou He didn't. It looked worse than it was.

She rubs her arm.

Boff He treats you really badly. He won't let you join in anything, he takes the piss out of you, he beats you up.

Lou He loves me very much. Brothers and sisters always fight a lot. That's what my mum says. It's called sidling ribaldry.

Boff Go home and go to bed, Lou.

Lou (*showing her stuffed doggie*) He bought me Richard, that's how much he loves me. For Christmas when I was a baby. The best dog in the world.

She hugs Richard.

Boff Look. You don't want Richard to get hurt, do you?

Lou No.

Boff Then go home and tell your dad what's happened. Someone needs to do something to stop all this . . . craziness.

Lou Tell my dad? That would be crazy. Have they gone in already?

Boff Yes. I mean, no.

Lou What?

Boff No. They haven't. They've all, er, gone to look round the back. The front door's all locked up. We probably can't get in.

Lou I've got a rope! We can climb up to a window and pull each other up!

Boff Don't be silly. I'd go home if I was you, before Kal catches you.

Lou No.

Boff He'll tell everyone that thing you're scared of.

Torchlight shines in the upstairs window. They both see it.

Lou What's that light?

Boff What light?

The light shines again.

Lou That light.

Boff Er . . .

Lou I thought you said they hadn't gone in?

Beat. The door swings open with a creak. Pause. Lou looks at Boff.

Lou I thought you said the door was locked.

Boff Please don't go in there, Lou.

Lou You come in too if you're worried about me.

Boff I'm, er, on lookout.

Lou Look out for what? The scary stuff's in there, isn't it? Not out here.

Boff No, but . . . there might be police coming. Or something. Or your dad! So I need to . . . look out.

Lou You're going to let me go in by myself, aren't you?

Pause. Boff looks away. Lou shakes her head sadly.

See ya, Boff.

Lou goes into the house, possibly sidling like a spy along the wall on the way in. She picks up the axe left earlier by Mal. The door swings shut behind her.

Boff Why won't anyone listen to me?

SCENE FIVE

Inside the house: upstairs landing. Ro and Tilly enter, clinging to each other. There's a room to the side of the stairs with the door closed. They shine their torches on it and go towards it.

Tilly Jaz! Mal!
Ro Kal!

They stop outside the door.

Tilly They're not in the bathroom.
Ro They're not in the boxroom.
Tilly They're not in the cupboard.
Ro They're not downstairs.

They stop outside the door.

478

Tilly This is the only room left.
Ro The front bedroom.
Tilly His room.
Ro Yeah.

Pause. During the following, The Man comes quietly onstage. He is very neatly dressed in a plain suit. He walks silently and slowly across the landing until he is standing behind Ro and Tilly. He has his Monkey with him on a lead. Tilly and Ro don't see him.

Tilly (*whispers*) What if they're dead?
Ro Don't say that.
Tilly We've been calling them and calling them. Why haven't they answered?
Ro Maybe they've gone back outside.
Tilly I hope so.
Ro Why don't we just go?
Tilly We've got to look in there first. What if they're in there and they need our help? We'd never forgive ourselves.
Ro I've got a very bad feeling about that room.
Tilly I thought you wanted to show 'em how brave you can be.

Beat.

Ro (*gulps*) Right. We'll just open the door quickly. Look in, quickly like. Then go home.
Tilly (*nervous*) Okay.

Tilly and Ro hold hands. They take a step towards the door. Ro puts his hand on the handle.

The Man (*calmly*) I wouldn't go in there if I was you.

Tilly and Ro jump, screech. They turn round to see The Man. Silence for a moment. He looks at them, they look at him. The Monkey sniffs them.

Tilly (*terrified*) Who are you?

The Man Who do you think I am?

Tilly I don't know. Where's our friends?

The Man Your friends?

Ro Are . . . you . . . him?

The Man Him?

Tilly Is this your house? Our friends came in here. They didn't mean to trespass or nothing. It was just for fun.

The Man Ah. Fun. I see.

Ro (*trembling*) They didn't mean any harm. Please let them out. We all just want to go home. Don't we, Tilly?

The Man You think I've got your friends in that room?

Beat.

Ro Yes.

Tilly No!

Tilly (*squeezing Ro's hand*) No. Course not. Is this your house?

The Man This house is dangerous. But if you come with me and do as you're told, I'll make it safe.

Tilly Thank you. But I think we're gonna go now, eh, Ro?

Ro Er, yeah. We're gonna go.

Ro and Tilly start edging towards the stairs. The Man watches them for a moment.

The Man Don't you want to know about my monkey?

Ro No, we'd better be . . .

Suddenly there is a call from in the room. It sounds like Jaz.

Jaz (*offstage*) Tilly!

Tilly's name echoes loudly. Ro and Tilly stop.

Tilly What was that?

The Man I didn't hear anything.

Tilly I thought I heard my best mate. Jaz.

The Man Stay here and talk to me. I might have seen her.

Ro Tilly, let's go.

Beat. Tilly takes a few steps back up. She swallows.

Tilly What did you say your monkey was called?

The Man Its called Monkey. Do you want to stroke it?

Tilly Yes.

Tilly goes to Monkey. She stretches her hand out to pet it. Suddenly, Monkey grabs her. Tilly struggles but Monkey holds her tight, covers her mouth.

The Man Don't be frightened. If you do as I say, all will be well.

He opens the door to the bedroom. We can't see inside.

The Man (*to Ro*) You'd better come too. Monkey gets a bit over-enthusiastic sometimes. Your friend might need your help.

Monkey pushes Tilly hard into the room. Ro, sobbing and shaking, follows. The Man lets them through the door, then slips in himself. The door closes quietly behind them.

SCENE SIX

Outside the house. Boff is looking towards the house. He wants to go in after Lou but he's really scared, and upset with himself for being scared.

Boff (*trying to convince himself*) I can be brave, I can be brave, I can be brave. I can.

Pause. He looks at the house.

Oh God.

He paces a bit. Makes a few steps towards the house, hears a noise, runs back again. He starts hesitantly to recite 'Lions and tigers and bears, oh my', from The Wizard of Oz.
    He builds up his confidence and starts to sing more loudly as the song goes on (or recites 'Lions and tigers and bears' louder and faster). He is just about to march confidently singing into the house when the light in the upstairs window comes on full and a small, crashing sound is heard. He stops in his tracks, stares in horror at the window, then turns on his heel and runs offstage.

SCENE SEVEN

The bedroom. Lights up on Kal, Mal, Jaz, Tilly and Ro, who are tied up and sitting on and around a stained old bed in the middle of the room. There are strange drawings and paintings on the walls of the room. We can still see the landing at the other side of the bedroom door. There is a broken glass on the floor. The Man stands watching the children. The Monkey sweeps up the glass with a dustpan and brush.

The Man Thank you, Monkey. Clumsy boy, Ro!

Tilly (*to Jaz*) What's going on?

Jaz I dunno.

Kal He's mad, that's what's going on. My dad's gonna kill you if you do anything to us.

The Man Who said I'm going to do anything? We were having an interesting talk before your friends decided to join us.

Kal I don't think it was interesting.

The Man About fear, wasn't it?

Kal You're weird and sick.

The Man What's your biggest fear, Kal? Come on.

Kal I don't have no biggest fears.

The Man Come on. I'll let you go if you tell me.

Beat.

Ro (*scared, to Jaz*) Does he mean he'll let us go if we tell him what we're scared of?

Kal Don't tell him anything, Ro.

The Man Don't listen to Kal, Ro – what does Kal know? It was, after all, Kal's idea to come here.

Beat.

The Man So. Who wants to leave?

Jaz Why tie us up like this? You could've asked us what we were scared of when we first came in.

The Man You were trespassing on my property. Isn't a man allowed to make his own house safe from intruders?

Kal We're ten years old, we're not very big intruders.

The Man (*snapping nastily*) Children can be very bad. Don't you watch television?

Pause.

Jaz Nobody has lived in this house for years. How come it's your property?

The Man That's true. No one has lived here. But there has always been an owner, and now the owner's back.

Beat.

Tilly Are you the owner, then?

The Man Yes.

Kal So where've you been?

The Man Let's just say I've been away.

Kal Why do you want to know what we're scared of?

The Man It's a . . . project I'm working on.

Mal I'm doing a project at school! It's about Queen Victoria.

Kal Shut up, Mal.

Mal Sorry.

The Man So don't any of you want to leave?

Mal I do!

Kal Mal, shut up.

Mal But . . .

Kal (*to The Man*) What are you scared of?

Beat.

The Man Mm. Interesting question.

Kal I bet you won't tell us.

The Man I could say ghosts. Or witches. Or monsters or banshees or spectres or demons.

Beat.

Jaz So? Which one is it?

The Man None of them. Not really. People aren't really frightened of things like that, because things like that don't really exist, do they? They're just stories. They're just figments of the imagination.

Mal I've got a figment in my imagination! My mum says that when I've been lying about something.

The Man Kal's got a good imagination, haven't you, Kal? Good at stories, aren't you? Good at telling lies.

Kal Fuck off!

The Man But lies aren't real. And people are really scared of real things. Things that could really happen to them. Plane crashes, diseases, earthquakes, hurricanes, guns, bombs.

Kal (*to Monkey*) Knives?

Monkey flinches a little.

Mal I ain't scared of plane crashes and that.

The Man Aren't you, Mal?

Mal It's really funny what I'm scared of.

Kal Mal . . .

Mal It's stupid really. Cos, really, they're meant to make you laugh, not scare you. But it's their faces, the make-up. It doesn't look funny to me. It looks horrible.

Jaz Mal!

The Man (*playful*) Ah! I think I can guess what you're talking about, Mally.

Mal (*pleased*) Go on then! I bet you can't!

Kal Mal will you . . . (*shut up*).

The Man (*cutting in*) Is it . . . something to do with the circus?

Mal (*amazed*) Yeah!

Kal Mal, shut up!

The Man It's clowns, isn't it?

Mal Yeah, man! How did you guess that?!

Jaz Mal, you idiot!

Mal What?

Jaz You've told him!

Mal Oh.

The Man Don't worry, Mal. That's fine. You've told me. You can go.

Monkey unties Mal. Beat.

The Man Off you go.

Mal Fabaluccio! Look, he's letting me go. You just have to tell him.

The Man opens the door for Mal. Mal gets up and goes out.

See you soon, guys.

Mal goes through the door. The Man closes it behind him. He stays facing the door, as if he can see through

485

it. On the landing, weird distorted circus/fairground music starts playing. A sign on the wall lights up: 'House of Fun'.

Mal What's this?
Echoey Voice (*offstage*) Welcome to the House of Fun, Malcolm.

Cackling, distorted laughter starts echoing round the landing. Harsh and nasty, an enormous clown comes bouncing onto the stage. He has really horrible make-up on, a grimacing red smile and a big garish clown suit. Mal screams. The clown envelopes him inside his suit in a big suffocating embrace. Other clowns follow: they bounce all over the stage, cackling maniacally. Mal screams and struggles, but he can't get free. They carry him away. During this, The Man faces the door from the other side and watches. He enjoys Mal's fear. It's as if it's giving him nourishment. Once Mal has been carried off, The Man turns back to the room.

The Man There you are, simple as that. Tell me what you're scared of and I'll let you go.

Beat.

Ro I'll tell you.
Kal Ro!
Ro (*scared*) I want to get out of here, Kal. We can all get out like Mal if we just tell him.
Kal No way. I'm not gonna tell him anything. Don't tell him! He's up to something!
Ro You're not the boss, Kal. We don't have to do what *you* say all the time. (*To the Monkey and The Man.*) You can untie me.

The Man gestures to Monkey. Monkey unties Ro.

Kal Ro!

Ro I just have to tell you, then I can go?

The Man Yes.

Ro It's vampires.

The Man Vampires. I see. What is it about them?

Ro (*duh*) They sink their teeth into your neck and suck out all your blood?

The Man And how would that feel?

Ro It'd . . . it'd feel like . . . like fainting, like going dizzy and sick and falling and banging your head on the ground. And your neck, them big teeth in your neck, that'd hurt, man. That'd really hurt. And it'd be really messy too. The blood'd get all over your nice clean clothes and mess 'em up. That'd be terrible.

Beat.

The Man Thank you. You may go.

The Man goes to the door and opens it for Ro.

Ro See! Don't listen to Kal. We just have to tell him! Just tell the guy what you're scared of, Tilly. I'll see you outside.

Ro goes through the door and onto the landing. The Man closes the door behind him. Standing on the landing is a vampire. It is animalistic and savage-looking.

Oh shit.

Ro turns to run away, but too late. The vampire grabs him. Other vampires come. Ro is paralysed with fear. The vampires crowd round him in a huddle. They attack his neck violently. The man watches 'through' the door. At the same time, in the bedroom, Kal struggles and bangs about.

Kal He's doing something to them, I know he is! Let us go, you freak! Let us go!

He bangs against the bed frame, straining to break his ties. The Monkey jumps on Kal and wrestles him to the ground. Sits on him. Finally, the vampires carry Ro offstage, bleeding. The Man turns back to the room. He sees Kal with the Monkey restraining him.

The Man Oh dear. You're being naughty, Kal. Now I'm *really* going to have to dish out some punishment.

Lights go out on the bedroom.

SCENE EIGHT

The landing. Lou sidles out of the shadows. She has been watching.

Lou There's definitely something weird going on here.

She sidles along the wall and listens at the bedroom door. She paces a bit. She looks worried, angry, ready for action. She delves into her backpack. She takes out a few things. The compass, the map, an Action Man magazine, the knife, a poster of McFly (or other current boy/pop band), a toy walkie-talkie. Finally she finds a toy spy headset. She puts the other stuff back in, then wraps the headset round her head. It has an X-ray vision eyepiece on it. She goes to the door and tries to stare through it with the X-ray eye. It doesn't work. She takes it off and throws it to the ground. She picks up Richard.

(*To Richard.*) Well, Richard, it looks like the batteries have run out on the X-Ray Spex Super Vision Eyepiece. Again. We're going to have to try something else. We must be clever, it's our Most Important Mission Ever. Only you and me can rescue these kids from this terrible nightmare.

She reaches back into her backpack again and brings out the axe she picked up earlier. The door creaks. Lou runs back into the shadows. The door opens and Monkey comes out. Monkey runs across the landing and exits. Lou steps out of the shadows and watches him go off through a toy telescope. A few seconds pass. Monkey comes back, dressed in a dentist's coat and mask. He/she is dragging a dentist's chair on wheels which squeak. Lou hides. Monkey goes back into the bedroom, closing the door behind him. Lou steps out of the shadows, runs up to the door and goes to hit it with the axe. The head of the axe falls off. Lou stares at it.

Mm. I thought Daddy said he was going to fix that. (*To Richard.*) Right. We'll have to think of something else, Richard. But be careful. That monkey looks really strong.

Richard whispers something in Lou's ear.

What's that? Richard, you're a genius!

She takes the rope off her shoulder and looks at it.

I think it'll be long enough.

She exits down the stairs, sidling like a spy.

SCENE NINE

The bedroom. Kal is tied up more firmly to the bed and he has also been gagged. Tilly is strapped to the dentist's chair. The Monkey is standing over her. It has an enormous syringe in one hand and a hand-powered drill in the other. It is wearing plastic hygiene gloves. Tilly is shaking with fear.

The Man So. Jaz. Tell me what you're scared of. (*Nastily.*) Or Tilly gets it right in the teeth.

Jaz You said we could go if we told you our fears!

The Man Yes, but then Kal was naughty, wasn't he?

Jaz But Tilly wasn't naughty! Tilly *told* you what she's scared of and now you've done this to her.

The Man Yes, because Kal was naughty. And now we know what scares Tilly. And a very understandable fear it is. I never liked having my teeth drilled either. It's a horrible *noise*, isn't it?

Monkey gives the drill a quick whizz. Tilly screams.

Jaz But why aren't you punishing Kal? This is all Kal's fault, Kal got us into it in the first place!

The Man Yes. He's been bad. And here you see the consequences of his actions. Too late for Kally. But *you* can be good. You can save Tilly. If you'll only tell me, you and Tilly can walk free.

Jaz I dunno, I . . .

The Man leans over Tilly and looks into her mouth.

The Man Oh dear. I think Tilly's been eating too many sweeties. We're going to have to drill them all out.

Monkey switches the drill on and moves it slowly towards Tilly's mouth.

Jaz Alright! Alright! I'll tell you.

Monkey switches the drill off.

The Man Good girl. I knew you'd see sense.

Pause. Jaz struggles with herself.

The Man Come on, Jaz. We're all *dying* to hear. Aren't we, Monkey?

The Monkey puts its hand to its ear and cranes towards Jaz. Jaz looks down.

Jaz (*mumbling*) It's to do with my mum.
The Man Pardon, Jasmine? I can't quite hear you.
Jaz My mum. I'm frightened of anything happening to her.

Beat.

The Man Really?
Jaz Yes. I've been like that since I was little, since my dad . . .went away. I don't even like her going out at night. You know, out with her friends for a drink or something. I always think something's going to happen to her.

Beat.

The Man What kind of things?

During the following, The Man seems to puff up and grow taller.

Jaz (*shrugs*) Could be anything. She could get run over by a car, or fall in front of a train, or get shot by accident in a bank raid. Or she could catch some terrible illness or choke on a fishbone or get bitten by a rabid dog. She could eat something dodgy and get salmonella and get admitted to hospital only to catch a terrible hospital bug. And if she ever manages to recover from that she could catch Legionnaire's Disease from the jacuzzi down the gym and just die anyway. I get these terrible dreams. My mum, lying in a coffin, dead. And I'm looking down on her. She looks beautiful. At rest. But suddenly she opens her eyes, she looks at me hard, her hand comes up and she grabs me.

Pause. Everyone is quiet for a moment.

The Man Thank you so much for sharing, Jasmine. (*Nastily.*) Personally, I think a coffin's the best place for a mother.

Monkey and The Man both snigger horribly.

You can go now, Jasmine. Bye-bye.

Beat.

Jaz What about Tilly?
The Man Tilly's coming soon.

He opens the door. Jaz stands up.

Jaz (*hesitating*) I dunno.
The Man (*impatient*) Oh, do get a move on, Jaz.

He pushes Jaz through the door and slams it behind her. A coffin rolls onto the landing with 'R.I.P. Mum' written on it. Jaz stares gobsmacked at it. The coffin lid creaks open and we see Jaz's mum lying inside. Jaz walks towards it like a zombie. She leans over. Jaz's mum opens her eyes, grabs Jaz's arm and drags her into the coffin. Jaz struggles, but the lid closes on her and the coffin glides back offstage. Simultaneously, in the bedroom, the Monkey leans over Tilly, brandishing the drill and syringe. It drills viciously at Tilly's mouth. Tilly tries to scream. There is blood. Kal struggles, bangs about, furious. The coffin by now has gone off. Finally, Tilly lies limp. Monkey opens the bedroom door and pushes Tilly out, chair wheels squeaking. It wheels the chair across the landing and off, then returns, pulling off its plastic gloves. During this The Man watches Kal. Kal stares back at The Man, defiantly. Struggling.

Did you want to say something to me Kal?

Kal tries to speak through his gag.

Monkey, I think Kal has a comment he wants to make.

Monkey takes Kal's gag off.

Kal (*angrily*) I know what you're doing, you fucking
freak!

The Man Oh, do you, how interesting. Do tell.

Monkey and The Man sit down and listen attentively.

Kal You're feeding off people's fear, aren't you? Like it's
food or something. Well, I'm not going to give you
anything more to eat. Because I'm not scared of
anything, okay? And if I was I wouldn't tell you and
you wouldn't be able to do anything about it because
no one's left. You've got no one left to threaten me
with!

*Just then, the bedroom window flies open and Lou
jumps in with a flourish and a yell, landing on the
floor in front of them. There may even be a crash of
breaking glass as she jumps through. She has her
balaclava rolled down. She takes up a martial arts
stance and yells out:*

Lou You leave my brother alone!

The balaclava muffles her.

The Man Beg pardon?

She rolls the balaclava up.

Lou You leave my brother alone!

Kal Oh for fuck's sake, Lou!

Lou (*hurt*) What? I'm here to save you!

Kal You've just ruined everything, you stupid *cow*!

Lou (*near tears*) But I, I climbed all the way up and
everything. I've grazed both my knees. You never want
me to join in anything!

She starts wailing.

Kal Shut up! Stop being such a baby! And that's *my*
backpack.

Lou (*shouting*) It *used* to be yours. You gave it to *me* last
week!

Kal Did I?

Lou Yes.

Beat. Lou looks at The Man.

Lou Who're you?

The Man I'm your friend, Lou.

Kal Don't listen to him, Lou. He's not anybody's friend.
And don't, whatever you do, tell him that thing you're
scared of.

Lou I won't. You're the only person in the world that
knows that. You and Mum.

Kal And Dad.

Lou And Daddy. And Richard. And Suzy next door.
That's all.

The Man (*delighted*) Ah. A Great Big Secret. How
wonderful!

Lou I'll never tell you. It's very, very embarrassing.

The Man If you don't, my Monkey will kill your brother.

Beat.

Lou What?

*Monkey goes to Kal. It puts its hands round Kal's
neck, and pushes his head back, ready to strangle him.*

Lou Kal!

SCENE TEN

*Outside. Boff creeps back onstage, looking warily
towards the upstairs window, which is now open with
Lou's rope dangling down from it. He stops and stares up
at the window.*

Boff Lou!

> *Boff runs to Lou's rope, dangling from the window.
> He grabs it. He looks up, braces himself for the climb.
> He tugs on the rope and puts one foot on the wall,
> ready. The rope falls down and lands in a pile beside
> him. Boff runs to the door and goes to open it. He
> pulls on the handle. It won't open. He pulls harder.
> No joy. He rattles and pulls and pulls. It won't open.*

(*frustrated*) For crying out loud!

> *He kicks the wall in frustration. A bit too hard. He
> hurts his foot.*

(*Hopping about.*) Owwww!!

SCENE ELEVEN

*The bedroom. Monkey has Kal round the neck, strangling
him. Kal chokes. Lou watches in horror.*

Lou Please. Please! Make it stop!
The Man If you tell me what you're scared of, I will.
Lou Okay! I'll tell you! I'll tell you.
Kal (*in between chokes*) Don't tell him, Lou!
The Man I promise not to tell another living soul what
it is.
Lou It's . . . it's . . .
Kal No! Stop! Stop! Let her go. *I'll* tell you, alright?

> *Monkey loosens its grip on Kal's neck.*

Kal (*defeated*) I'll tell you what I'm scared of. Let her go.

> *The Man claps his hands together.*

The Man Oh goody! Got you! I knew I would in the
end.

Lou Kal!

Kal goes quiet. Pause.

The Man (*excited*) Come on then, fire away!

Another pause. Kal struggles with himself.

The Man Oh, do hurry up, Kally, the suspense is killing me.

Kal It's . . . my dad.

The Man (*beat*) Ah. Like Jaz with her mum!

Kal No. Not like Jaz with her mum! It's him. Himself. I'm frightened of him. I'm frightened of my dad, okay?!

Beat.

The Man Why?

Kal Because he's scary! Why d'you think?! I'm not the only one that thinks so. A lot of people are scared of my dad.

Lou I'm not.

Kal No. Cos you're his little princess, aren't you?

Lou I'm not! I don't even like princesses.

The Man (*very interested*) Is he . . . cruel to you?

Monkey whimpers.

Kal No, not cruel, firm. And a bit shouty sometimes. But he has to be, doesn't he? He has to be with me because I'm out of order sometimes and he can't put up with *that*, can he?

The Man Does he shut you up in dark cupboards?

Monkey whimpers some more.

Kal No!

The Man Does he burn you with his cigarette?

Kal Of course he doesn't! He doesn't even smoke!

496

The Man Does he make you sit in a bath of freezing cold water, in the middle of winter, for fifteen long and torturous hours?

Monkey holds The Man's hand and strokes it, comfortingly.

Kal No.
The Man Then what's to be scared of?!

Beat.

Kal He, well, sometimes I think he . . . sometimes, when he's cross with me, I think – (*Mumbles.*) He doesn't like me.
The Man Speak up, Kal!!!
Kal He doesn't like me.

Pause. Kal is on the verge of crying. Lou goes to him and puts her arm round his shoulders.

Lou He does like you.
Kal How do *you* know?
Lou He says it. He's very proud of you, that's what he says. That time when you got best marks in the Maths test. And when you made that really good *Dr Who* Tardis out of egg boxes. I heard him telling Mum.

Beat.

Kal Well, he never said anything to me.
Lou Maybe he feels embarrassed.
Kal D'you think so?
Lou Yeah. Cos men're *like* that, aren't they? That's what Mum says, anyway.

Beat.

The Man Is that it, then?
Kal (*embarrassed*) Yes.

The Man (*scornful*) Your dad's a bit strict with you?
That's it?

Kal Yes.

The Man (*slowly, with actions*) Loser, loser, double loser,
take a picture. Look at the minger.

Kal (*upset*) Shut up! You ain't even got a dad!

The Man Oh, boo-hoo. You've got no idea.
(*Disappointed.*) Untie him, Monkey. I thought it was
going to be something good.

Monkey unties Kal. The Man holds the door open.

The Man Bye-bye, boring boy.

Kal What about Lou?

The Man Lou hasn't told me her secret.

*Monkey goes behind Lou and holds her by her arms,
behind her back.*

Kal If you don't let Lou go then I'm not going either.
Don't tell him, Lou.

The Man Goodbye, Kal.

Kal I'm not going.

The Man Goodbye!!

*He starts pushing Kal through the door. Kal pushes
back. They struggle for a moment. Lou looks around
desperately, then sees her Batman backpack.*

Lou (*quickly*) It's knives!

Kal What?

The Man What?

Monkey whimpers.

Lou That's what I'm scared of. (*Hinting to Kal.*) You
know, Kal. Grandad's nasty scary old knife.

Monkey whimpers.

Luckily I haven't seen it for a while.

She nods towards the backpack. Kal twigs, takes a sudden lunge away from The Man and grabs the bag. He turns it upside down. All the stuff, including Richard, falls out. Kal grabs the knife. Lou meanwhile makes a sudden twist out of the Monkey's grasp. They fight. Lou stamps hard on Monkey's foot, Monkey whimpers and hops. Lou punches Monkey. At the same time, The Man goes to grab Kal, but Kal slips away. He grabs Monkey and holds the knife to its heart. The Man grabs Lou. Stand-off.

Kal Let my sister go or I'll kill your dirty, mangy flea-bitten stinking old ape!

Monkey is terrfied of the knife. It whimpers and shakes.

The Man (*very worried*) Please. Please. Not the knife!
Kal That's what *you're* scared of, isn't it? Someone sticking a knife in your precious Monkey's heart.
The Man Please.
Kal It's your only friend isn't it? A dirty minging animal.
The Man You mustn't hurt it.
Kal Let my sister go.

The Man hesitates for a moment, then lets Lou go.

Run, Lou!

Lou runs out.

The Man Let go of my Monkey, please.
Kal Bring my friends back first.
The Man Your friends have gone.
Kal Bring them back or I'll kill it.

Kal brandishes the knife at Monkey's throat. Monkey screeches.

499

The Man (*panicking*) Alright, alright. I'll bring them back.

He clicks his fingers. Music. The children are escorted back onstage by their respective 'fears': Mal is brought back by a clown, Ro by a vampire, Jaz by her dead mum and Tilly by a dentist. The 'fears' now seem kind and caring. They deliver the children, then leave. As this happens, The Man seems to become smaller, weaker.

Tilly Ro?
Jaz What happened?
Ro I dunno.
Mal Where are we?

Kal sees them through the open door.

Kal Right.

He edges to the doorway, still holding Monkey. When he gets into the doorway, he throws Monkey to the floor. Monkey weeps. The Man goes to it. They hug. The Man weeps.

The Man My precious. My angel.

Kal slams the door shut on them.

Kal (*to the others*) Run!

They all run offstage as quickly as possible. Music.

SCENE TWELVE

Outside the house. Kal and Lou are in the middle of explaining to Boff and the other kids what happened.

Kal And then the Monkey drilled your teeth out!
Tilly (*amazed*) What?

Mal A monkey? Drilling teeth? Fabaluccio!

Kal You *must* remember!

Boff This is ridiculous. (*To Jaz.*) This is just one of his stories.

Lou It's not! My brother is not a liar!

Beat.

Kal Thanks. Lou.

Kal gives Lou a quick awkward pat on the back. She looks made up.

Boff (*to Lou*) You're just sticking up for him again. You know it's not true.

Lou No I'm not!

Jaz (*to Kal, cutting in*) Your imagination is really out of control you know, Kal. Or is it just an excuse? Because you came screaming out of that room like a little baby!

Tilly (*cocky*) Yeah, me and Ro didn't find it scary in there at all, did we, Ro?

Ro (*evasive*) Er, no. Not at all.

Kal Look. I don't care what you think. We need to get away from here.

Lou Please listen to him!

Boff (*sighs*) Just because he bought you Richard doesn't mean you always have to stand by him. *He* probably didn't even buy Richard, it was probably your mum!

Beat.

Lou RICHARD!

Kal Oh God.

Lou RICHARD!

Kal We can't go back in there, Lou.

Lou (*wailing*) RICHARD!!

Kal For fuck's sake. It's just a bit of stuffed fur!

Boff That's not a very nice thing to say about Richard!

Kal What's it got to do with you?!

Boff Nothing. I just . . . I understand about Richard, that's all. Cuddlies are very important to people.

Kal (*beat*) You've got one, haven't you?

Boff Shut up.

Kal You have. Boff's got a cuddly!

Jaz Actually, Kal, so have I.

Tilly And me.

Ro Er, yeah. I've got one too.

Mal I've got a T-Rex!

Jaz T-Rexes aren't cuddly, Mal.

Mal You're telling me. Those teeth don't half hurt when you lie on them!

Boff Richard is more than just a bit of fur.

Kal (*to Boff*) Alright then. If Richard is so important, you go back in there and get him.

Beat. Boff hovers.

Come on, Boff. If what I told you ain't true, what's to be scared of?

Lou sobs.

Come on. I've been in, Mal's been in, Jaz's been in there. Even Ro and Tilly.

Ro and Tilly look proudly at each other.

Boff I did *try* and get in, you know.

Kal (*disbelieving*) Oh yeah?

Boff Yes! The door seemed to have locked itself up again, and the rope fell down.

Kal Yeah, right. Chicken boy.

Boff I'm not chicken, I . . .

Kal Little girl.

Boff I *did* try. We don't all tell lies all the time, Kal.

Kal Stop calling me a liar.

Boff Well, it is all a bit far-fetched. A monkey dressed as a dentist!

Kal So go in and get Richard, then. Do something brave for once in your life.

Pause. Boff takes a big breath.

Boff Alright. Alright. I'll go.

Boff takes a deep breath, then moves purposefully toward the house. He's about to reach the door when:

Kal (*bit worried*) Boff.
Boff What?
Kal Er, take this. In case I'm telling the truth.

He takes the knife out of his pocket and gives it to Boff. Boff pockets the knife. The door is already open. They all watch. Boff hesitates, turns his torch on, then suddenly runs in, very fast. The door doesn't shut. We hear Boff singing 'My Favourite Things' (or 'Lions and tigers and bears') inside the house as he runs upstairs. Torchlight flashes in the upstairs window. A flurry of shadows is seen. Suddenly, there is a loud scream.

Tilly Oh my God!!
Jaz Boff!
Lou Richard!

Jaz and Kal run towards the house but Boff comes running out, fast as he can, carrying Richard. He has no knife. He runs right into Jaz and Kal. Jaz throws her arms round him.

Kal What happened?!
Jaz Are you alright?

Boff hugs Jaz back for a sec, then they both realise what they are doing and jump apart. Boff gives Richard to Lou. She cuddles him happily.

Lou Richard!

Mal What happened, Boffy?

Boff (*still scared, out of breath*) I went upstairs.

Mal Yeah?

Boff It was really creepy in there. And very dangerous.
    I'm surprised none of you broke their ankle!

Kal What did you see?

Boff I went in the bedroom. It was really dark and quiet.

Kal And?

Boff There was a bed.

Tilly I'm scared.

Boff And lying on the bed was a stuffed toy monkey.

Beat.

Kal A toy?

Boff Yeah. And Richard was lying next to him. So I went
    to grab Richard. And just as I put my hand on him
    I swear I saw the monkey move!

Ro No!

Boff Yeah! It must have been a trick of the light. But
    I panicked. I screamed and I stabbed it. I stabbed the
    toy monkey in the heart!

Beat.

I'm sorry, Kal. Your knife's still in him.

Beat.

Kal He can keep it.

Lou (*to Boff, hugging Richard*) You *saved* him!

Jaz You were very brave.

Beat. Boff looks coy.

Kal (*awkwardly*) Yeah. Well done.

*He slaps Boff on the back, a bit too hard. A man
comes on stage. A Night Watchman.*

Night Watchman Oy!

The kids all jump.

What you kids doing here? This is private property.
Boff We, er . . .
Mal We're doing a project!
Night Watchman Bit late for that kind of thing, isn't it?
Jaz It's, er, about Things That Go Bump in the Night.
Lou I bet you get a lot of night bumps in your job!
Night Watchman I could tell you a thing or two.
Boff Do you know anything about this house?
Night Watchman Oh yes. I've been keeping an eye on this place for more than thirty years.
Kal Can you tell us who it belongs to?
Night Watchman Doesn't belong to anyone any more. The guy who owned it died last night.

Beat.

Kal Last night?
Jaz What?!
Ro Did he . . . did he still live there?
Night Watchman You must be joking. No one could live in there. It's a deathtrap. No. No, he died in jail. He'd been there for years. (*Scary voice.*) People say he murdered his mother.
Jaz What . . . what would he do that for?
Night Watchman She was cruel to him apparently. He was brought up on fear. She locked him in cupboards and burnt him with cigarettes. That sort of thing. And then one day, he turned. Apparently he had a pet monkey, and she'd killed it.

Beat.

Tilly That's horrible.
Night Watchman Yes. Still. It's all in the past now, eh?

He moves off.

All in the past now.

He exits. The children look at each other for a moment, gobsmacked, terrified. Then they all run offstage as fast as they can.

SCENE THIRTEEN

Kal's bedroom. Kal, Mal, Ro, Tilly, Jaz and Boff are settling down in sleeping bags on the floor.

Ro You could've let Lou sleep in your room after all that, Kal!

Kal *No.* She's not allowed. It's *my* sleepover. Not hers.

While they're talking, Lou runs on and settles down in her own sleeping bag outside the door.

Jaz Come on, Kal. Before you go to sleep. Tell us what *you* were scared of.

Kal No.

Tilly Oh, *go* on, Kally.

Kal No.

Jaz Let's see if we can guess it.

Mal Yeah! Is it ghosts, Kally?

Kal No.

Boff Is it snakes?

Kal No.

Ro Spiders?

Kal NO!

Mal Is it zombies?

Kal Go to sleep.

Boff Is it a person?

Kal *(beat)* What?

Jaz It is! It is! He didn't say no. It definitely is.

Boff Is it someone you know?

Kal Look. It's not, alright? But if you really have to know a secret, I'll tell you that thing that Lou's scared of.

Lou's head bobs up out of her sleeping bag.

Boff You can't do that, you promised.

Kal Well then, let's go to sleep, shall we?

Boff (*beat*) Alright.

They turn the lights off.

Mal (*after a moment*) Just whisper it to me, Kally. I won't tell anyone.

Lou I'm right outside the door, Kal!

Kal sits bolt upright.

Kal What?! I told you to go to bed!!

Lou I'm not *in* the room, I'm outside. And I can hear every word you say. So you'd better not.

Kal Go back to your room or I will.

Lou No! I'm not even *in* the room. And if you tell them, I'll tell Daddy.

Kal Right. Here comes your first clue everybody.

Lou I'll tell Daddy!

Kal (*donkey noises*) Eeyore! Eeyore! Eeeeeeeeyooooore!

Lou (*wails*) I HATE YOU!

Mayhem. Mal laughs his head off. Ro and Tilly also laugh. Lou bursts into the room and jumps on Kal, starts trying to beat him up. Kal responds. Boff tries to drag him off. Jaz tries to drag Lou off. A light comes on on the landing.

Voice (*offstage, loud*) What the hell is going on in there?!

They all stop in their tracks.

Kal Dad!

Everyone immediately assumes sleeping positions and starts to snore. A shadow looms on to the landing. The shadow is followed soon after by The Man. He stands on the landing and watches the children sleeping. Lights fade.

End of play.

Production Notes

The title of the play came from its content and the slight
pun on *Scary Movie*. There was an old empty house near
the end of the street where Judith grew up which was
surrounded by stories of this kind. She and other kids
used to sneak into the house, and there was a rumour of
a dead monkey with a knife in its heart in the bathroom.

SLANG ACTIONS

'Your mum works in McDonald's', 'Your mother's a
minger', and 'Loser, loser, double loser – take a picture,
look at the minger' all require hand movements.

The first two involve making an 'M' with thumbs and
forefingers and swinging this round to form a 'W', then
turning it back down as the 'M'. The same 'M' symbol
is used for 'minger'. The final movement involves making
an 'L' with thumb and forefinger first with one hand and
then the other; these then come together and are brought
down to do a camera action and the 'M' for 'minger'
sign.

SCALES OF FEAR

The fears affecting the characters differ in order and
severity. Some of the fears are amusing and others have
a more serious tone, but all of them are real for the
children. It is only through Kal's actions that they can
be liberated from their fears. If it wasn't for him, they
would still be trapped by them. There is a fine line
between fear and laughter and it is important to find
where that line falls.

The Man is able to see through the door. Decide who can see what and when, so that the characters are only reacting to what *they* see and are experiencing at a particular time. There will be more going on onstage than the kids can see. Kal is the only one who does clock what The Man is doing, and he seems to realise this from the start. This is because he is so familiar with the language of horror movies and has been watching The Man much more keenly than the others.

Judith is deliberately working with ambiguity between The Man, the Night Watchman and Kal's Dad. It may be that the whole play is in the imagination of Kal, resulting from his fear of his dad. The ambiguity makes the play exciting and could be explored further. For example, the voice of Dad could be the same as that of the Man.

EXERCISES

The characters in the play have been deliberately chosen as 'stock' characters, but they must be real. Here are some useful exercises which will help the actors to discover who they are and how they feel about other characters.

EXERCISE 1

Walk around the space.

Walk around the space and make eye-contact.

Walk around the space, make eye-contact and say, 'Oh yes.'

Walk around the space, make eye contact, say, 'Oh yes,' and then turn to face the audience before walking on.

Walk around the space and don't let your bottom be pinched.

Walk around the space as puppies.

In pairs:

Person A Do you know a trick?

Person B Oh yes. (*Does trick.*)

Person A Is that it?

Person B Oh yes.

The 'Oh yes' provides thinking time and also lifts the energy level, because it is difficult to say the phrase without lifting at the end of it.

In the case of The Man, this could be quite a good state to be in:

Person A Do you have a secret?

The Man Oh yes.

EXERCISE 2

Find a person in the room whom you fancy without letting them know and walk around the room.

Find a person in the room you are frightened of without letting them know and walk around the room.

Do those exercises at the same time.

Ask 'What does the exercise do to you?' and 'What does the exercise do to the group?' This exercise is important in enabling the actors to get in touch with their internal rhythm and to make them aware of how this changes depending on who is in the space.

EXERCISE 3

One character is in the middle with eyes closed (e.g., Kal).

Other characters adjust their position in terms of how much they like that character (e.g., Kal) in the play.

Other characters adjust their positions depending on the extent to which Kal would protect them if something nasty happened.

This exercise can be adapted to different characters and different examples of what other characters think of them – e.g., Lou, and how clever the others think she is; or Boff, and how good the others think he would at getting them out of trouble.

This exercise is useful when blocking and thinking where characters would be in relation to each other. These relationships also vary between scenes so it can be useful to do the exercise scene by scene. It is important, however, that the character in the middle has eyes closed so that he/she is not aware of the differing relationships.

EXERCISE 4

Hot-seat the characters at particular moments in the play.

EXERCISE 5

Ask each actor to read the play and write four lists about their character:

- Facts about the character and things they do.
- All the character says about him/herself.
- All the things others say about the character.
- All the things the character says about others.

This is a good tool because it encourages the actor to take control. It also means the actor has to read the play very carefully a number of times.

EXERCISE 6

Exploring a character's posture and movement and thinking about where he/she holds tension can be helpful in characterisation.

Get an actor to walk around the room in character.

Encourage the other actors to copy this actor and then to parody him/her.

This exercise is useful because the actor becomes more assertive in their character as he/she sees him/herself being parodied. It can also lead to him/her finding out interesting things about the character.

Build on this by drawing out non-psychological ways of getting into character through explaining the concept of the body as a mask which can portray different types of people depending on its position:

King – all needs met, satisfaction everywhere.

Madonna or Christ – head turned and tilted slightly upwards.

Fool – both eyebrows up.

Trickster – one eyebrow up and one down.

Baboon – cheeks blown out.

THE MONKEY

The Monkey should be real. Have the actor playing him watch a monkey video, or better still, visit a zoo, see one live and really try and embody its characteristics. If the actor is playing a monkey through movement, s/he doesn't necessarily need to be shown through a monkey suit.

The Monkey as a puppet. This would overcome the problem of the reality of the Monkey. It could also draw out a parallel between the Monkey and Richard – both are real to their respective owners, but whether they are actually real may be questionable. The puppeteer could either be someone in black or The Man.

The Monkey as a feral child. Given the way The Man was treated as a child, the monkey could be a child, but referred to as Monkey. This would become difficult at the end, though, when there is a clear image of a dead monkey with a knife through its heart.

The schizophrenic nature of the Monkey needs to be put across. One minute it is sweeping the floor, the next it is attacking someone. The audience need to think, 'I don't know what is going to happen next.'

STAGING THE PLAY

SCENE ONE

The first scene begins in the middle of the sleepover. The actors are already onstage, busy at Spin the Bottle or playing with torches. (The actors are led on with a torch.)

Music clearly indicates the actors arrival onstage, now the play starts. If music is used, it could be a feature throughout the play over scene changes.

Dad is always present in the background of this scene, with Kal terrified of noise levels rising. There could be a game preparing for this scene, like a grandmother's footsteps where Dad can come in at any time.

In telling the story, Kal needs time to draw people into it. It needs to be done slowly, with pauses for effect, and every word needs to count. The contrast between Kal holding attention when telling a story and the interruptions needs to be stark. This is a status issue – who is telling the story? – which clearly comes out in Boff's interruption, when he is shot down straight away.

The story is very real for Kal; and the others, in listening to it, want to be scared. It becomes more real for them when Kal brings out the knife, and the timing needs to be clear between the knife sinking into the bed, Tilly's scream and the door swinging open, with a pause to separate the build up of tension and its dissipation.

Whether the visit to the house is in Kal's imagination or not, the effect on staging wouldn't be different: in the theatre dreams are acted out in the same physical space as reality.

SCENES TWO AND THREE

The challenges in these scenes involve moving from the scene outside the house, with its door, window and bushes being key features, to being inside the house.

The shadow in the window could be created using a silhouette or lighting on the floor. Or, if the staging is end-on, the audience could be in the house, which would completely distort perspectives and also open the play outwards. Alternatively, projections could be used to draw out aspects of the house.

Simple is often best: the use of lighting and tokens or props could work better than having cumbersome pieces of set.

SCENE FIVE

The location of the door and the exit route are important in this scene. Perhaps work diagonally across the stage. Or, if the play is being performed in-the-round, the corridor could be marked by a shaft of light. The door and the fear surrounding it need to be powerful, so a distance between Ro and Tilly and the door will have to be kept. Fear is behind the door so it must be terrifying when behind them they hear, 'I wouldn't go in there if I was you.'

Decide whether the entrance of The Man and the Monkey is through a wall or behind Ro and Tilly. Also how long they have been watching Ro and Tilly.

The breadth of the corridor is important to think about here. It needs to be communicated that Ro and Tilly are trapped, with the door on one side and the Man on the other. The audience needs to feel, 'What would I do?' Then the unexpected question comes, 'Don't you want to know about my monkey?'

The dilemma is heightened by the shout from Jaz. Tilly needs to save her best friend, so her decision is made. Ro could leave, but he doesn't: decide why. Is it because of his promise to Tilly? It is important to add a human dimension and to capture Ro's dilemma.

SCENES SEVEN, EIGHT AND NINE

The presence of the door between the bedroom and the landing is important. It could be on wheels so that it is easily movable.

Tactics from horror movies could be used, showing what is happening from a distorted or different angle.

SCENES NINE, TEN AND ELEVEN

These scenes move between the bedroom and outside. Lou's entry and Boff's reaction could be shown happening simultaneously. Alternatively, it will need to be very clear that it is the same action – that Lou's entry from the house is being seen from different angles. This could be clarified by Boff being to the side of the stage where Lou enters the building, or the set could turn around to show Boff on the outside.

The window might be a paper window, or there could be net curtains shown from different angles.

Lou's entry needs to be big, but its speed could be fast or slow.

Diagonals are always friendly, and lighting and sound effects can help to indicate where actors are. Both are excellent tools for creating and dissipating fears. Working with different levels could be helpful, with a creative use of ramps and steps.

Workshop facilitated by Edward Kemp
with notes taken by Daisy Lloyd

SHOW AND TELL

Laline Paull

Laline Paull wrote her first play, *Eskimo Sisters*, in 1999. It was shortlisted for the Verity Bargate Award, and opened at the Southwark Playhouse in April 2000. Her second play, *Bone in the Teeth*, was workshopped at the Bush Theatre in February 2003, and her third, *Boat Memory*, was written for *Connections* in 2004. In May 2003 she contributed a very short play, *Red on Red*, as part of the Young Vic Studio's exploration of dramatic response to the war in Iraq. She has worked as a screenwriter in the US and in the UK, and continues to write also for film and television, including the Channel Four drama series *Ny-Lon*, broadcast in 2004. She has also written for the hit TV series *Cold Feet*. Her new full-length adult play, *Radiance*, is about female spies in the Second World War.

Author's Note

Too silly, very juvenile, and full of fart jokes – a comedy seemed to be emerging out of my laptop, with little regard for my past subjects or style. I didn't want to question it too much – it was enough that it was gathering, page by page, into *Show and Tell*. Comedy has always been my ultimate refuge as a reader, but for some reason I'd never tried writing it – perhaps put off by the number of times I'd heard how hard it was. Yes – but no harder than any other kind of writing, as far as I can tell. There are always leaves that need to be swept up, tea made, navels gazed into, before the serious business of sitting down and staying there until you've done it.

'Actually you've written a farce,' I was advised by those who know, 'and farce has rules.' Interesting to discover, but a bit irritating too, as I'm not generally that keen on following rules. But it was worth testing them out – even if what I'd initially thought of as a bit of fun, had also to become as painstakingly structured as a tax return. Goodbye spontaneity, hello structure. Structure. And more structure.

And then, something really surprising happened. That reported writer's experience I'd always secretly questioned came true. As a reward for my attention, the characters started to come alive on their own and make their own plans. Bunce, who was initially, in my imagination and first notes, the butt of all jokes, took centre stage as the real hero. Boisterous Toby, even while I was planning to give him to Jo in return for her obsessional devotion, inadvertently revealed his secret attraction to the unlikely (but yet so fitting once I saw it) Oli. Jo did thankfully have the reaction I expected – but then transferred her attention quite pragmatically to Alex, despite all her earlier protestations of undying love and loyalty to Toby. Alex came into focus as kind but no pushover – not bland and boring, as he and I had both secretly worried he was.

However, these signs of life must have been accreting quite subtly before I really noticed them, because one slow day I decided not enough was happening, and it was time to make my life really hard by throwing a hibernating hamster into the mix. Result: despite his comatose fictional state, Stephen the pedigree Syrian hamster ran amok through the plot, turning up when he wasn't wanted and, inconveniently, logically remaining in another location when he was. I wanted to delete him, but the very animated fictional voice of Jo absolutely refused to speak another word to me unless he stayed. She won, and was vindicated.

So – a liberation and a discipline to write sunny-side up. No volumes of historical documents to trawl for treasure (satisfying, but a great responsibility to real lives past). No misery in council flats or war-torn streets and no weeping women – I recycle that most days in the papers. And, of course, there is a vitally important place for writing about hard realities, and it is crucial that artists bear witness and speak the unspeakable, and do not look away. Sometimes. But possibly . . . it's not that much fun to write like that. And fun was definitely what I wanted when I was writing this. I laughed while I wrote *Show and Tell* – I hope you will when you read it.

LALINE PAULL

Characters

Oli
not more than fifteen or sixteen

Jo
her best friend

Toby and **Alex**
identical twins

Bunce
class nerd

Agatha
a girl

Other Kids
as desired in public and school scenes

Miss Harris
a supply teacher

Liz
Toby and Alex's mother

Becca *and* **Tom**
Oli's parents

Barry *and* **Claire**
Jo's parents

Monica *and* **Garth**
Bunce's parents

The Telly
one or four voices

Stephen
a hamster

School neighbourhood. February.
Before and during half-term.

SCENE ONE

After school, freezing cold. Push and shove as kids hurry home. Toby is responsible for most of it. Oli and Jo walk together, deep in conversation – mainly Oli's. Bunce tags along, gets caught up in scuffle, falls down. People step round him.

Alex Oy, watch it – you're hitting people –
Toby Look to yo own side, bro, don't be steppin' to me.
Alex You sound like a wally, do you know that?
Jo (*deliberately getting in his way*) Hi, Toby.
Toby (*ignoring her*) You is hearin' but you is too slow to be followin', know what I'm sayin'? Cuz you come out second so you always last, bro, uh uh, the Tobester the T-Star, the Tobosaurus Rex, the Tobosaurus Rocks, unh, unh – (*Etc.*)

Jo giggles, until she sees Oli looking at her.

Alex Why wasn't I an only child?
Oli It's pretty good, actually.
Toby Hey, you dissin' me, bro? You dissin' me to Etna? Huh? You is, you are, you won't get far –
Alex Just shut *up*.
Oli My name is Oli.
Toby No one tells the T-Star to shut up.
Alex Except Mum, all the time!

Toby grabs Alex's hat off his head. Alex lunges for it, they struggle.

Kids (*filming on their phones*) Fight, fight, fight –

Toby tries to use Oli as a human shield. She shoves him off.

Oli Get off me, Toboid Growth!
Toby What's that, Etna? Can't hear 'cause of the huge spot on your chin.
Oli (*hand flying to it*) It's gone and I hate you!

Toby and Alex keep struggling for the hat. Bunce gets shoved, grabs on to Jo.

Jo Go away, Bunce, how many times do I have to tell you?

Toby has Alex in an armlock, winning very meanly.

Toby (*to the kids*) T-Star, T-Star: come on or you're next –
Kids (*frightened*) T-Star . . . T-Star . . .
Oli How can you like him? He's a neanderthal.
Jo My love would change that.
Bunce It's all the red meat they eat. Though it looks like maybe Alex eats more chicken . . .
Alex Shut up, Bunce –

A Man in an overcoat and hat pulled down low, steps over the scuffle and rings a doorbell. A Woman in an immaculate white coat opens the door with a big smile. Everyone, including Toby and Alex, freezes and stares.

Toby (*letting go of Alex*) Miss Harris!

The Man goes in. The door closes. Alex gets up with his mashed hat, shoves his brother and goes off. Entranced, Toby doesn't notice.

Bunce (*to the other kids*) Disperse, please, no more violence today. Become vegetarian and –
Oli – fart like you, no thank you.

Bunce Pity the meat-eaters – I forgive you for that, Oli.

Jo (*going to Toby*) Oh you poor, poor thing – are you alright? Are you bruised, are you shaken? (*Feeling under his coat.*) Are you?

Toby (*wriggling away from her*) Oy! Hands!

Jo Toby. Come and lie down at my house for a while.

Toby Uh . . . why?

Jo You're in shock.

Toby Yeah! Did you see Miss Harris!

Jo What about her? Anyway, you need first aid. Look, just come on –

Toby Phwoar! I'm in love! (*Runs off.*)

Jo turns to Oli, stricken.

Jo In love? Have you been keeping it from me, trying to spare my feelings? We vowed no secrets, ever, didn't we? Oli, didn't we?

Oli Yes . . .

Bunce By the way, in our house, what you call 'farts', we call 'secrets'.

Oli Except yours aren't.

Jo Other girls are bound to try to take him from me . . . but a teacher?

Bunce Only when I'm nervous – if I'm just, you know, walking around quite relaxed, they're pretty discreet.

Jo It's because he's so gorgeous –

Oli Jo, stop it.

Jo I don't want to. I can't. I have to have him. He's sexy gorgeous misunderstood completely fit ohmygod when I put my hand on his stomach I made sure I counted the whole six pack – it was rock hard –

Bunce I can make mine hard too, here, feel –

Jo/Oli Eurgh!!

Jo Oli, I can't stand it, I really can't, if he's two-timing me –

Oli For that you have to be going out with him.

Jo Go on, then, be all scientific and technical about it –

alright, we haven't exactly specifically been on a *date*, but you saw how he was with me just now, didn't you? How he looked into my eyes? Don't tell me that's not a relationship. (*Pointedly ignoring Bunce, who gazes meaningfully at her.*) You vowed to support me in my Quest for Love.

Oli Can't you pick someone better?

Bunce Hear, hear!

Jo You're always hanging around him trying to be friends, Bunce – what does that make you?

Bunce Desperate. I know.

Oli Never in fashion . . .

Jo Desperation, creative visualisation – who cares so long as I get him? I've even thought of getting Dad to arrest him and question him about his true feelings for me. Only he'd know it was my dad, wouldn't he?

Bunce Hey, I've got a brilliant idea: use me to make him jealous!

Jo Oli. Tell him.

Pause.

Oli Um . . . Bunce? Don't you think you should try to find some more . . . appropriate friends? Instead of dripping along behind us all the time? What about from your animal rights chatroom?

Bunce It's all gone quiet – I think they're ignoring me too. But look. (*Produces wallet with cards in it.*) Junior Opera Club, Young Chemists' Forum, Local Government Youth Opinion Panel . . . it's not like I don't try, but they're all nerds!

Jo Coming from you, Bunce . . .

Bunce Exactly! And now Mum wants to do a class tea at our house so your parents can tell you to be my friend. She keeps trying out new menus and my dad's going to sing arias like some sort of cabaret from hell – I'm going to kill myself!

Oli Class tea? At your house? Your dad wants to . . . sing . . . to my parents?

Bunce Don't even go there.

Oli Wow.

Jo Oli, could I have some attention please? My heart is breaking in pieces and lying in the freezing slush –

Bunce Here's my shoulder, Jo. Use it. Get it really wet. It's okay.

Jo Uh, I'm suddenly a lot better. But thanks.

Bunce Or you, Oli – either of you – my parents would be so relieved if I had a girlfriend. (*On their incredulous looks.*) I hate opera so much, I hate it I hate it I hate it – (*Pause.*) Listen, we wouldn't have to Do Anything. Why are you both looking like that?

Pause.

Jo Bunce, are you secretly gay or something?

Oli Just come out if you are, everyone's cool about it.

Bunce I am not gay! I want a girlfriend. And you two are obviously available –

Jo No, I am not.

Bunce Well, you like Toby.

Jo Toby is an alpha male.

Oli Oh rubbish –

Jo He is.

Oli He so is not.

Jo Oli's free, though, Bunce, she's not getting off with anyone in a hurry.

Oli Thanks! Bunce, not to hurt your feelings or anything –

Bunce coughs loudly, flaps his coat behind him. Jo and Oli hold their noses.

Bunce Sorry, sorry – you made me nervous. Girls are just so scary.

Jo Then why have you been standing here talking to us?

Bunce (*going inside*) I live here.

Pause.

Oli We are not scary.

Jo You are. Because you're so clever. I'm the cute one. Oh, why does he have to fancy Miss Harris? She's old! And she's only a supply teacher, not even a proper one – trying to boss us around like she knows us or something – Hello, Oli, I'm talking to you.

Oli How many men have we seen going in there in the last two weeks, Jo? That was the third or fourth, wasn't it? Are they boyfriends?

Jo Brothers. Checking up on her. Large family of boys probably. And if my stupid parents had organised it properly I'd have an older brother and he'd have loads of gorgeous friends so Toby would have to fight for my attention and then he'd realise –

Oli And in that tight white coat – every time.

Jo White's the new black. Duh.

SCENE TWO

Class next day. Everyone messing around, general disorder. People not very surreptitiously send and receive texts, completely disrespecting Miss Harris, who is now conventionally dressed.

Miss Harris As I was saying last week, though no one is listening, the point of our work on observation is to enliven us, to actively connect us with our world rather than encourage the passive consumption of media and advertising messages –

Jo enters, heavily accessorised in white, carrying a hamster cage. She slips into her seat.

Jo (*mumbles*) Sorry I'm late. Bit of a domestic.

Miss Harris I'm very sorry to hear that. Are you okay?

Jo (*re cage*) Fine, now I've brought him out of harm's way. Soon as my back's turned, my mum's trying to chuck Stephen in the bin! I mean, can you believe it, like hibernating's a crime! Not even a proper burial and service – the bin!

Miss Harris Something in there is hibernating?

Jo Mmhmm. Having a nice sleep aren't you, Stephen? Oli, don't look at me like that, he *is*. You don't make droppings when you're dead, do you?

Oli New ones?

Jo That would be proof, wouldn't it! That's what I'll do, I'll count them – Oli, you're so clever.

Miss Harris Jo, this isn't Show and Tell, you know. Pets are not allowed in class under any circumstances.

Jo Then you're sentencing an innocent hamster to death.

Toby Good. They're disgusting, they're like rats.

Miss Harris Returning to our work on observation –

Jo Stop it, Toby – Stephen and I grew up together.

Oli Jo, maybe your mum's right.

Miss Harris – we can slowly raise our level of awareness.

Jo (*to cage*) Stephen, darling, I know you're alive. Don't you worry.

Miss Harris It's a choice we can make.

Oli Okay. But he'll start to smell soon.

Jo It's the natural fragrance of a filigree Syrian hamster, they're famous for it.

Toby Like Bunce –

Miss Harris (*louder*) Or give over to other people, who make it for us –

Toby (*sniffing*) Urgh – he's done one, I saw him tilt –

Miss Harris (*shouting*) We can listen when we hear!

Alex Die when we're gassed –

General flapping of exercise books, groaning, holding noses. Jo grabs the cage and holds it high away from Bunce.

Bunce Do you realise pet-keeping is another form of animal exploitation? A perpetually infantile state of dependency –

Toby Get that dead rat away –

Jo Hibernating hamster! And if you'd just come over after school I could help you with your phobia.

Alex (*chanting*) Toby's got a phoby, Toby's got a phoby –

Toby (*leaping at him*) Shut it –

Kids (*camera phones out*) Fight, fight, fight!

Miss Harris Dear God, please make Mr Dixon well soon so I can leave this place.

Toby (*stopping mid-thump*) Miss, Miss, this isn't your real job, is it?

Miss Harris Don't tell me you were paying attention, Alex?

Alex (*back to his seat*) I'm Alex Miss, that's Toby.

Toby No, I'm Alex, Miss, that's Toby. It's hard when we're identical, but I'm the clever one.

Alex Stop it, Toby.

Toby I'm not Toby, I'm you. Oy, everyone, I'm Alex, aren't I? Anyone says 'no' gets thumped after –

Kids start shouting and pointing.

Forget the rat, Miss, I'll be teacher's pet – oh, please, Miss, will you wear your white coat to school? Pleeeease?

Miss Harris Alex, Toby, whichever you are, and I don't know why you're in the same class, it's quite ridiculous –

Alex Because he cries if he can't see me, Miss, ever since we were babies.

Toby For happiness – you're still sulking 'cause you were born last –

Alex Only 'cause you shoved me out of the way –

Toby Prove it – he'll never get over it Miss, always being second to the Tobester, the T-Star, the Tobosaurus Rex, the Tobosaurus Rocks –

Miss Harris Your poor mother.

Toby I know. I need more love, Miss, can I have some? I'm so ready, know what I'm reprazentin to you?

Miss Harris Probably Attention Deficit Disorder.

She walks around giving back assignments. Groans as people see their marks.

Oli Excuse me, Miss Harris.

Miss Harris Yes, Oli, what is it?

Oli Olivia. I never get Cs. Ever.

Miss Harris You will if you're average.

Oli If I'm –

Jo I got a B! Wow! Oli, look, I won!

Miss Harris It's not a competition, Jo.

Oli 'Average'?!

Toby Was that your boyfriend, Miss? That you wore the coat for? Little nursy ting going on, you looked like one big sexy icicle, Miss. Listen up now, cuz, I did a rap for you and it go like dis:

Ah Miss Harris you is so buff,
An I bin missin' dat juicy stuff –
Cuz dere ain't no booty call in dis lame class,
So you jus gimme yo' nice round . . . um . . .

Miss Harris gazes at him. Toby has a coughing fit.

Miss Harris Thank you, Toby. (*Her phone rings, she answers.*) Hello? Oh yes, hi, he said he'd recommended me . . . no that's fine. (*Even more quietly.*) No no, cash is absolutely fine, I understand . . . Five, okay, great. (*Hangs up.*) So. We've been discussing the quality of observation, what we notice about ourselves, others, and our environment.

Oli Miss Harris, we are not even allowed to send texts in class and you just took a call which did not sound as if it was about the curriculum –

Miss Harris You're absolutely right, Oli. Since I've been here there's been nothing but wilful disrespect – thank God I have a life outside this room. Now, who has a mobile phone on them? (*Every hand goes up.*) Good. Send someone in class words to this effect: half-term homework, if you consider yourself mature –

Toby You need a mature man, Miss, you come see me –

Miss Harris – then please complete an intensive field study of a living thing. However, if you're still a child –

Toby She's looking at you, bruv.

Alex Shut up –

Miss Harris – you can bring something for Show and Tell when we get back. Though Jo seems to have done it already. Anyway, your choice – I've had enough of you.

Jo Being loyal to my hamster does not make me a child.

Everyone gets out their phone and starts texting. Sniggers and frowns.

Toby 'You're so fit – from Miz Harris.' Same to you, Miss.

Alex Such a liar.

Oli 'You are my bestest friend' – thanks, Jo.

Jo 'You could do much more than model.' Oli, that's not very supportive – I thought I could be whatever I wanted?

Alex 'Toby is a silly git' from everyone –

Toby You're the liar, you liar –

Bunce stares at his silent phone. Miss Harris sits on the edge of his desk.

Miss Harris Marcus.

Alex Don't make him nervous, Miss –

Bunce I'm fine, Miss, really, don't worry about me – oh dear – oh dear –

Toby Bunce's batty blaster – take cover!

The bell rings, everyone runs away.

Miss Harris Marcus, if you have Irritable Bowel
 Syndrome, there are things –
Bunce Oh Miss, you're just making it worse –

He flees, flapping his jacket.

SCENE THREE

*Evening. The four different rooms in which Oli, Jo, Alex
and Toby, and Bunce sit with their respective parents,
all watching the same natural history programme on
television.*

Voice of the Telly (*whispers*) And now, high above, the
 forest floor . . . the incoming younger male makes his
 move. Who will he choose first?

Simultaneously:

*Oli's mum, Becca, is busy with a calculator and big
ring-bound file. Her dad, Tom, looks like he's
dropping off behind his newspaper. Unimpressed, Oli
watches them.*

*Jo's mum, Claire, half-watches, half-reads a gossip
magazine while her dad, Barry, seems to be dealing
with indigestion. Jo keeps one hand on Stephen's cage,
writes a text message with the other.*

*Toby and Alex's mum, Liz, sprawls exhausted, drink
in hand. Toby and Alex gurn at each other behind her
back, making the occasional monkey sound.*

*To Bunce's great discomfort, his parents, Garth and
Monica, sit cuddled up very close, watching avidly. He
puts his hands up like blinkers to shut out the sight of
his parents getting jiggy.*

Voice of the Telly And there she is – the large female . . . obviously in heat . . .

Bunce Can we watch something else please?

Mrs Bunce It's nature, Pumpkin.

Voice of the Telly From the front, she seems to be calmly eating berries –

Jo's Mum Jo, love, that thing's starting to smell. Go on, love, let me take him.

Jo No.

Voice of the Telly Whilst from behind, in the shaking foliage –

Bunce There's a really good sudoku programme on the other side.

Jo's Dad Health risk, love. Listen to your mum.

Jo Smelling doesn't make you dead. Duh.

Jo's Dad We'll buy you another one. It's only a bloody hamster.

Jo No. My love is true and steadfast to the end. Which is not yet.

Voice of the Telly The other females have seen. The new, younger male, might be in trouble of a different sort now.

Garth and Monica Bunce give each other meaningful looks. Bunce pulls his jumper over his head.

Toby (*watching*) Oh, that's a bit much, isn't it? Are they trained to do that?

Alex What's the matter, you're the one who can't get enough action.

Toby and Alex's Mum Still virgins, then, are you?

Toby/Alex Mum!!

Voice of the Telly But look! The youngest female . . . there she goes . . . jumping the queue –

All the families stare . . .

Mr Bunce God, it's good. Bloody good documentary . . . Look at that . . .

Mrs Bunce Can't wait, can she? (*Looks round.*) Where's Pumpkin? Did he go up?

Mr Bunce Must have done – come here you big bouncing Brünhilde!

Bunce runs from the room, jumper still over his head. They look up briefly, fan the air, continue.
   Jo and her family watch TV uneasily.

Jo's Dad You won't get up the duff now, princess, will you?

Jo Dad, do you mind?

Jo's Mum She's chosen him, though, haven't you, love? Like I chose your dad. His name's Tony.

Jo Toby! And I refuse to talk about him.

She exits with Stephen's cage.

Voice of the Telly The older, alpha male moves further away from his females, in search of choicer fruit. Does he know he is being usurped?

Oli's dad, Tom, begins to snore. Her mum, Becca, goes back to her calculations.

Oli Have you and Dad always been like this? He might as well be a baked potato, look at him – no wonder I'm an only child.

Oli's Mum That's not very nice, is it?

Voice of the Telly The young challenger watches . . . and waits . . .

Oli Sex is not supposed to be 'very nice'. It's supposed to be exciting and dangerous and passionate!

Oli's Mum Oli, do you have PMT again? And what on earth do you know about sex?

Oli Nothing! Nothing whatsoever! And I probably never ever will. Do you know what they call me at school? Etna! And today I got marked – average!

She exits.

Voice of the Telly What a privilege . . . to witness . . . the moment of congress . . .

Toby and Alex's mum, Liz, looks at her sons. Neither of them can meet her eye.

Toby and Alex's Mum Now I don't want to hear about you getting some nice girl in trouble, do you understand? Don't just nod at me. Have you had sex yet?

Toby and Alex look at each other.

Alex/Toby Homework!!

SCENE FOUR

Sunday afternoon. Jo's bedroom. Music. Jo finishes tanning her face orange, while Oli struggles to copy a hairstyle from a magazine. Jo stares into Stephen's cage, silently counting.

Jo It's hard to know if they're fresh or old without disturbing him . . .

Oli Tell me you're not counting them.

Jo Trying to, but then Toby comes into my mind and I have to start all over again . . . Toby, droppings, Toby, droppings –

Oli When you finish, you could maybe consider getting a life?

Jo I know you think I'm obsessed, but love is more natural to me than breathing. Anyway, I'm fed up waiting for the stupid wally to make his move – pretending he's not interested – all that avoiding me. I mean, who's he fooling? Himself. That's who.

Oli Jo . . .

Jo No no, put the feather thing back in, I liked it. Trust me – there . . . very directional.

Oli I look stupid.

Jo But how do you feel? Are you in touch with your emotions? Or are you living out someone else's lifescript? There's a brilliant quiz on page twenty-three. I should really do it with Toby –

Oli Josephine! I'm sick of hearing about him and I'm freaked out you're keeping your dead hamster with you all the time –

Jo (*calmly*) / He's not dead.

Oli – and I'm sick of my parents and school and my spots and my hateful boring life and – Aargh, get these stupid things out of my stupid hair!

Jo (*finishing her own make-up*) The natural look is by far the best on you. Really. Don't be upset at one style failure, Oli, you've got so much going for you. Really you have.

Pause.

Oli Like what?

Jo Um . . . lovely eyes, you're very clever with a great personality . . . you understand poetry really well and all that.

Oli More stuff like eyes.

Jo Um . . . your horoscope's always really good – and you are very much above average in all ways.

Oli Except looks.

Jo You're fine.

Oli Really?

Jo And . . . your hair is in great natural condition.

Oli Thanks. (*Pause.*) Sorry about that. It's stupid to care so much about external things.

Jo No it's not, it's good. (*Pause.*) So can we talk about Toby again now, without you getting annoyed? (*On Oli's nod.*) I need to tell you a secret. Swear you'll never tell a soul. Okay. (*Whisper.*) I want to have sex with him.

Oli Everyone knows that.

Jo Well, he obviously doesn't, or he would have arranged it by now, wouldn't he? Unless . . . unless he doesn't . . .

Silence. A terrible possibility begins to dawn on Jo.

Oli Jo, listen. Sometimes things happen the way we want, like . . . I don't know . . . I get all As – and you find a fake tan that really works for you.

Jo (*tearful*) Don't joke, streaks look really common.

Oli Yes, they do, but sometimes, Jo, things don't happen like we want. And we have to . . . accept them.

Pause.

Jo You mean, like, Jo, wake up: Stephen's dead, Toby's never going to marry you, and you haven't a hope in hell of becoming a model?

Oli Kind of.

Jo Oli, you're my best friend and I love you, but I'm afraid sometimes, like this actual minute, you're extremely and very averagely wrong about my whole entire life and future. And probably everything else too. Okay?

Oli Okay. I never said I was always right.

Jo Good. Because you're not.

Oli Right.

Jo Fine.

Silence.

Oli What shall we talk about, then?

Jo You know everything, you decide.

Oli Okay. Miss Harris.

Jo That man-eater. Oli, those are not her brothers.

Oli They're not, are they?

Jo But it's a lot of boyfriends, even for a man-eater.

Oli If they are, actually . . . boyfriends.

Jo Why would a boyfriend give you cash? To send you shopping?

Oli Or . . . to pay you for Something.

Jo What could they buy from her though?

Oli Think about it.

Jo I'm not that clever.

Oli Of course you are.

Jo Am I? Oh yes, that's right, I got a B and you only got a C – don't look like that, you just told me I'm clever. Okay, I'm definitely thinking what you're thinking – which is what again?

Oli All those men, coming and going, in and out – that phone call in class – 'Cash is fine!' she said, her pitiful teaching salary, her body her greatest asset in a material world –

Jo Huh, it's not that good.

Oli It is, admit it.

Jo Yeah, alright, but time is on my side.

Oli And the damning detail: the nurse's costume.

Jo Oh my God! You mean . . . our supply teacher is secretly a . . . a . . .

Oli Yes. The world's oldest profession! And who can blame her? Jo, don't you realise? We've already started our observation project, we've already worked out Miss Harris's dark secret, the terrible burden she bears, which makes her so bad-tempered and horrible to me in class and mark us so erratically –

Jo She's on the game! She's a ho!

Oli Of course she is: her casual attitude to our education, her 'life outside the room' that she's embraced in desperation –

Jo Yeah, but it's probably better than teaching a bunch of ungrateful, badly behaved –

Oli No no no, that's not the direction of the film at all.

Jo Film?

Oli You're right – documentary's much better. Who says homework has to be on paper? My dad's got an old video camera he'll never miss, we can use our phones – Jo, we're not being horrible to her, we're supporting her struggle for economic dignity by exposing her plight! When she makes a fortune from the tabloid interviews, she'll thank us.

Jo Even when she loses her job?

Oli Absolutely. You'll present it, I'll direct, and together we'll save Miss Harris from the gutter, and make our names as compassionate yet hard-hitting young film-makers of tomorrow.

Jo And Toby will have to have me when I'm on the telly!

SCENE FIVE

Monday. Toby and Alex's house. Alex is absorbed in his MP3 player. Toby watches, idly throwing socks and underpants at him.

Alex Try to grow up . . .

Toby I have, bruv, but I'm waiting for you! (*Pause.*) Come on, you're so boring.

Alex Then go away and find someone interesting.

Toby Can't we have a fight or something? What if I just –

He pulls out Alex's earphones. Alex picks up a book.

Alex If you're so bored, you should have helped Mum with the shopping like she wanted.

Toby She said don't bother.

Alex It's called sarcasm.

Toby Don't you like the Tobester any more?

Alex No.

Toby How about the T-Star, the Tobosaurus Rex, the –

Alex None of them.

542

Toby Yes you do – why don't you?

Pause.

Alex Because you're always making fun of me and trying
to make me look stupid and you never listen and
you're always talking in that stupid rap.

Toby Don't you call it stupid, Stupid.

Alex Leave me alone.

Toby You leave me alone first.

Alex There – (*Returns to his book.*)

Toby You still in my face, steppin' to me dissin' me,
givin' me grief – you is axin' for a Brazilian waxin', my
friend.

Alex I'm not your friend.

Toby Mum! He said he's not my friend!

Toby and Alex's Mum (*offstage*) I'm not surprised!
Visitor coming up –

*Bunce walks in, with a great big coffee-table book.
Toby and Alex's jaws drop at the sight of him.*

Toby/Alex Mum!!

Bunce (*in a big rush*) I'm not staying long because I
know you think I'm really boring and square and I fart
uncontrollably and I never do anything interesting but
here – (*Dumps the big book on Toby's lap.*) You're
always going on about boobs and things so I brought
you this to look at – but if you want to borrow it, you
have to make a deal with me.

Toby and Alex look at the book.

Toby Ah man, proper! Bruv, look, they're all Doing It!

Alex Bunce, where did you get this?

Bunce My parents have got loads of them.

Toby Look at that one! Alex man, look! Good on you,
Bunster, it's well sick!

Bunce (*slamming the book on his hand*) You like it?
Want to deal? Then this is what has to happen –

Alex Bunce, you're trying to bribe us with porn?

Bunce Fingers crossed. Look, I don't care if you like me
or not, but would you just come out with me in public
and pretend that you do, so that it looks like I've got
friends? Not opera-chemistry-nerdy ones; rough,
tough, common, football types. That'd be so cool.
(*Pause.*) I know I'm embarrassing myself. But if it
looks like I'm friends with you two, people might
think it's okay to talk to me, and my parents will stop
worrying. And don't worry about my secrets, I've
taken something to bung me up. Loads of it, in fact.

Alex Too much information, Bunce.

Toby Give us that book again . . . (*Leafs through.*) Go
on, bruv, off you go.

Bunce (*to Alex*) Charity. Do it out of charity. The
goodness of your heart. Help a poor flatulent nerd.

Toby Can't say he doesn't need it, bruv. Go on.

Pause.

Alex (*taking Toby's jacket*) I'm wearing this, then.

Toby It's too cool for you, man, don't embarrass
yourself. (*Re the book.*) Serious . . . you have got to be
kidding me – oh man, no way . . .

*Alex puts the jacket on. Bunce gives him the thumbs
up. Toby doesn't notice their exit.*

SCENE SIX

*Monday afternoon. Stake-out, outside Miss Harris's
house. Heavily bundled with camcorder, binoculars,
thermos, etc., Oli and Jo (still orange) crouch concealed.
Oli is filming, Jo presenting.*

Oli *Cash is King*, take six, and . . . rolling!

Jo And here we are, stuck in a bush freezing our tits off –

Oli Cut! Take seven –

Jo Here we are, outside Miss Harris's flat – no, um . . . her . . .

Oli (*whispering*) Modest home.

Jo Ow – a thorn's in my bum –

Oli Cut! Cut cut cut! Is it really that difficult?

Jo Oh, Oli, can't I just walk by and be interviewed in soft lighting, from the left ideally? Don't look at me like that – you know how I feel about my nose, I'm the one who lives with it and I'm telling you it's definitely a bit wonky and I –

Oli (*handing her the camera*) Here. You film it.

They switch places, don't notice Alex and Bunce approaching, and stopping, fascinated.

Jo *Cash is King*, take nine –

Oli Eight. Take eight.

Jo I said eight, and rolling –

Oli You said nine –

Jo Cut!

Oli Oh for goodness' sake, Josephine –

Jo What, Olivia? I'm so cold I can't feel my hands, I'm worried to death Mum's going to recycle Stephen while we're doing this – Ohmygod is that Toby?

Oli / Shh!

Jo Yoohoo, Toby! (*As Alex steps out of concealment.*) Oh. It's you.

Alex Only me.

Bunce (*appearing*) But hey! Here we all are! Practically a jolly old gang!

Alex/Oli/Jo Shut up, Bunce.

Jo Why are you wearing Toby's jacket? Is he dead?

Alex He's not the only one who can wear cool clothes.

Jo Only asking, don't get in a huff.

Bunce Jo, why are you orange?

Jo What is wrong with everyone? I'm bronze.

Alex Okay. What are you filming, anyway?

Oli Major undercover nation-rocking society-reforming scandal happening right here under our noses. Don't blow our cover.

Alex But everyone can see you.

Jo Not from up there.

Bunce Miss Harris's?

Oli Shh!

Bunce I spy on her too. FYI to any film crews, you get a much better view from my bedroom.

Oli We are not spying.

Jo Aren't we?

Oli Is CCTV spying? Or is it protecting our common interests? Exactly.

Alex/Bunce / Spying.

Oli I don't care. What we're doing / is –

Jo Exposing Miss Maneater Tobysnatcher Harris for the ho she is.

Alex Can you speak normally, please? He's not here.

Oli What Jo means is that we have deduced that Miss Harris's stream of male visitors, together with her willingness to take cash, and her proclivity for nurse's outfits, can only mean one thing.

Bunce She's a nurse?

Oli She's on the game! With a niche market in nursing fantasies –

Bunce 'Oh no. Too vanilla.'

Alex What does that mean?

Bunce No idea. Just repeating what my parents say. Something about sex, probably, that's all they think about. They're maniacs. They try to cover it up with really loud opera, but it's no good. (*Whispers.*) I hear it all.

Jo Poor Bunce!

Bunce Thank you, Jo. Thank you.

Oli What are you two doing together anyway?

Alex Oh . . . just hanging. You know.

Bunce Yes! Just hanging around, chewing the fat, kicking back – hey, why don't we all go to my bedroom? We've got a great view, we can have hot chocolate –

Jo Bunce, dream on. I am never going in your bedroom.

Bunce Not in a torrid, relationship sort of way. In a well-scrubbed, platonic way. Please?

Alex Bunce man, don't beg –

Bunce It's okay. They already know I'm desperate. And don't worry, I've taken something to bung me up so – (*Nudged hard by Alex.*) Ow –

Alex – so why don't you come, Jo, it'd be fun. I'll watch out for you.

Oli and Jo look at each other.

SCENE SEVEN

Monday evening. Toby and Alex's house. Toby vegges out in front of the TV. Alex comes in, flops down, happily exhausted, chucks the jacket to his brother. Finally:

Toby You were gone ages.

Alex Was I?

Toby Really boring, was it? Bunce going on and on, you feeling rubbish in my jacket 'cause it's way too sick for you. Never mind –

Alex Pretty good fun, actually.

Toby No, it was not.

Alex Okay.

Toby What did you do, then?

Alex Had a laugh with Jo and Oli.

Toby You were supposed to be with Bunce.

Alex Yeah – all of us.

Toby Together?

Alex At Bunce's.

Toby No way – they'd never go there. Doing what?

Alex Not allowed to say. Top secret project.

Toby Crap. Come on, bruv, give it up – where were you really? Down the library, being all speccy with Bunce? Swotting away together and then you saw Etna there too, that's what happened, isn't it? Can't hide the truth from the Tobosaurus.

Alex You got me. It's like you were there. Only better, 'cause you weren't.

Toby Okay, I get it. Trying to make me jealous, making out you had a good time being all intelligent together with Etna –

Alex And Jo, and Bunce.

Toby Making out you're all pally with them and I don't matter – (*Jumping on him.*) What secret project? Tell me!

Alex Ow – aargh – alright. We were doing our homework together – now get off me –

Toby releases him. Alex dusts himself off, his good mood gone.

Toby Suppose the Batty Blaster can't wait to come back tomorrow and go out in public with the Tobester.

Alex Actually we're going back to his again.

Toby We?

Alex Me and Jo and Oli.

Toby And me.

Pause.

Alex No.

Toby What do you mean, 'No'?

Alex No as in, we don't want you.

Toby Don't be stupid, course you do. (*Pause.*) Why don't you?

Alex Because you're loud and obnoxious and you're always shoving people around and making fun of everyone, especially me, and we are all sick of it.

Toby You talked about me? Put the boot in to the Tobester behind his back?

Alex Not once. No one mentioned you.

Toby Not even Jo? Aha! She still likes me. The rippling torso of the Tobosaurus Rex drives them all insane. (*Pulls up his T-shirt.*) Look –

Alex She's too nice for you.

Toby Think I should have Etna, do you, the really scary one? That's the sort of bruv you are, is it? Going off with Bunce and leaving me alone all day to ruin my eyesight?

Alex Stop whinging, you've been desperate to get some porn –

Toby How come you're all kind to Bunce and mean to your own bruv? Eh? Let me come and I'll be the perfect Tobester. If I even diss you once, I'll snog Etna Pterodactyl as punishment, how's that?

Alex Or I get your jacket. For ever.

Toby But that's from Santa! He gave you the MP3 player and / I asked for the –

Alex Toby, Mum is Santa. (*On Toby's stricken look.*) You did know that, didn't you?

Toby Yeah. Course. Think I'm a little kid or something?

Alex Funnily enough –

Toby Just shut up – I'm coming, right?

Alex Only if you behave.

Toby Totally absolutely one hundred per cent.

Alex Diss me even once, and you snog Oli.

Toby Not going to happen, bruv. No way.

SCENE EIGHT

Tuesday. Stakeout outside Miss Harris's house, Jo and Oli already concealed in position, Bunce conspicuously disguised with raincoat, hat, sunglasses, newspaper. Silence. Broken by Toby's noisy rhythm as he bops along beside Alex.

Jo Toby!

Toby Hey babe.

Jo 'Babe!' Oli, he said –

Oli What are you doing here?

Toby Come to lively tings up, haven't I?

Alex Oh man, we talked about this.

Toby What? I'm not doing anything wrong – is that where she lives?

Bunce Don't point!

Toby Who's that?

Bunce An anonymous stranger in transit.

Toby Bunce?

Everyone Shhh!!

Toby No one shushes T-Star!

Alex Then you better go.

Jo / No!

Oli Yes, he should – Alex, why did you ask him?

Alex I didn't –

Oli Light off in the hallway – second position!

Jo/Bunce/Alex Roger –

Everyone takes up their new surveillance position. Toby bursts out laughing.

Oli Quiet on the stakeout!

Toby Oy, Bunce, there's steak involved, you shouldn't be here.

Oli Synchronise watches.

A Man comes out of Miss Harris's door, walks off.
Bunce follows, Oli films, Jo makes a note, Alex takes
a photo with his phone.

Toby Was that Roger?

Bunce (*returning, out of breath*) He got in a car – and
drove off!

Oli Make of vehicle, registration plate:

Bunce Um . . . blue? More sort of teal.

Oli Bunce!

Toby Etna, it's a shambles, obviously I should be in
charge –

Oli This is my project, Toboid.

Jo And mine – maybe he could help, Oli?

Toby Course I could. Look, bruv over there's the anorak,
he does all the writing down, Jo's the presenter, doesn't
matter what Bunce does.

Bunce Excuse me, I'm the location manager, aren't I,
Oli?

Oli Yes, Bunce, stop asking me that. (*To Toby.*) Alright,
be a silent extra then, if you have to be here.

Toby Cool – see, bruv? T-Star to the rescue. Right – first
thing – (*Grabbing the camcorder.*) Give us that –

Oli Get off –

Toby (*struggling with Oli*) Just let me see the light meter
thingy –

Oli (*hanging on*) It's fine –

Something breaks. Toby quickly releases his hold.

Toby Cheap rubbish, was it? Get what you pay for, I
know.

Oli It's my dad's!

Alex What did I tell you? Oh man –

Miss Harris (*emerging behind them*) Hello!

She hurries down the street and out of sight.

Oli Toby, you have just completely and utterly ruined our surveillance!

Toby No, I never.

Bunce Yes, you did.

Alex Course he did –

Toby Jo, I never ruined anything, did I?

Jo Well . . .

Toby Then it means Etna didn't organise it properly. Doesn't it?

Oli Everything was fine until you turned up!

Toby Wasn't.

Oli Yes, it was! Why are you always having / a go at me!

Toby You started it.

Oli I didn't!

Toby Did.

Alex Tobe, go home. Go on.

Toby Shut up, Skidmark.

Pause.

Alex What did you say?

Bunce He called you Skidmark.

Toby Cheers, Bunce. What I meant, bruv, was –

Alex Don't bruv me – give me the jacket. Or you've got to do it.

Toby (*staring at Oli*) I can't. Don't make me.

Oli I'm not making you do anything – what are you talking about?

Alex Do it . . .

Jo Do what? What's the matter, Toby?

Toby You think I'm scared, Etna. (*Running away.*) But I'll be back –

Everyone stares, bemused.

Mrs Bunce (*offstage*) Pumpkin!! Time to go!

Bunce Oh no . . . I forgot. The opera trip.

Mrs Bunce (*offstage*) We're going to the car, Pumpty, come on!

Bunce groans, exits.

Alex (*exiting too*) Sorry about the stakeout.

Silence.

Jo Oli, why was Toby staring at you like that?
Oli How on earth should I know?
Jo Are you sure?
Oli Oh Jo, don't go thinking –
Jo What.
Oli I don't know.
Jo Yes, you do, just say it.
Oli Alright, that you're getting paranoid about everyone fancying him.
Jo Paranoid.
Oli Alright then, living in some fantasy world – being a model, Stephen's not dead he's just hibernating, I've got this secret thing with Toby – wake up, Jo, get a grip!

Bunce comes running back, out of breath.

Bunce I've thrown a sickie, I'm not going with them. Everyone come over to mine tonight and we'll do a surveillance sleepover while they're away – Toby and Alex, you two, me. Oli, the film's practically in the can –

He runs off.

Oli Wow. Think of the filming opportunity . . . Shall we? Shall we go? (*On Jo's still sulking shrug.*) Then again . . . it is a long time to all be together though, at Bunce's. It could be tricky . . . the intimacy of the stakeout . . . bonding through the small hours . . . seeing the dawn –
Jo Course we're going, don't be stupid. One little problem, though. I'd have to be staying at yours.
Oli And I'd have to be staying at yours.

They look at each other.

Oli/Jo Just this once.

Jo So now can I get back to Stephen? I turned the heat up in my bedroom to see if it makes any difference and maybe he's on his wheel right now and wondering where I am . . .

Oli I understand.

Jo Oli you're still my best friend ever.

She runs off.
    Left alone, Oli settles herself into a new place of concealment, ready to film again. Toby comes skulking back. She ignores him for as long as possible – difficult when he's staring at her. Finally:

Oli What is the matter with you?

Toby Doing the stakeout with you, aren't I?

Oli I don't want to do it with someone who hates me.

Toby Well, you hate me more.

Oli No, I don't.

Toby Yes, you do.

Oli Do not –

Toby Do do do a million times – (*Pinching her.*) – and no returns.

Oli Ow! (*Pinching him back.*) You're such a child!

Toby Man –

Oli Child –

Toby Man man man man man –

Oli Shh!

Miss Harris hurries back with a bag of shopping. Oli films. Miss Harris lets herself into her flat.

Toby Look at me – what am I? Tobe in the hole. The perfect stakeout partner.

Pause.

Oli You know Jo really likes you, don't you?

Toby Why me and not Alex?

Oli Do you know, I've never thought about that . . .

Toby Alex this, Alex that, why does everyone always like him more? You fancy him, don't you? You think he's more interesting than me. Alex can come on the stakeout with you, Alex can hang out with you at Bunce's –

Oli Oh my God! (*Putting a hand over his mouth.*) Look!

Oli starts filming. Jo's dad, Barry, in his policeman's uniform, walks down the street, glances around when he's outside Miss Harris's house, then rings the bell. She opens the door to him, doing up the last buttons of her tight white coat.

Miss Harris Hello! Come in! – I don't think I've ever had a policeman before, that's great –

He goes in, she closes the door. Oli turns to Toby.

Oli Oh my God. Not only is Jo's father being unfaithful, the whole police force must be completely corrupt! Now do you see how serious this is?

Toby Yes.

Oli No, you don't, your eyes have gone all funny –

Toby (*robotically*) I have been instructed to snog you. To save my jacket from Alex – I must snog Etna in penance –

Oli (*shoving him back out*) Who do you think you are? I've never been so insulted in my life. You don't seem to have the slightest idea of how terrible this situation is – and what about Jo? If she knew you even – ugh – I am never snogging you, do you understand? Ever! (*Shoves the camera at him.*) Right: you can stay here and interview him when he comes out, seeing as you ruined it all earlier.

Toby Why me?

Oli I can't do it, he knows me. Anyway, it's freezing, I've
been here hours, and you're so tough you don't feel it –
isn't that right?

*She goes. Toby tries to get comfortable in the cold with
the camera. It's all gone pear-shaped.*

SCENE NINE

*Split between Toby shivering outside Miss Harris's, and
Oli and Jo in the warmth of her bedroom. Jo finishes
packing a bag. Oli looks into Stephen's cage.*

Oli How are your parents?
Jo He's never known them. Poor thing.
Oli Yours! Are they, you know, okay?
Jo Oh. Boring as ever, why?
Oli No reason.

*Jo's dad, Barry, emerges from Miss Harris's – walks
past Toby, who sneezes.*

Jo's Dad What you doing in there, matey?
Toby (*frozen, barely able to speak, pointing camera at
him*) C-c-confess everything –
Jo's Dad Come on, matey, up you get – in a spot of
bother, are you?
Jo Why? Are yours okay?
Toby C-c-confess –
Oli I think so, but you never know, do you? You can
think things are one way, but then you find out they're
all different and then what do you do, and how do you
tell someone their whole world –?
Jo Oli, you worry too much about things.
Jo's Dad (*arm round Toby*) Look a bit rough, mate –
what happened? Run away from home? (*Re
camcorder.*) What's that, then?

Toby (*teeth chattering*) It's not mine. Confess now –

Jo's Dad That's right: get it off your chest. Everything gets better when you just come clean. You could always return it – ever thought of that? Is that possible? Could you do that, son? Eh?

Toby I know – I'm going to –

Jo's Dad You do that. We can all do things we never thought we had the courage to. (*Winking.*) And we feel like we've shed a load, I can tell you that much. Well done, lad.

Jo's Dad goes off, whistling. Jo picks up her bag and Stephen's cage.

Oli Jo, maybe we shouldn't be doing this.

Jo Oli, this is my big chance with Toby. We are *so* going.

They exit. Toby stares up at Miss Harris's flat. Glances around – anyone looking? Rings the bell.

SCENE TEN

Bunce's house, stakeout. Alex, Oli, Jo (with Stephen's cage) and Bunce, all eating crisps, playing music, are taking it in turns to watch Miss Harris's from the window.

Jo But why isn't he here? The whole thing's ruined if we're not all here together.

Alex I don't know where he is every second of the day, do I?

Bunce Is he his brother's keeper?

All Shut up, Bunce.

Bunce Shut up, 'Location Manager'. Owner of location, in fact. *In loco parentis*, as it were. Ah . . . just think, right now, they'll be drinking champagne in their box, humming along to *Aida*, tears in their eyes . . . and later . . . They never care that I can hear! Is it any wonder I'm like I am? From now on, I'm just going to be sick every time and not go. It's the only way. (*Pause.*) I love them, but not their behaviour.

Everyone glances at one another. Bunce is just too strange.

Jo But did he say he'd come later?
Alex Jo, I don't know, I haven't seen him for ages.
Jo Have you, Oli?

Doorbell rings.

It's him!

Bunce goes. Jo quickly puts on some more lip gloss, before Bunce comes back with Toby.

Toby (*gives Oli camera*) Ask me how I am. I'll tell you – Knackered! (*Throws himself down.*) The Older Woman falls for the charms of the Tobosaurus Rex . . .
Alex Mum's the only older woman you know.
Toby Mum . . . and Miss Harris.
Jo You never –
Toby I, the Tobester, the T-Star, the Tobo –
Oli (*checking playback*) Well done – you filmed the inside of the lens cap.
Toby Should have had a warning or something then, shouldn't it? Told you it was cheap rubbish. Anyway . . . Miss Harris, eh? Wore me out. She's a one, I'm telling you.
Alex In your dreams.
Toby Right then, how would I know she's got a purple duvet cover, eh? Or a blue kitchen, or pink loo roll in the loo, so huh huh huh to you, you're the wally –
Oli So no confession?
Toby Uh . . .
Jo Toby, what were you doing at Miss Harris's?
Toby Wouldn't like to say . . . Just got to get some shut-

eye first – worn out, I'm telling you. Phew – (*As Alex jumps on him.*) What's that for!

Alex Come on, tell us the truth.

Toby It was amazing. Her words. Ah, champagne – well done, Buncy.

Alex (*to Bunce*) You sure they're gone for the night?

Bunce A box for *Aida*, followed by a bargain jacuzzi suite hotel break? They're definitely gone.

Jo Are you trying to say you and Miss Harris Did It?

Toby Babe, don't get jealous –

Jo Don't call me babe any more.

Toby (*to Oli*) I thought you said she liked me.

Jo You told him I liked him? Oli!

Oli It's not exactly a secret –

Jo Not any more! (*Breathes very deeply.*)

Toby What you doing?

Jo Keeping calm so I don't go completely nuts at you.

Toby Good plan, I'm worn out.

Alex Jo, he's lying, I can tell.

Toby How? No, I'm not.

Oli Well, did you at least get a scale of charges for various lewd acts?

Jo Oli, don't sound like you're okay with what he's done.

Toby Uh . . . she didn't want to talk money. Experienced, in her prime –

Jo Aargh!

Toby What's the matter? I haven't done anything to you –

Jo Why not?

Toby yawns again, settles down to sleep. Leaps up when he sees he's near Stephen's cage.

Toby Urgh! Rodent corpse alert!

Oli But did you pay her? If you did –

Toby Freebie. On the house. Who could blame her . . .

Jo bursts into tears. Alex puts his arm round her.

Alex (*to Toby*) Shut up, you stupid wally.

Bunce (*putting his arm round Jo too*) I'm here for you too, Jo.

Jo (*shaking Alex and Bunce off*) Oli, this is all your fault –

Toby Can I help it if women find me irresistible?

Oli I certainly don't.

Toby You're not a woman, you're Etna.

Oli Shut up.

Toby (*aside to her*) Ah, but you can't make me now, can you? Or I'll tell . . .

Jo Tell what?

Toby The secret.

Oli Toby!

Alex/Jo/Bunce What secret!

Toby Oh. Em. Nothing. About anyone. Or anyone's parents. Especially anyone's father –

Oli Toby wanted to kiss me.

Toby Quick snog – don't get carried away, Etna.

Anxious eyes on Jo, who struggles to absorb this.

Jo *Kiss* you. Kiss *you*, Oli. My so-called friend.

Oli Only as penance, Jo, to get his jacket back from Alex. Not because he liked me or anything. It was extremely insulting.

Toby How'd you think I felt, having to do it?

Oli Not as bad as I did.

Toby Much worse!

Oli No, you didn't.

Toby Yes, I did –

Oli Did not!

Jo I don't care, I'm going to kill myself anyway!

Alex Don't, Jo.

Jo (*at Oli*) I will!

Oli Jo, it wasn't my –

Jo (*sobbing noisily*) Yes, it was!

Bunce Jo, think of Stephen. You can't leave him alone in
  the world.

Alex (*to Toby*) Can you go anywhere, or do anything,
  without upsetting everyone?

Toby Didn't upset Miss Harris, did I?

Bunce We'll find out. (*Bringing out big book.*) Right,
  Toby, did you do . . . (*Opens it.*) This?

*Everyone gathers round, even the tearful Jo. Their eyes
all widen.*

Toby Blimey. Not that exactly.

Oli Bunce, where does that come from?

Alex His parents have got loads –

Jo You're all sex-mad aren't you – what about romance,
  and courtship? (*Sobbing again.*) And True Love?

Toby What's that got to do with anything?

Bunce Alright then, did you do – that?

Toby Oh . . . that's proper . . .

Jo You did that?

Toby Saving it for later.

Bunce What about that?

Toby Steady –

Oli (*turning pages*) That? This? Like that?

Toby Um –

Alex Did you use one of those?

Toby Certainly not –

Jo (*forgetting she's angry*) Look, Oli, how disgusting –

Oli Urgh, gross –

Jo Go away, you're not my best friend ever again.

Bunce snaps the book shut.

Bunce He didn't do anything.

Alex It's all in his head.

Oli And if he really *was* there –

Toby I was!

Oli – he should have got evidence. He wasn't supposed to be doing it for fun.

Toby Yes, I was –

Alex Time for the truth.

He jumps on his brother.

Where's Stephen?

Toby The rat?

Jo (*getting him*) Syrian hamster –

Alex Everyone – keep him down. (*To Jo.*) Take him out.

Toby (*struggling*) No, don't, bruv – Bunce. what's happened to you?

Bunce The power of being a location manager has warped me.

Jo (*taking out a bundle from the cage*) Hello, Stephen darling . . . I know you can hear me . . .

She puts him against Toby, who shrieks.

Feel – he's warm.

Toby No, it's not! Get it away –

Jo You don't know anything about hamsters –

Alex Tell him, Jo. In great detail.

Jo Okay . . . Look, Toby, here's his cute little stumpy tail . . . and if he was to open his eyes they'd be like little bulging rubies . . . Would you like to cuddle him?

Toby No – please –

Alex Don't forget the see-through ears –

Jo That's right, see how the light shines through? All transparent aren't they, with little veins . . .

Toby I'm not looking –

Oli You are now –

Bunce Give him air, we don't want him passing out under questioning.

Toby Bunce! What about cruelty to animals?

Bunce I would never hurt a living thing.

Oli See, Jo? Even Bunce thinks he's dead.

Jo No, he isn't, and don't talk to me. Scratchy little feet
that scurry about – or used to, didn't they, Stephen?
Here, feel one anyway –

Oli (*as Toby grabs her*) Get off me, I'm not saving you –

Jo Still trying to snog her, are you? And by the way,
Olivia, they stop pooing when they hibernate, so there
goes your dropping count theory.

She sprinkles Toby with hamster bedding.

So don't worry, those are dry old ones . . .

Toby Urgh! It's going down my neck –

Jo (*hand down his top*) Keep still, that one's stuck,
maybe it's fresh –

Toby Aargh! Aargh!

Alex Great – keep going, Jo, he's nearly ready to talk.

Jo It's definitely stuck to your skin –

Toby I'll talk! Get it off me please! Just stop!

*Alex holds up his hand. Jo stops. Impressed, Bunce
quietly copies him. Toby sits up, shakes himself out.*

Jo (*putting Stephen back in his cage*) Well done. (*Sadly.*)
Good boy.

*Only the audience might spot that the door is not
properly closed . . .*

Alex Go on.

Toby You got me at it, Bunce, with your parents' porn –
and you, Oli, going on about Miss Harris being a ho
and everything – and then there was that monkey
programme –

All I saw that!

Toby So when the stakeout went wrong –

Oli Completely ruined by you.

Toby Yeah, whatever, I thought I'd try to get in there.
And I did! She does have a purple duvet – I saw it
through the door.

Bunce You really did get in there? Cool!

Toby But she said no, 'cause I'm a pupil – even though it's half-term so it shouldn't count. Or we'd have Done It, I know we would. I was right in there.

Silence.

Alex Access to the surveillance site. Fair play, bruv.

Oli Not bad. So we need to send in another agent. Is it too late?

Alex Bet she does business quite late.

Oli What do you think, Jo?

Jo We're not talking, remember?

Toby I could try again –

Jo Alex. You go.

Bunce In disguise, though.

Alex I don't have any.

Bunce But in my parents' bedroom there is a box . . .

Alex exits. Jo cries.

Oli Jo . . .

Jo Never speak to me again. My life is an aching void.

Silence. Bunce points to his shoulder.

But I'm just about managing.

SCENE ELEVEN

Miss Harris's flat. She is in her white coat. Alex wears something velvet and gothic with what could be a highwayman's hat.

Miss Harris So, Mr . . . Turpin.

Alex Call me Dick.

Miss Harris You found out I was in practice here from . . .?

Alex Um . . . uh . . . the last bloke who was here.

Miss Harris Barry Evans?

Alex (*stunned*) Sergeant Evans, Jo's dad?

Miss Harris Such a nice chap. What's the matter?

Alex Nothing – (*He fiddles with something in the pocket of his coat, coughs loudly.*) Testing, testing –

Miss Harris Testing?

Alex Ahem – testing your services, comparing like with like, you know. Now Miss Harris, what do you charge for your services?

Miss Harris Depends on the client.

Alex (*holding out his pocket*) Could you repeat that please?

Miss Harris It depends on the client's pockets.

Alex What would you charge me, for instance? For everything. Full service.

Miss Harris Richard, I know you're a professional highwayman not a car going into the garage.

Alex I'm a courier. Highwaymen don't exist. How stupid would I be to say I was that?

Miss Harris Courier, exactly – but you really do remind me of someone. Are you by any chance . . . a twin?

Alex I'm nothing like him. No, I'm not.

Miss Harris Then I must be mistaken. It's just . . . I keep wanting to call you Alex for some reason –

Alex Don't you like Dick?

Miss Harris Mr Turpin, listen to me: I provide a very important and intimate service, for people in need.

Alex Normal people in need . . . who come to professionals like you.

Miss Harris Yes.

Alex That's well sick.

Miss Harris Sorry?

Alex You know, Miss, like cool.

Argh. Wrong. Miss Harris stares at him, straight-faced.

Miss Harris Right. Into the bathroom, everything off

below the waist, paper coat on, and come back out
here. I'll take your clothes – (*As he jumps away from
her.*) What's the matter now?

Alex Ah, terrible headache – brain tumour probably –
better come back another time –

He runs out. Miss Harris smiles to herself.

SCENE TWELVE

*Bunce's house. The place is well on the way to being
trashed, and there are a couple of empty champagne
bottles on the floor. Everyone crowds around Alex, who
holds up a little dictaphone. Bunce turns off the music.*

Alex Listen – (*Only a harsh crackle.*) I made sure it was
working – (*Tries again.*) Oh, I don't believe it –

Toby Who's the wally now, huh? Huh? HUH?

Jo You!

Bunce We need a longer lens. We need sophisticated
listening devices. We need to mount round-the-clock,
twenty-four-seven surveillance and maybe put bugs in
the walls. We could get a decoy construction crew to
work in the street to cover the noise of our drilling –

Alex Bunce. Stop.

Bunce I don't want to. This is the best fun I've ever had.

Oli Maybe we all have to. Maybe it's just too difficult.

Silence.

Jo You're giving up?

Toby I want to try again.

Alex I shouldn't have run away.

Bunce It's okay – I do it all the time.

Toby Bruv. Doesn't matter. I'm the brave one, you're the
brainy one.

Alex Yes, it does . . .

General gloom. Bunce goes round with a new bottle of champagne, refilling everyone's glass.

Bunce Every stakeout has its dark moments. Now – bottoms up!

Oli Bunce, your parents –

Bunce Stop fussing, we'll have a big tidy before they come back. (*Puts on some lively music.*) Come on, Jo – (*Pulling her up.*) Let's dance – one, two, three and one-two-three – that's it, you can do it.

Jo (*flung around*) Can't you see I'm heartbroken and betrayed? What are you doing?

Bunce Teaching you salsa. Come on – (*Twirling her wildly.*) That's it, that's it, you're doing it!

Bunce loses control of the struggling Jo and she goes flying. Alex catches her.

Alex Are you okay?

Bunce Sorry, Jo, won't happen again –

Alex That's right –

Bunce I can dance with her –

Alex She doesn't want to dance with you.

Jo Are you two fighting over me?

Bunce Would you like us to?

Jo Maybe . . . it might cheer me up at bit.

Oli Jo, that's terrible.

Jo It's true!

Bunce Very well: I challenge you to a duel, sir, and I will have my satisfaction!

Bunce prepares to fight, shadow-boxing, a few kung fu moves . . .

Alex Give over, Bunce.

Bunce Oh, thank God.

Oli What's happened to us all . . . ?

Bunce You need another drink, Oli. Here. Lighten up.

Oli Impossible. I'm cursed with seriousness.
Bunce Try, anyway.

Oli drains her champagne. Burps. Toby looks shocked.

Jo You'll never get a husband like that.
Oli I'll never get one anyway. (*To Toby.*) I'm Speccy
Etna, aren't I?

Pause.

Toby Right then, everyone, I'm taking over the operation
now, and I'm going in again, so give me one of your
dad's business suits, Buncy-Wuncy –
Bunce Don't call me that.
Toby Buncy-Wuncy? What's wrong with that? Go on, go
and get us one of your dad's –
Bunce I am not being called Buncy-Wuncy on location –
do I make myself clear?
Everyone *Oooh* . . .
Toby Right then. I'll get one myself, shall I?
Bunce You do that.
Toby I will then.
Bunce Okay.
Toby Um . . .
Bunce In the bedroom. (*To everyone else.*) What's wrong
with salsa, anyway? Nothing.
Alex Bunce . . . you're really drunk.
Jo (*sounding it too*) Really really plastered . . .
Oli So am I.
Bunce Oli, while you were wallowing in misery –
Oli I'm still there –
Bunce Toby staged a coup, and he's the director now.
Oli Who cares?
Jo I can't believe you're saying that. What about the
awards and everything?
Oli Fantasy.
Jo No! It isn't!

Bunce No one's taking Location Manager away from me!

Alex Oli, listen. We're going to make it happen. Jo's going to be a brilliant presenter.

Jo (*recovering her good humour*) Am I? Why?

Bunce I was born to it –

Alex You're all sparkly and funny.

Jo Am I? That's nice . . .

Bunce It makes me feel free –

Alex And Oli's got loads of good ideas.

Oli I do?

Jo Usually.

Bunce It releases something in me –

All No! Don't let it do that –

Bunce Charm, I was going to say. I've taken loads of Diocalm for the other thing.

Toby (*offstage*) Stand back for the Tobester – the T-Star is coming through in all his manly glory! Push the crowds back, for the human phenomerone that is, The One –

Alex (*calling*) Hang on a mo –

Toby (*offstage*) The Only –

Alex (*whispering*) Hide!

They just finish cramming into a hiding space as Toby bursts in, dressed in a Chippendales-style fireman's costume.

Toby Love God and Tobosaurus Rex! (*Pause.*) Where'd you go?

The others struggle not to laugh. Silently, Alex puts his arm round Jo, who pretends not to notice.

Very funny – I'll just finish all your champagne –

He cruises around, downing their drinks, throwing some moves, until:

Mr Bunce (*offstage*) Call that a jacuzzi? Totally and utterly ridiculous. I'm so keyed up – if putting them all in modern dress wasn't bad enough – (*Entering.*) That's it, no more package – (*Seeing the carnage.*) – deals . . .

Toby crouches down behind a piece of furniture.

Mrs Bunce *We've been burgled!*
Mr Bunce Stay here – (*Runs out, comes back in brandishing a golf-club.*) They might still be here –
Mrs Bunce Our beautiful home . . .

Stephen suddenly scoots across the floor and into where Toby is hiding –

(*Shrieking, jumping on a chair.*) A rat! It's a rat! It's gone behind there – kill it –

Golf club raised, Mr Bunce steps out to get it – reels back as Toby the Fireman leaps out, jumps on a chair. Alex stops Jo from shouting out.

Toby It's alive! It's alive!
Mr Bunce Hold it right there, sir, or you'll be the one with the handicap!
Mrs Bunce Very good, dear, very masterful.
Toby Sir, that means you think I'm an adult, doesn't it?
Mr Bunce Monica! Call the police!
Mrs Bunce Not while there's a rat on the loose –
Toby Sir – about how old would you say?

Mr Bunce grabs the phone, dials with one hand while keeping an eye on Toby.

Mr Bunce Old enough to go to prison!
Mrs Bunce Take that outfit off, it was bought for a very specific purpose.
Toby I can't, I'd be naked! Anyway keep your hair on, Bunce said I could borrow something –
Mr Bunce (*into phone*) Police! Emergency!

Mrs Bunce Bunce?
Toby You know, Pumpkin.
Mr Bunce Yes, that's the location – (*Seeing Stephen move.*) There it is! (*Hurls phone at it.*)
Mrs Bunce Did you hang up first?
Jo He's alive! (*Bursting out.*) Leave him alone!
Mr Bunce Is this your accomplice?
Mrs Bunce Where's my Pumpkin!? There it goes!
Mr Bunce I'm going to get it –
Jo Stephen, look out!

> *Mr Bunce chases Stephen with the golf-club. Toby leaps out of the way.*

(*Crawling around.*) Come to Mummy!
Mr Bunce (*now after Toby*) Stop thief!
Toby You're going to break something with that!
Alex (*jumping out to block Mr Bunce*) Leave my brother alone!
Mrs Bunce (*grabbing at Toby*) Get that uniform off, young man –
Toby (*as she rips at his clothes*) / Help!!
Mr Bunce Control yourself, Monica!
Mrs Bunce (*shaking Toby*) Where's Pumpkin!
Oli (*jumping out*) Leave him alone!
Mrs Bunce There's the rat!

> *Stephen scoots across this floor. Toby falls off the chair, Mrs Bunce on top of him.*

Jo / Don't crush him!!
Mr Bunce (*roaring*) Monica!
Mrs Bunce / Now I've got you, young man –
Toby Help!

> *Mr Bunce seizes Toby's leg. He struggles.*

Mr Bunce You're going to pay for this –
Alex It's not his fault!

Mrs Bunce (*top volume*) What have you done with my Pumpkin?!

It stuns them all into silence. There's a loud fart.

Bunce (*emerging*) Hi, Mum. Hi, Dad. Uh . . . how was the opera?

Mr Bunce You're not responsible for this carnage, are you, Marcus? You were overpowered by these juvenile delinquents –

Toby But first they reckoned I was an adult burglar – how cool is that!

Mrs Bunce You know rats carry bubonic plague, don't you, Pumpkin? You're always so careful about washing your hands – here, let me smell them –

Bunce Mum, get off!

Mr Bunce The police will know what to do with these youths.

Jo Police? No!

Toby We're only kids!

Mr Bunce A short sharp shock's what you need –

Bunce Don't, Dad. These are my friends.

Mr and Mrs Bunce Friends? Really?

Good question. Bunce looks at them.

Alex/Jo/Toby/Oli Yes.

Mrs Bunce How wonderful! Garth, Pumpty's got friends at last! Let's see now, two boys, two girls – oh that's just so healthy. I thought you'd maybe get one or two at most –

Bunce Mum, will you stop it?

Mrs Bunce Though I don't like the way that big one's wearing your dad's special outfit.

Alex Yeah, Toby, well-stupid outfit.

Mrs Bunce Excuse me, Garth looks very masculine in it.

Mr Bunce Thank you, Monica.

Bunce Lalalala, can't hear you, don't want to know –

Mrs Bunce Toby . . . now would that be the school bully?

Toby Who's calling me that?

Jo/Oli/Alex/Bunce We are!

Mrs Bunce And his brother is . . . no, don't tell me, let me think . . . Alex –

Alex Hi.

Mrs Bunce Who likes Jo, but Jo likes Toby, is that right?

Bunce I'm really sorry about my mum.

Oli Mine's just as bad. It's okay.

Mrs Bunce Now you two lovely girls . . .

Jo See Oli? You're lovely too.

Mrs Bunce You must be Jo, and you're Oli?

Jo/Oli (*butter wouldn't melt*) Hello, Mrs Bunce.

Mrs Bunce And Oli and Toby like each other –

Oli/Toby No we don't!

Jo, Oli, Toby and Alex stare accusingly at Bunce.

Bunce Well, I have to talk to them about something, don't I?

Toby hiccups.

Mr Bunce I want the phone numbers of all your parents so that I can inform them of your outrageous conduct. (*To Bunce.*) It's all very well them coming round here and abusing your facilities – let's see how friendly they are with you when you're back at school.

Oli I hope you're not accusing us of exploiting Pumpkin.

Bunce Oli!

Oli Sorry, of cold-heartedly exploiting Marcus.

Jo We like him.

Bunce Do you really? Honestly?

Jo Yes. And if you could find Stephen, I would even love you.

Bunce Jo, it's done.

Alex Anyway, you're the only one in trouble about all this.

Toby Funny that, bruv, eh?

Alex Yeah.

There's a hammering on the door.

Jo's Dad (*offstage*) Open up! / Police!

Jo No!

Mrs Bunce runs to the door, returns with Jo's dad in uniform, Jo's mum, Oli's parents, and Toby and Alex's mum.

Toby/Alex/Jo/Oli Mum!

Jo/Oli Dad!

Oli's Mum Did we bring you up to lie?

Jo's Mum If you think you're going to the fashion show after this –

Jo's Dad What seems to be the problem –

Toby and Alex's Mum Tell me you've used condoms –

Toby/Alex Mum!!

Jo's Dad Are you girls alright?

Oli's Dad What other lies have you told us, Olivia?

Oli I haven't!

Jo's Mum It was only by chance I bumped into Becca –

Oli's Mum And I asked how you two were getting along –

Jo's Mum This is what happens when they go boy-crazy.

Oli/Jo We are not boy-crazy!

Toby / Why not?

Alex Go on.

Bunce I'm a boy.

Jo Anyway, Mum, Stephen is alive after all, so I was right, and, Dad, you're in the police and you wanted to put him in the bin so that would have been murder and you could have been struck off –

Jo's Dad (*looking at Toby*) Do I know you from somewhere?

Toby Nowhere. Ever.

Jo's Dad I do . . . Anyway – what exactly has been going
on here? I hope you haven't been wasting police time –

Mrs Bunce Oh no, Chief Inspector, it's lovely to see you.

Jo's Dad 'Officer' will do.

Mr Bunce Of course, Superintendent, we were just
labouring under a genuine misapprehension that –

Jo's Dad Jo. What's going on.

Miss Harris (*coming in*) Maybe I can help. I couldn't
help seeing the commotion – I live across there, as
some of you might know . . .

Bunce Do you, Miss?

Miss Harris And I thought I might just step over and
have a word with the young people . . . You left the
door open, did you know that?

Jo Stephen! He might have run into the road!

Jo's Mum You're staying right here, young lady. (*To Jo's
Dad.*) What's the matter? Why are you looking like
that?

Jo's Dad Um . . .

Miss Harris I'm Penny Harris, the supply teacher.

Alex and Toby's Mum Oh, the one my sons go on about.
Toby, her breasts are not that gigantic at all –

Alex/Toby Mum!

Miss Harris I'm quite happy with them, thank you, but
I'm not here to discuss that. I'd like to talk about the
special interest your children have taken in my private
life of late.

*All the parents stare at the children, who are acutely
embarrassed.*

I think it's time we cleared the air, wouldn't you say,
Barry?

Jo 'Barry'?

Oli Don't, Miss Harris. Don't destroy her world.

Jo Dad?

Jo's Mum Yes. Come on then, it's just a fact. I don't care.

Jo You don't *care*, Mum?

Mr Bunce Excuse me, we are taxpayers, we did call the police for our own situation, not to have a marriage guidance meeting.

Mrs Bunce Shh, I think it's fascinating – go on, Penny. Share.

Miss Harris Maybe one of my pupils would like to explain their fascination?

Silence. Slowly, everyone is looking at Oli.

Oli Alright! We know what you do, Miss Harris, and we understand you need to make more money and that's fine, but we don't think you appreciate how you're just buying into a corrupt and patriarchal system not to mention destroying families by selling your body!

Miss Harris As a colonic hydrotherapist?

Jo's Dad has a violent coughing fit.

Jo's Mum (*patting his back*) Stop it, Barry, there's nothing to be ashamed of.

Jo Will someone please tell me what's going on!

Jo's Mum Nothing, Jo, your dad just goes along to Miss Harris and gets a tube up his bottom, and some water gets swooshed around and flushes him out. That's all.

Jo Mum, that is not nothing. Dad, tell me you don't –

Mrs Bunce Plain water?

Miss Harris Of course there's herbs in it, and depending on the levels of toxicity . . . Anyway, everyone seems to be catching on to the benefits –

Toby So I was never going to get a feel, Miss?

Miss Harris 'Fraid not. Either of you.

Alex and Toby's Mum Nice try, boys. (*To Bunce.*) Are you the one who lends them porn?

Mr and Mrs Bunce Erotica –

Bunce Whatever!

Oli's Dad Olivia. Have any of these boys tried to . . . interfere . . . with you? Because they'll have me to deal with if they have.

Oli Oh, Dad, you're alive! That's so nice of you.

Oli's Dad Don't you 'Oh Dad' me, you're in big trouble.

Toby It's not her fault –

Alex/Jo/Bunce Oooh . . .

Miss Harris I would just like to say, that if anyone has been spreading rumours that I operate any kind of illegal activity – I would be extremely upset. And could even sue for defamation.

Parents (*ad lib*) Oh no. / No, you wouldn't want to do that. (*Etc.*)

Mr Bunce I'll tell you whose fault it is – that bloody sat nav, sending us halfway up the country in the wrong direction – and that money-grabbing hotel, telling us we were in the honeymoon suite – never seen such a dump – and as for what some people call a jacuzzi – I mean, forget the modern bloody dress opera, the whole bloody thing's been a fiasco from start to finish. I just need to kill that rat and I'll feel a lot better –

Jo No!

Mrs Bunce There, there, dear. Now let me apologise to everyone for the place being such a mess, it's like my worst nightmare come true.

Parents (*ad lib*) No it's not. / Haven't noticed a thing. (*Etc.*)

Mrs Bunce But seeing as we're all here, and Pumpkin has already started on the champagne, why don't we all have a nice drink together?

Parents (*ad lib*) How nice. / Thank you very much, so nice to meet you at last. (*Etc.*)

Jo's Dad Just tea for me, still on duty.

Jo Miss Harris, I'm so glad you're not a ho.

Toby Me too, Miss, 'cause you're not some sket, you're well sick in that white coat, know what I'm saying?

Miss Harris The gist seems polite.

Oli You didn't seem to care about us, you didn't seem to bother.

Miss Harris Respect must be mutual, Oli.

Oli Yes. Sorry.

Miss Harris Thank you. You're an A student really, I know. (*To Alex.*) And I must say, I did like the hat. Dick.

Mrs Bunce (*drawing Miss Harris over*) Miss Harris? Would you give us a little chat through the process? It's something Garth and I have wondered about.

Jo's Mum Barry's been a new man, I must say.

Jo Don't want to hear!

Jo's Dad Then don't listen.

Miss Harris (*joining them*) I'd be delighted.

Bunce It just gets worse . . .

Oli, Jo, Toby and Alex stand watching the adults talking and laughing.

Oli Sorry everyone. I was . . . wrong.

Toby Fun though, wasn't it?

Oli Was it?

Toby Yeah. It was.

They look at each other.

Jo Ahem. Oli, could I please have a word?

Oli Excuse us.

Alex Bruv. Over here.

Bunce is left alone. Again. He sighs, throws himself down in a chair. Farts. There is a strange squeak. He reaches under the cushions and pulls something out – Stephen.

Bunce No!

A blast of adult laughter – but not at him. Jo, Oli, Toby and Alex are still deep in conversation. Bunce cradles the hamster.

God, you know I'm a vegetarian, so you wouldn't make this happen, would you? Please say I haven't killed Stephen after everything he's been through –

Jo (*returning*) Oh Bunce, you found him! I can't believe it!

Bunce Me neither.

Jo (*kissing his cheek*) For this I will be your loyal-but-never-more-intimate-than-that friend for ever.

Bunce Wait –

Jo No, Bunce, I'm too happy – and to seal our pact, I'm going to give you my dearest Stephen, to be your boon companion, for as long as you both shall live. (*Pause.*) I've actually grown out of him, I didn't realise, so don't feel you're depriving me.

Bunce Oh. Okay. Thank you.

Alex And Bunce, man, sorry about this, but Jo's now officially my girlfriend, so if you want to teach her salsa, she better agree or you'll be answering to me, okay?

Jo Oh, Alex, you're so butch.

Bunce Who knew . . .

Alex (*digging Toby in the ribs*) Go on –

Toby Oliwillyougooutwithme?

Oli Look, you don't have to say things like that because you feel bad about the jacket thing.

Alex He's given it to me.

Oli (*not listening*) I mean, I've obviously got everything wrong myself so who am I to, to, you know.

Toby Oli, will you go out with me?

Oli I suppose what I mean is to say that if someone gets it wrong, oh, then punish them for ever, because people are only human and even I can make a huge, massive, ridiculous –

Toby (*shouting*) Oli, will you go out with me!?

Everyone turns to stare.

Oli – mistake.

Toby It's not a mistake.

*He steps forward and kisses her. Everyone claps. Even
Bunce, forgetting he's holding Stephen, who bites him –
suddenly hanging off his hand with his teeth.*

Bunce Aargh – argh –
Jo Naughty Stephen!
Bunce (*hopping about, trying to shake him off*) No, it's
fantastic, thank you. God. Mum, I'm fine –

*The doorbell rings, insistently. Mr Bunce goes, Bunce
hops about in pain, trying to grin. The adults are still
laughing and talking in their huddle.*

Adults (*ad lib*) So the herbs help the process? / Do you
think I should let myself go grey or fight it all the way? /
About twice a week if we have time. / Much worse
with PMT. / Gets if from you, love. (*Etc.*)

*Mr Bunce returns with a cool, punky-looking girl.
Jo, Oli, Alex, Toby and Bunce stare at her.*

Girl I'm Riotgrrl. Where is Firefox?
Bunce (*hamster still hanging from hand*) Uh . . . here.
All Firefox?
Girl My real name's Agatha. Laugh if you want, I'm used
to it.
Bunce Riotgrrl! Wow! Why did you stop emailing? I
checked every site but you'd gone.
Agatha I decided I was getting too dependent on digital
media and I needed to go live, so I went cold turkey on
the website and came to find you instead.
Bunce So you weren't ignoring me, then, because I'd
annoyed you?
Agatha No. You have the heart of a lion.
Bunce Everyone! This is Riotgrrl from the animal rights
website! She's a real person and she's come to visit me!
She's a real actual friend I haven't bribed or begged or
paid in any way!

Agatha Here – (*Swiftly detaching the hamster.*) Let me.
Bunce Ouch – thank you. That's Stephen.
Agatha (*deftly turning him upside down and back*)
Stephanie. It's female.
Jo Really? All this time?

*Agatha and Bunce gaze at each other. Bunce farts
loudly.*

Bunce Aargh –
Toby Oops, sorry, that was me.
Jo No, it –
Toby Yes, it was –
Agatha That's okay. I fart myself.
Bunce You do?!
Agatha Sure. We're human animals, aren't we? (*Seeing
cage, and putting Stephanie in it.*) Looks like your
parents are partying. Want to go somewhere else
where we can talk?
Bunce Can my friends come too?
Agatha Oh sure. I need some normal people in my life.

*Bunce puts his arm round Agatha, Alex round Jo,
Toby round Oli.*

Jo/Oli/Alex/Toby/Bunce That's us!

End.

Production Notes

Comedy has to be real and truthful; but directing comedy is fundamentally different from directing *Hamlet*. Think very carefully about how to physicalise it – particularly how to get the actors on and off the stage, as comedy can completely die between the scenes. It doesn't matter how fast and light a scene is, if it is followed by a long scene change it will die for certain. The trick is to start the next scene before the previous one has finished.

Ask what is the least amount of *stuff* you can do the show with. Many shows (and comedies in particular) are killed by being overloaded with 'stuff' – a particular bugbear being the *burglars* (men in black who creep on between scenes and steal the furniture). Laline always tries to write with as little need for 'stuff' on stage as possible, preferring to see things implied rather than explicitly there. But obviously in *Show and Tell* there are scenes where people have to hide, and enter and exit, so there has to be a bit of a physical set – and in terms of a minimal set, doors are very useful in a farce. Make it your duty to present the audience with something as slick as possible. The whole production could be about doors and curtains – what's open or shut.

Think about the staging of the first two scenes. Could sound effects be enough to create the locations? Scene One has street noises (perhaps with passers-by) and in Scene Two there is the general hubbub of a classroom.

Moving from Scene One to Two as swiftly as possible could be achieved with an invasion of the space by the

actors with chairs to create the buzz of the classroom.
Getting onstage should always be part of the story –
coming on, taking positions, *then* starting the scene is not
interesting. A chaotic entrance would also be a contrast
with the boredom/torpor when we start mid-lesson

SCENE ONE

Ask: What do we know from the scene? • What do we
know about the people? • What are the clues?

When new characters enter it should be as if they are
colour-coded – immediately they come on, they should be
saying to the audience: 'I'm this person and this is what
I do.' 'This is what is interesting about me.'

All the characters in the play are self-aware.

BUNCE says straight away that he knows he is a geek,
but he is also intelligent and has a keen sense of humour.
He is not a stereotype. We find out about his home
life – he is a vegetarian and is ashamed of his parents.
He probably always does his homework. But he puts a
lot of energy into trying to be part of the group. Although
he is low-status, he plays low-status with high status.
When Laline first started writing, Bunce was very much
laughed at – but as the story developed, she realised he is
in fact the hero.

THE TWINS (TOBY AND ALEX) are like two sides of the
same coin. Decide if you're going to make them identical
or if there is visual comedy in them being different – e.g.,
one very tall and one very short. The slang that Toby uses
(e.g. 'Toboid') gives the impression that he is not very
bright. He might muck around and underachieve. His
jacket needs to be very cool and genuinely desirable. Toby
does have style, flamboyantly so.

JO AND OLI can be irritable with each other, as they always know what the other is about to say. Oli is the leader – she often talks down to Jo. While Laline imagines Jo and Oli as equally attractive, Oli prides herself on being the wiser, so Jo takes on the role of fashion adviser and 'the pretty one'.

The scene changes when Bunce exits. There is a different feel – it is a coda.

SCENE TWO

We need to bring attention to the fact that Miss Harris isn't a regular teacher – the phone call shows us this. Toby has 'found her out'.

Oli finds her too familiar and doesn't like her. She in turn asserts herself over the essay marks.

In Miss Harris's speeches about *observation* there are really important key words and ideas:

- *Noticing surroundings.*
- *Living things.*
- *Intensive field study.*
- *Show and tell.*

These should have lots of air around them – not so much stressing these parts of the speech or saying them loudly, more about giving them interest and 'capital letters'.

Experiment with the staging of the scene. It could be side-on or on a diagonal. It would also work with the teacher walking around. It will be necessary to experiment to find the right and strong place for Toby in this scene. Is he gazing at Miss Harris from afar or is he as close to her as possible?

Decide how the actors make clear that no one is listening at the top of the scene. Is it silent, or is there general low-level noise throughout? Since Bunce's main goal is to fit in, it might be interesting to have him mirror everything that Toby does, but with a beat's difference.

Get Toby on his feet as soon as possible – so that he can rule the class. Maybe as soon as: 'No, I'm Alex, Miss.'

THINGS TO THINK ABOUT

The farting. Laline doesn't want non-specific farting. Bunce uses his flatulence as a way of making a statement. There doesn't have to be sound. *Corral the audience into the same place to get one big laugh.* Suggest that all that is needed is for the person next to Bunce to move.

Interrupted lines. The actors should *always keep going* (and therefore need to be clear about what the remainder of the line would be), as their character doesn't know that they are going to be interrupted.

Additional actors could be used for the scenes in the street and in the classroom. Although potentially distracting, they could bring real life to a scene. Make sure you know what the most important part of the scene is – a whole football team could come on as long as they are focused on the main action. You could use the ensemble to change or set the scene. Those who appear in the street or classroom at the beginning could take responsibility for the staging of the play. They could invade scenes and change locations – could change people's costumes in view of the audience.

Have the actors create a character dossier to help them. Exercises could include: Writing 'a day in the life of' their character – a page from Jo's diary. Oli and Jo could make a video about their friendship. Alex and Toby's Mum could give a speech about them at a family gathering.

Have actors play their scenes with heart and exuberance. Farce will really take off when the stakes are high and characters have a lot to lose (particularly their dignity). The fact that here they are all teenagers obsessed with appearances and how they come across to each other is perfect, as are their painful romantic obsessions – the more their pain, the more we laugh.

The backstory is very important – the actors should know what the previous scene was if it is not in the play. This way they will bring energy and intention onstage.

Work on the difference between *pace* and *speed,* as this is crucial in comedy. It is not necessary for every line to go fast, but it is necessary for the actors to pick up the cues. They should work towards the last and first consonant of each line being slammed up against each other. (But not at the beginning of rehearsals, as the shape of a scene needs to be right first.)

Show and Tell is a metaphor for the idea that there are parts of ourselves we are prepared to reveal and others that we hide, and how we are defined by this. Also how what you are and what you want to be can be quite different.

Avoid making the parents stereotypical. They should have a genuine concern for their children. Bunce's parents may be slightly barking, but they love him and just want him to be happy, which is very touching. The more truthfully they are played, the funnier (and more profound) they will be. Steer clear of things like stick-on moustaches to age-up.

Encourage the actor playing Miss Harris to observe teachers in action.

The young people in the play are wrong about Miss Harris, but they are also wrong about themselves.

EXERCISE

Ask the actors what would be their character's worst nightmare and their best dream come true.

Jo – dream would be to be a celebrity model, and nightmare would be to be seen looking awful by a boy she fancies.

Oli – dream would be to accomplish something extraordinary or highly academic. Her nightmare – no recognition.

Alex – dream is to be the opposite of his brother, his nightmare to be like his brother.

Toby – dream is adoration, nightmare is exclusion.

Laline sees Toby as the most vulnerable person on the stage. Alex is much more cool and doesn't feel the need to appear mature and grown-up.

STAGING

Be consistent in the way you tell the story. It's important to set up conventions and use these throughout. If the scene changes are to be done by the actors, this should be consistently so.

Scene One (after school on the street): a door for Miss Harris to appear at. Or two doors? One for Bunce's house?

Scene Two (classroom): chairs (door can stay).

Scene Three (watching TV in four different rooms): chairs can make sofas – no need for TVs.

Scene Four (Jo's bedroom): a large cushion? Chairs could be 'disappeared' by the departing parents. Or chairs could remain and space be defined by lighting.

Scene Five (twins' bedroom): as previous scene.

Scene Six (street): as in Scene One.

At the end of Scene Five there could easily be an overlap with the beginning of Scene Six: as Bunce is referring to the girls, they could already be there. Any way of starting the next scene before the previous scene is finished is money in the bank. It is very useful for *the lighting to slightly precede the action* – i.e., the lighting state changes and the character follows it. This will give the impression that *the lighting belongs to the play and the play knows where it is going.*

It might be useful to have a costume rail in Scenes Eleven/ Twelve. The idea of dressing up/disguise is thematic – as well as the obvious (Bunce's parents, the disguises when they visit Miss Harris's flat, the surveillance outfits, Toby in the fireman's costume, etc.), there is the way Toby dresses in exaggerated street clothes, the way Jo disguises herself with her fake tan/lipstick and so on.

Looking forward to the last scene, the costume rail (or even two) might make a good alternative to a cupboard. Actors could easily appear, talk and disappear from behind hanging clothes, etc.

Having focused so far on using the minimum to suggest location, towards the end of this play (from Scene Twelve, when the location remains Bunce's house) it would be possible (and useful) to start filling the stage – secure in the knowledge that it doesn't have to be got off until the

end of the play. There could now be an escalation of *stuff* –
furniture, costumes, streamers, bottles, party-poppers –
that could be used to enhance the mayhem necessary for
the last scene. Also there's great comic potential in
bringing more and more stuff on.

If you choose this option you will have to design/organise
the wing space as much as the stage. There's nothing
worse than seeing actors unable to make a decent exit or
entrance because there is stuff in their way.

WAYS OF STAGING SCENE EIGHT

Place Miss Harris's door downstage right. Have a row
of bins downstage centre with a downstage-left bin being
Bunce's bin. Discover whether it is necessary for the
characters to have something that they can actually hide
behind or whether it could just be dustbin lids. You could
use wheelie bins, but with the bottoms cut out so that the
actors can move them around, pop up out of them, etc.

Avoid placing the action too far downstage, and so forcing
the actors to play across the stage rather than using the
diagonals. This could be solved by placing Bunce upstage
centre, as if at the bus stop. There's no need for a bus
stop to be there – Bunce reading a newspaper tells us
where he is. His face should be completely covered by
the paper. Bunce could say his line, 'Don't point', from
behind the paper and then reveal himself.

The 'second position' should be just that – a new hiding
place for each of them, allowing the scene to be opened
up/shaken up. The girls could move to press themselves
against an imaginary wall. The door could have trellis/
greenery attached to it to create a hiding place. Wherever
they go, Toby should be momentarily isolated centre

stage as he doesn't know what is going on – then perhaps he should copy the girls.

Give the actors the objective to make it the most professional stakeout of all time. Ask them to think about how many hours they have been there. What time of day is it? How cold is it? Then, when Jo goes and ruins it in her excitement over Toby's arrival, the stakes are much higher.

Oli should clearly be in charge. Before the boys arrive they could also have a moment when they think something is happening, then stand down. Ask the actors to think about why Alex and Toby are arriving late. Who enters first? Alex is probably late because he has been trying to shake off Toby. Ask the actors to think about volume – all of them should be talking in whispers except Toby.

Toby needs some kind of fanfare announcing his arrival – perhaps some kind of syncopated/beat-box-type rhythm that he creates himself. Also his hyperobjective should be to laugh at them all.

When the man leaves Miss Harris's house (and the actor playing him should remember as he walks across the stage that he has just had colonic irrigation!) is it the end of the stakeout? The characters could then take up new positions.

Now try the scene with no doors – there could be an imaginary door in the audience, so that the actors are watching them. Place bins downstage left, bus stop centre stage. When someone comes out of Miss Harris's house, we could see him as a projection (on a screen on the back wall) as if Oli is filming him. The image could start with a blur and then focus in on the door.

The video would be prerecorded. Work this through. You could hit a problem with the entrance of Miss Harris. She has to be onstage, where the man was on the screen. Could the logic be that we only see on the screen what Oli sees through her camera, and everything else is onstage?

Any such use of video would have to be clearly thought through. For instance, would you film the man leaving a real house/flat? How would this work if in other scenes you were using a single chair/cushion to represent a bedroom?

A third way could be to use two doors upstage on a diagonal for Bunce's house and Miss Harris's house – almost like an entrance from the wings. Avoid having the actors ending up in a straight line across the stage.

A useful exercise: at any point in the scene, whoever is in charge (however momentarily) should take centre stage. This exercise helps to find ways to keep everyone moving. It's important to do this to resolve masking issues and also to keep shuffling the pack and re-establishing status. There is a formality to the stakeout that needs to be mucked up.

A fourth option would be to place the door offstage left and a row of wheelie bins across the stage. Put Bunce inside one of the bins, but make sure he can pick it up and move with it. Play the scene with the actors using bin one as first position, then moving to bin two as second position, etc. Think about how you would get four large wheelie bins onto the stage. Is there a way to make their arrival part of the scene? We could see the ensemble putting their rubbish out . . .

Rather than stopping every few lines to make suggestions, give the actors the opportunity to run the scene. This offers them the chance to self-correct and removes their fear of doing something 'wrong'. It also helps to create conditions for discovery and allows them to feel where a scene may be going. See what the actors bring to the scene before making concrete choices.

Try where possible not to impose moves on an actor. Their instincts are often right.

WORKING ON THE FINAL SCENE

The hamster is either hibernating or dead. Everyone except Jo thinks that it is dead and wants her to bury it. Jo has brought the hamster with her to Bunce's house to make sure her parents don't bury it. At the end of the play the hamster should be triumphantly alive! Whatever is used, there are a few moments where a fake hamster has to have capacity for movement – e.g., hanging off a finger by its teeth. A key prop throughout the play is the hamster cage.

The hamster could be a toy on elastic, a battery-powered, radio-controlled toy, or something on a track. A number of fake hamsters could be revealed (and then concealed) in various places on the set – and then a real hamster used at the end.

Think about the effect that you want to create and what the point of the hamster is.

Play the mole-under-the-carpet game in a circle – the imaginary mole moves around the circle, and one after another everyone jumps over it and follows it with their eyes to demonstrate how we could see an imaginary hamster moving around the stage.

When approaching this type of big climactic scene it's very important within the chaos and activity to have moments when everything stops and we can focus – for example, on the moment when Bunce reveals that Oli and Toby like each other.

Work through this scene with your actors to clarify exactly who knows what about each character/situation. Work out the time-line – the parents need to have been away long enough for them to get tipsy, etc., but their return is also early enough for people to be calling round.

People's obsessions need to drive the scene. Ask: why have they come onto the stage? Why they are there and what do they want to happen?

Focus on the moment that Bunce tells Toby to shut up. This is an important turning point – Bunce standing up to him triggers the rest of the group into ganging up on Toby, and sets up the discovery by the parents.

It doesn't matter what you choose for Toby's disguise, but it would be interesting if it was something from Bunce's parent's collection that gave us an insight into the nature of their dressing up, as well as reinforcing Toby's desire to be more grown up than he is. It could be a cowboy outfit, a Chippendale-type fireman's outfit, a builder's, or something in studded leather. Whatever it is, it should be both masculine and ludicrous.

Look at the build up to the emergence from the cupboard (or whatever it is) – a classic piece of farce. You could use the costume-rails idea, or have the actors hiding under a table with a tablecloth so they can peer out from underneath it to say their lines. The crucial thing is that they should be squashed in like sardines – contained and close to each other. This should build to them exploding out of their hiding place because of Bunce's explosion and the exploding of the whole misunderstanding.

From here on the chaos should build rapidly, and there probably needs to be music from this point to the end – or at least until the moment that the parents go into a huddle to discuss colonic irrigation.

Think carefully about entrances in this scene – they need to be strong, and with so many actors onstage there could be a problem with masking. It is important to keep everyone moving and constantly forming new groupings.

The hamster and the characters' fear of it could be used to move people around the stage. Also people jumping up on chairs, etc., could be used to create different levels.

Find ways to bring people off and on again to relieve congestion – although it is also this congestion that makes the scene manic.

At the end of the play we should feel that Bunce has almost achieved coolness – but then, as the others pair off, he is left with the hamster. Then Agatha enters: it doesn't matter what she looks like, but we should understand that to Bunce she is the most beautiful girl in the world.

Workshop facilitated by Jeremy Sams
with notes taken by Paula Hamilton

A YEAR AND A DAY

Christina Reid

Christina Reid wrote *The King of the Castle* for *Connections* in 1999 and *The Gift of the Gab* for the NT *Assembly* series in 2003. Her other plays for stage, screen and radio include *Tea in a China Cup* (Thames TV Playwright Scheme Award, 1983), *My Name, Shall I Tell You My Name*, *The-Bomb-Damage-Sale Wedding Dress*, *Sex and the Single Granny*, *The Belle of Belfast City* (George Devine Award, 1986) *The Last of a Dyin' Race* (Giles Cooper Award for Best Radio Plays of 1986), *Did You Hear the One About the Irishman?* (Ulster TV Drama Award, 1980), *Joyriders* and its sequel *Clowns*. She has also written episodes of the TV series *Streetwise* and *Pie in the Sky*. In 2002, Methuen published six of her stage plays in a single volume, *Christina Reid Plays: 1*. Additional information on all Christina's work is available from the Christina Reid Collection in the Theatre Archive of the Linenhall Library, Belfast.

Author's Note

The story that led to the writing of this play began in
my head nearly twenty-five years ago, when I heard
the novelist Mervyn Wall tell a tale about a haunted
churchyard.

We were part of a group of a dozen or so Irish artists
and writers who were living and working in the Tyrone
Guthrie Centre, Annagmakerrig, Co. Monaghan – where,
it is said, the ghost of Lady Guthrie walks along a corridor
and looks out of an upstairs window. (None of us had
actually seen her, but, as is the way with such stories,
there were, of course, a few residents who claimed that
they knew somebody who knew somebody who knew
somebody who had.)

Most of us (artists and writers are nothing if not
imaginative) had other stories to tell of strange happenings
we'd heard of or experienced. The storytelling, the whiskey
and the wine flowed through the evening into the night.

There was one sceptical, sober artist there who dismissed
all word-of-mouth stories as unreliable myths, urban
legends that couldn't be proved. Mervyn smiled and told
his tale.

He said that there was, not too far away from Annagh-
makerrig, an ancient Irish churchyard. If you ever go to
a funeral there, don't linger afterwards. Don't be the last
to leave. Don't look back. Because, if you do, you will see
a beautiful young woman and you will fall in love. And
she will tell you that she has to go away until this time
next year. And she will promise that when you come back

to the churchyard she will be there, waiting for you. And this time next year you will return to that churchyard. In a coffin.

And then he smiled again and said that if anyone listening wanted to prove or disprove the story of the beautiful ghost all they had to do was go to that churchyard on the day of a funeral. And linger afterwards. And look back. And find out for themselves if it was a fact or a fiction. None of us, including the sceptic who didn't believe in ghosts, had the courage in us to tempt fate by going there.

The story stayed in my head. And every now and again it floated to the surface and I'd find myself wondering who the beautiful young woman was in life and how she became the bringer of death. Years later I used the basic storyline to write a short piece for BBC Radio 4. Last year, I used it again to write this play for *Connections*.

My basic storyline began in my head with a Storyteller, a Girl, two Ghosts, two Tribes and a lot of questions. Who? Where? When? What if . . .? When I began to write I didn't know that these characters would be joined by Pontificators, Acolytes, Traders and Kritters. Once they arrived, I had a play. My own ghost story, with music, singing, dancing and a terrible scream.

I wrote it with the intention of scaring the audience.

If you're a sober sceptic, if you don't believe this story, will you have the courage in you to look back at the end of the play?

CHRISTINA REID

Characters

The Storyteller
The Singer
The Musician
The Girl

The Kritter
an anthropoid more man than ape
The Landkritter
an animal-like creature
The Treekritter
a bird-like creature
The Waterkritter
an amphibious creature

The Silver Pontificator

The Crimson Pontificator

The Silver Acolyte

The Crimson Acolyte

The Silver Trader

The Crimson Trader

Tribe One
Children of the Silver Stars
Tribe Two
Children of the Crimson Moon

Twilight. Mist. Silence. An empty space, surrounded by stark bare trees.

The Storyteller asleep, on the ground, on the edge of the trees. Alongside her, The Kritter sleeps, unseen, completely hidden under a blanket.

Sound of The Singer and The Musician, from behind the audience. The melody is eerie, seductive. It begins with The Singer – a child's sweet voice singing 'La-la La-la-la' (a haunting version of the childish mocking 'na-na na-na-na' taunt).

Then The Musician is heard, playing the same five notes on a penny whistle. This is repeated, softly, insistently. Secret lovers calling to each other. With each repeat, the sound moves forward, from the back of the auditorium, through the audience, to the stage, past The Storyteller, into the trees.

The singing and the music merge into one, then stop abruptly.

A sudden, shocking, very, very brief glimpse of The Singer and The Musician in the trees – two ghastly, ghostly shades. Accompanied by a terrible, terrifying scream as they immediately vanish.

The Storyteller wakens, listens for a moment to the silence, moves towards the audience.

The Storyteller (*to the audience*) Be still. Be calm. Don't get your knickers in a twist. All you saw, all you heard – it was only me, dreaming. A dark dream. A trick of the light. Twilight time is not to be trusted. Now you see it, now you don't.

Trust me. I'm a storyteller.

Relax.

Things always look better in the morning, after a good
night's sleep.

Well, nearly always.

What?

You're not scared of the dark, are you? Big boys and girls
like you?

Do you want me to tell you a nice little bedtime story?
Do you?

The Kritter sits bolt upright. Throws off the blanket.

The Kritter (*to the audience*) No, you don't! (*Moving
towards the audience.*) Whatever you do, don't get her
started, or we'll be up all night. She could talk the hind
legs off a donkey, that one. (*To The Storyteller.*) Miles
you've walked me today. Miles and miles and miles.
And my feet are killing me. And I am very, very, very,
very tired. And I would like to go back to sleep, now.
Okay?

The Storyteller What wakened you? Did you hear
something?

The Kritter Yes.

The Storyteller What?

The Kritter You! Rabbiting on! Natter-natter. Chitter-
chatter.

The Storyteller Nothing else?

The Kritter I don't dream. You have enough imagination
for both of us. I would like to go back to sleep now.
I would like you to go back to sleep now. (*To the
audience.*) And you!

He goes back to the grove of trees, muttering to himself.

The Storyteller (*to the audience*) He's old. His bark's
worse than his bite.

The Kritter I am not a dog!

The Storyteller Goodnight!
The Kritter Goodnight!

He lies down, pulls the blanket over himself.

The Storyteller (*to the audience*) And a good night to
you too. Sweet dreams. Think beautiful thoughts.

*She goes back to the edge of the grove of trees. Lies
down.*

Darkness.
  A grey dawn. The Storyteller is wakened by:

*Offstage, in the distance, approaching – a slow
repeated drumbeat: na-na na-na-na rhythm.*
  *A drummer enters, at the head of a funeral procession.
A child's shrouded body or a small coffin carried and
followed by mourners. The Storyteller watches the
procession as it crosses the stage and exits.*
  *The last mourner is The Girl. She stops, looks back
at The Storyteller. The Storyteller shivers.*

Don't look back, child. Don't look back.

The Girl exits.
  The drumming fades into the distance.

(*To the audience.*) Another day. Another war. Another
dead child. Will there ever be an end to it?

While she is speaking The Girl re-enters.

The Girl (*peering out at the audience*) Who are you
talking to?

Behind her, The Kritter flings off the blanket.

The Kritter (*shouts*) Anybody who's daft enough to
listen to her! Day or night!
The Storyteller Pay him no heed. He thinks he's a tiger,
but he's just a big soft pussycat really.

603

The Kritter I am not a cat!

The Girl Who are you? What are you doing here? Don't you know there's a war on?

The Storyteller We're just passing through.

The Kritter She's a conjurer of tall tales.

The Storyteller And he is my constant companion. And my best pal, when he's not being a bear with a sore head.

The Kritter I am not a bear!

The Storyteller He's my dear old Kritter. And we've travelled the world together for a long time.

The Kritter Too long.

The Storyteller He thinks it's time we settled down and grew old gracefully.

The Kritter My last Storyteller didn't traipse me all over the world. She had a nice little cottage. We sat by the fire. She didn't go gadabout. People *came to her* to hear the old stories. Happy days. And then she went and passed me on to this one.

The Girl Passed you on?

The Storyteller He comes with the job.

The Kritter And goes with the job.

The Storyteller You'll miss me when I'm gone. (*Shivers, makes light of the feeling.*) Today, old friend, someone, somewhere, is walking on my grave.

The Kritter That is true of all of us, from the day and hour we are born.

Look at the state of you. Lack of sleep and no breakfast, that's why you're feeling shaky. I'll go and find us some food.

The Girl Me too. I'm starving.

The Kritter Don't you have a home to go to?

The Girl No, I don't.

The Storyteller Stay. Eat with us. I'll tell you a story to pass the time, till he gets back. It's the oldest story I know.

The Kritter And her excuse for wandering the world.
No matter how many miles you travel, no matter how
many times you tell this terrible tale, it won't change
anybody or anything. There will always be wars. There
will always be children like her, with no home and no
hope. It's how it is. It's the way of the wicked world.

He gets his blanket, wraps it round himself.

(*Calls back, as he is exiting.*) My last Storyteller liked
nice fairy tales, with happy-ever-after endings! And
roses round the door! And a roof over her head!

He exits, muttering to himself.

The Storyteller I was one of the many children who
heard the lovely fairy tales in her cottage. I loved them.
I still do. I still tell them, as I promised her I would.
But, unlike her, I also tell the story-that-has-no-ending.
It was passed down through the ages by all the
Storytellers who went before her. But she kept it to
herself, until her dying day.
And at the end, she passed it on to me, with The Kritter.
Would you like me to pass it on to you?
The Girl Yes, I would.
The Storyteller (*to The Girl and the audience*) Sit by me.
Listen. Look. See the world as it was.

Warm light.
    The Storyteller begins her tale.
*The Landkritter, The Treekritter and The Waterkritter
come onstage.*
    The Landkritter has a wheelbarrow of props.
    The Treekritter has a bird's-nest basket of props.
    *The Waterkritter has a shell or boat-shaped basket
of props.*
    *They create the set of the long-ago world as The
Storyteller conjures it.*

The Storyteller
Once upon a time.
Long, long ago.
When the world was very young.
There was a big beautiful garden.
Surrounded by an orchard of gold and green and copper
coloured trees.
A winding river, with multicoloured stepping stones of
amber and coral and lapis lazuli, flowed through the
garden.
And the Kritters of the land, the trees and the water
shared the plants and the fruit of the earth and the
river.

*The three Kritters, having set the scene, sit down
together on the stepping stones.*

And a year and a day passed.
And new creatures appeared in the garden.

*Four humans enter. A male and a female on each side
of the river.*
*The females are carrying a baby. The males carry
wooden staves. They thump the ground with the
staves: an aggressive na-na na-na-na rhythm, indicative
of a quarrel.*
*They stop. Stare across at each other with cold
hostility.*

The Waterkritter Funny looking lot, aren't they?
The Landkritter No fur.
The Treekritter No feathers.
The Waterkritter No fins.
The Landkritter They won't last.
The Treekritter/Waterkritter No chance.
The Landkritter This time next year, we'll have the place
to ourselves again.
The Treekritter/Waterkritter Yeah.

The humans exit.

The Storyteller
And another year and a day passed.

The humans reappear on each side of the river,
followed by all of their tribe.
    Pause as the Kritters take this in.

The Landkritter Got that wrong, didn't we?
The Treekritter/Waterkritter Yeah.
The Storyteller
The two tribes settled on opposite sides of the river.
And each tribe had their own language.
And their own way of living.
And dressing. And cooking.
And they worshipped different Gods.
And each tribe believed that they were the Chosen-
    People-of-the-One-True-God.
Because generations of Pontificator priests had
    mesmerised and terrified them into believing it was so.

A Pontificator dressed in silver and a Pontificator
dressed in crimson preach a variation on the same
sermon to the children of the two tribes on either side
of the river.

Silver Pontificator If you live your life according to the
    divine teaching of the Supreme God of the Silver Stars
    you shall ascend to His Heaven on star-spangled wings
    and live happily ever after.
Silver Tribe (*looking at their Pontificator, mesmerised*)
    Oooohhhh . . .
Crimson Pontificator . . . and the true believers among
    you shall ascend on rainbow wings to the Kingdom of
    the Almighty God of the Crimson Moon and live
    happily ever after.
Crimson Tribe (*looking at their Pontificator, mesmerised*)
    Oooohhhh . . .

Crimson Pontificator – but if you ever cross the river –
Silver Pontificator – to consort with the heathen on the
other side –
Crimson Pontificator – the heavens shall open –
Silver Pontificator – and the thunder –
Crimson Pontificator – and the lightning –
Silver Pontificator – of the wrath –
Silver and Crimson Pontificators – of the one true God –
Crimson Pontificator – shall strike you down –
Silver Pontificator – and the earth shall split asunder –
Crimson Pontificator – and the river shall drag you
down –
Silver Pontificator – and you shall descend into hell –
Crimson Pontificator – where your heavenly wings shall
melt in the flames –
Silver Pontificator – and your earthly body and bones –
Crimson Pontificator – shall blister and burn –
Silver and Crimson Pontificators – for ever and a year
and a day!
Both Tribes (*in unison, looking across the river at each
other, terrified*) Aaaaahhhh!
Silver and Crimson Pontificators Let us pray for God's
good grace.

The Tribes bow their heads and pray.

The Landkritter What a load of old cobblers.
The Treekritter Poppycock.
The Waterkritter Codswallop.
All Three Kritters Balderdash and Claptrap.
Silver and Crimson Pontificators Amen.
Both Tribes Amen.

The Pontificators exit, followed by The Tribes.

A girl (The Singer) is at the back of the Silver Tribe.
*A boy (The Musician) is at the back of The Crimson
Tribe.*

They turn, look at each other for a long moment, fall in love.
They speak in different languages.

The Singer If I could speak the language of your tribe, what would I say?
The Musician I wish I had the words to tell you how beautiful you are.
The Singer I would say that I do not feel afraid of you.
The Musician My grandmother told me that we all spoke the same language once –
The Singer I would sing for you.
The Musician – long long ago, when we were all one tribe –
The Singer I would like to dance with you.
The Musician – before we quarrelled and went our separate ways.
The Singer I wish I had the words to tell you how beautiful you are.
The Singer/The Musician You are my heart's desire.

They gaze longingly at each other.

The Landkritter We could put them out of their misery and translate for them.
The Treekritter Better to let the humans go on thinking we're dumb and stupid.
The Waterkritter If the Pontificators find out that we can talk among ourselves . . .
The Treekritter And understand what they say.
The Waterkritter And speak it, like they do.
The Treekritter They'll claim us as God's children.
The Waterkritter The lost tribe.
The Treekritter And make us into converts.
The Waterkritter And make us wear clothes.

They all shudder at the thought of it.

The Landkritter Better we keep it our secret, like we agreed.

The Treekritter/Waterkritter Yeah.

The Singer I have to go . . .

The Musician (*as she turns away*) Don't leave.

He plays the five la-la la-la-la notes on a penny whistle. The Singer turns back. Sings.

The Singer La-la la-la-la.

They repeat this, moving towards each other.

The Landkritter (*sniffs the air*) I smell Pontificator heading this way.

The Treekritter (*rushes to The Musician, who is about to play again*) Stop!

The Waterkritter (*rushes to The Singer, who is about to sing again*) Don't!

The Musician and The Singer stare in astonishment at the talking Kritters.

The Landkritter So much for keeping it our secret.

The Singer/The Musician You can speak.

The Treekritter/Waterkritter Don't tell the Pontificators.

The Landkritter (*sniffing*) They're very close!

The Treekritter/The Waterkritter They're behind you.

The Treekritter Turn away.

The Waterkritter Look away.

The Treekritter/Waterkritter Now!

The Singer and The Musician turn as The Silver and The Crimson Pontificators enter.
The Kritters go into dumb-animal mode.

The Singer I was just . . . (*puts her hands behind her back, slips a ring off her finger, holds it out*) I lost my ring. It's loose. It's always slipping off. (*Demonstrates.*) See?

Silver Pontificator I see.

He takes the ring from her. Looks from her towards
The Musician.

I thought I heard voices.

The Singer He came out of the trees and I was frightened
and I shouted at him to go away.

Silver Pontificator Good. May God guide you safely
home.

The Singer exits.

The Musician (*holding out the penny whistle*) I left this
behind.

Crimson Pontificator Careless of you.

He takes the penny whistle from him.

Was there anything else?

The Musician I shouted at a heathen girl for looking at me.

Crimson Pontificator God will bless you for it. Goodnight.

The Musician exits.
The two Pontificators walk to the river's edge. Face
each other. Hold out the ring and the penny whistle.
Drop them into the water
They exchange a conspiratorial smile, a slight nod
of the head. An unspoken agreement that it suits them
to keep the two tribes apart.
They walk away from the river and exit.

The Landkritter Miserable mangy mankers.

The Treekritter Bad cess to them and all their tribe.

The Waterkritter takes the penny whistle and the ring
out of the river.

The Waterkritter Not all. They kept our secret.

The Landkritter They won't be back for those. The
Pontificators are not stupid. They'll be watching their
every move.

The Storyteller Which indeed they did.

And The Singer and The Musician thought of each other every day and dreamt of each other every night.

And another year and a day passed.

The weather was perfect.

There was an abundant harvest.

And the tribes came to the river to celebrate and show off their good fortune and prosperity to each other.

The two Tribes enter, led by the Pontificators.

Silver and Crimson Pontificators God be praised! Let the celebrations begin!

Big cheers from The Tribes.

Big celebrations with ale, cider and wine. (Food is optional.)

Dancing. Clapping. Foot-stamping. Singing/ Chanting. (Musical instruments for the song/dance routine are optional, not essential.)

The verses of the following are to be sung or chanted. The Tribes can sing alternate verses or lines within each verse. The 'Yeah' at the end of each verse is a shout.

Song/Chant

We've got apples
We've got oranges
We've got mango and melons too
We've got mushrooms
We've got truffles
We've got more than you.
Yeah!

We've got apricots
We've got guava
We've got plums and peaches too
We've got tangerines

We've got nectarines
We've got more than you.
Yeah!

We've got onions
We've got beetroot
We've got peas and mangetout too
We've got marrows
We've got pumpkins
We've got more than you.
Yeah!

We've got barley
We've got lentils
We've got maize and millet too
We've got celery
We've got broccoli
We've got more than you.
Yeah!

We've got chicory
We've got zucchini
We've got yams and olives too
We've got aubergines
We've got artichokes
We've got more than you.
Yeah!

We've got lycees
We've got kumquats
We've got kiwi and pawpaw too
We've got chestnuts
We've got coconuts
We've got more than you.
Yeah!

All together:

Our corn is sweeter
Our fruit is juicier
Our wheat and rye grow taller than you
Our beans are broader
Our berries are bigger
We are better than you.
Yes!! (*Or 'Ooooh! Yeahhhhhhh!'*)

They go on dancing to the rhythm of the song/chant.
    The Pontificators are seen whispering to an Acolyte.
The Acolytes listen, nod, give a thumbs-up sign.
    The Silver Acolyte moves towards The Singer. The
Crimson Acolyte moves towards The Musician.
    The Pontificators look across at each other.
Exchange again a conspiratorial smile, a slight nod of
the head.
    During the dancing, The Singer and The Musician
keep trying to get to the river side to catch a glimpse of
each other. Every time they get close, the Acolytes
dance them away, back into the crowd.

The celebrations wind down. The drunk and happy
Tribes begin to wend their way home.
    The Singer and The Musician are among the last to
leave.
    The Acolytes make sure that they do.
The Three Kritters are left alone. They sit in silence for
a moment. The Landkritter sniffs the air.

The Landkritter All clear.

The Kritters produce the drink they've stashed.

All Three Kritters Mud in your eye!!

The Waterkritter and The Treekritter take a big swig
of their drinks.

The Waterkritter Bloody good ale.
The Treekritter Cracking cider.

The Landkritter takes his time. Sniffs his drink. Swirls it round his mouth before swallowing.

The Landkritter Full-bodied. Fruity. Hint of apricots. Their best year yet.

The Waterkritter and The Treekritter exchange 'get him' looks. The Landkritter sniffs again.

The Treekritter Oh for goodness' sake!
The Waterkritter Just drink the stuff!
The Landkritter (*sniffs again*) There's someone coming.

The Kritters hide the drink and go into dumb animal mode.
  The Musician enters.

The Musician (*smiling at them*) You don't fool me any more.

Pause. The Kritters don't move.

It's alright, I'm alone. I made sure I wasn't followed.

The Kritters stop acting dumb.

The Landkritter How did you get away from that creepy Acolyte?
The Musician Humans can act dumb too. I pretended to be asleep, until he fell asleep.

The Waterkritter gives him the penny whistle and the ring.

The Waterkritter Thank you for keeping our secret. The ring is hers. The Pontificators chucked them in the river.

The Musician puts the ring on his finger. Plays the five notes on the penny whistle.

Waits. Plays them again.
Waits. Is about to play again.
The Singer's voice is heard offstage. 'La-la la-la-la.'
She enters.

The Singer La-la la-la-la.

They walk towards each other.
Step into the river, on to the stepping stones.
They touch.
They kiss.

The Singer The heavens have not opened.

The Treekritter (*translating/agreeing*) The heavens have not opened.

The Musician The earth has not split asunder.

The Landkritter (*translating/agreeing*) The earth has not split asunder.

The Singer/The Musician The water does not drag us down.

The Waterkritter (*indignant*) There is no road to hell at the bottom of river. It's where I was born. I've got kith and kin down there. It's a myth.

The Singer Is heaven a myth too?

The Landkritter We don't know.

The Treekritter We're not like you.

The Waterkritter We live life here and now.

The Landkritter It's nearly dawn. You should both go home soon, before you are missed.

The Singer/The Musician Not yet. Not yet . . .

They stop, both puzzled by the same thing. Stare at the Kritters.

The Musician We both understood what you just said.

The Singer How is it that when you speak in my language, he understands too?

The Landkritter I wasn't speaking in your language. Or his.

The Treekritter We can also speak the old language.

The Waterkritter The one your ancestors shared, before they quarrelled and went their separate ways.

The Singer But how do we know it?

The Landkritter The memory of it is still in you.

The Treekritter You were born knowing it.

The Waterkritter And forgot about it, as you grew up and learned the language of your tribe.

The Landkritter You've just remembered it again, because you needed to, that's all.

The Waterkritter Just as you remembered the notes you sung and played.

The Treekritter (*sings*) La-la la-la-la . . . la-la la-la-la . . .

The Waterkritter It's one of the oldest sounds in the world.

A pause. The Singer and the Musician look at each other, lost for words.

The Landkritter Go on then. Say something.

The Treekritter You can do it.

The Waterkritter The old words are still there, in your head.

The Treekritter And your heart.

The Waterkritter Just open your mouth and let them all out.

The Landkritter Oh for goodness' sake, stop dithering and just go for it!

The Musician Hello.

The Singer Hello.

They gaze at each other, overcome.

The Landkritter Is that it?

The Treekritter and The Waterkritter exchange looks, nudge The Landkritter, make a head/eye signal.

The Landkritter What?

*The Treekritter and the Waterkritter repeat the nudge/
signal.*

The Landkritter What!?
The Treekritter I think they need a little bit of time
together.
The Waterkritter By themselves.
The Landkritter What for?

*Exasperated looks/gestures from The Treekritter and
The Waterkritter.
    The Landkritter gets the message.*

The Landkritter Oh, I see. (*To The Singer and The
Musician.*) Just going for a little stroll, in the orchard.
Alright?
The Singer/The Musician (*without taking their eyes off
each other*) Alright.
The Landkritter Shall we bring you back some apples?

*Stern looks from The Treekritter and The Waterkritter.
    They steer The Landkritter away from the lovers.
Into the orchard and offstage.*

The Singer Hello.
The Musician Hello.
The Singer You're wearing my ring.
The Musician The Waterkritter rescued it from the river.

*He takes the ring off his finger, puts it on her finger.
She removes it, puts it back on his finger.*

The Singer With this I make you mine.

*He takes his own ring from his finger. Puts it on her
finger.*

The Musician With this I bond you to me.
The Singer/The Musician For all our days. And all our
nights.
The Musician I am yours.

The Singer I am yours.

The Musician Never to part.

The Singer No one and nothing shall come between us.

The Singer/The Musician For as long as we both shall live.

The Musician I love you.

The Singer I love you.

The Musician I will love you for all of my life.

The Singer I will love you in this life and the next.

The Musician I will love you for ever.

The Singer I will love you for ever and a year and a day.

The Singer/The Musician You are my heart's desire.

They dance together.

The Musician Walk away from this place with me.

The Singer Let us follow the river and see where it leads us.

The Musician And never look back.

The Singer And never look back.

They walk, hand in hand, along the stepping stones, into the trees.

As they exit, the Silver and Crimson Pontificators enter. The two Acolytes are behind them.

Offstage, The Singer is heard singing the five notes. Then The Musician is heard playing the five notes.

The Pontificators gesture towards the trees. The Acolytes go after The Singer and The Musician.

Offstage, The Singer and The Musician are heard singing and playing the five notes in unison.

An abrupt stop to the sound.

A terrible scream, as heard at the beginning of the play.

Silence.

The Pontificators stand, impassive.

The Acolytes come out of the trees, carrying the blood-soaked bodies of The Singer and The Musician.

They throw them down at the feet of The Pontificators.

Crimson Pontificator Tell the tribe that The Children of
The Silver Stars have kidnapped and murdered our
musician.

Silver Pontificator Tell the tribe that The Children of The
Crimson Moon have captured and killed the singer of
our songs.

The Acolytes exit, shouting.

Silver and Crimson Acolytes Murder! Murder! Murder!

*The Kritters come out of the trees. Shocked. Trembling.
They sit down, huddled together on the stepping
stones.
The two Tribes enter. Weeping and wailing.
The bodies of The Singer and The Musician are
lifted. Ceremonially laid out, washed, wrapped.
They lie, side by side, separated by the river.
A Star-God shrine is placed around The Singer.
A Crimson-God shrine is placed around The Musician.
The Tribes kneel. The Pontificators raise their arms
heavenward, over the shrines.*

Crimson Pontificator In the name of the One True God –

Silver Pontificator In the name of the One True God –

Silver and Crimson Pontificators – I declare this a holy
place.

Silver Pontificator Weep no more. Her spirit has
ascended to the silver stars.

Crimson Pontificator Weep no more. His spirit has
ascended to the crimson moon.

Silver and Crimson Pontificators Arise! Rejoice!

*Big cheers from The Tribes.
They turn the two shrines into a focal point for
religious fervour and good business. Place flowers and*

offerings (candles, notes, cuddly toys) on the shrines.
Set up souvenir stalls.
The Three Kritters walk away, into the trees.

The Girl (*stands up, shouts to The Kritters*) Come back!
Tell them what really happened here! You saw it! Say it!

The Storyteller Hush, child. They can't hear you.

The Girl Was keeping their secret more important to
them than telling the truth of it?

The Storyteller The Kritters of the land, the trees and the
water were struck dumb with terror by what they saw.
They never spoke to the humans again.

The Girl And nobody questioned what The Pontificators
said?

The Storyteller Need and greed go hand in hand in the
marketplace.

Shouts from the traders in the Silver Shrine and
Crimson Shrine marketplaces. The pilgrim shoppers
gather round, react to the sales pitch.

Silver Trader Bangles and bracelets! Earrings and
necklaces! Silver stars for the Singer Saint!

Crimson Trader Flutes and whistles for the Martyred
Musician! Crimson ribbons and beads for your hair!

Silver Trader A star for each year of the life of the
martyr!

Crimson Trader A moon on a medal to ward off the devil!

Silver Trader A ring like the one that she wore when they
killed her.

Crimson Trader A plate with the face of our heavenly
saint!

Silver Trader A ball for a baby. She loved little children.

Crimson Trader A doll that sheds tears on the day that
he died.

Silver Trader A piss-pot engraved with the face of the
heathen!

Crimson Trader A curse on a candle, to cripple their
sons!
Silver Trader A picture of her with her wings all star-
spangled.
Crimson Trader His wings on a blanket, all fluffy and
warm.

*Silence falls as the Silver and Crimson Pontificators
enter. They are followed by the two Acolytes. Each
Acolyte carries a roll of cloth.*

*They go to the shrines. The Acolytes unroll the
cloths, which contain a selection of charms, relics,
miraculous cures and the like.*

*The Pontificators bestow a blessing, then leave The
Acolytes at the shrine, stroll through the pilgrim
shoppers. Look at the goods on offer on the stalls.*

Silver Trader Sugar-coated stars?
Crimson Trader Chocolate moons with raspberry icing?

The Pontificators take the offerings.

*The Traders hold out their hands for payment.
The Pontificators ignore them and stand, eating the
sweets, watching as the pilgrim shoppers move
towards The Acolytes to see what they have on offer.
The Traders are well miffed.*

Silver Acolyte Tears from the Sainted Singer's eye, that
fell on the lapis lazuli.
Crimson Acolyte Drops of blood from the Martyr's
shroud, that fell back to the earth on a crimson cloud.
Silver Acolyte Find true love with a bead of her blood, in
a tincture of rose and forget-me-not bud.
Crimson Acolyte A piece of red amber splashed with his
tears. Place under your pillow and banish night fears.
Silver Acolyte A testimony from a mother, whose child
failed to thrive. She gave her the saint's blood. And

kept her alive. She's a singer of songs now, that once sickly child.

Crimson Acolyte A premature baby born deaf, dumb and blind. The teardrops stained red cured his ears and his eyes. He speaks and plays music, that once silent child.

Silver Acolyte A piece of her robe.

Crimson Acolyte A lock of his hair

Silver Acolyte A nail from her finger.

Crimson Acolyte A lash from his eye.

Silver and Crimson Acolytes For health, wealth and happiness. Buy, buy, buy.

The pilgrim shoppers surge forward.
The Pontificators smile and walk away.
Behind their backs, The Traders pull a face/make a rude gesture. Get back to business as soon as The Pontificators have exited.

Crimson Trader Special offer!

Silver Trader For one day only!

Silver and Crimson Traders Buy one, get one free!

Crimson Trader Merrie Musician Potency Pills!

Silver Trader Sexy Singer Soap-on-a-Rope!

Some of the pilgrim shoppers move back towards the traders. Some stay where they are.

The Storyteller And another year and a day passed.
More perfect weather.
And an even bigger harvest than the year before.

Big cheers from The Tribes.
A reprise of the harvest celebration song/chant/dance. The Pontificators and The Acolytes looking on, very prosperous and pleased with themselves.
The sound of The Musician playing, followed by the sound of The Singer singing, is heard. The tribes stop dancing. Listen.

Silence.
The lovers call to each other again. And both Tribes
hear:
Softly, from inside the Crimson shrine – the sound
of The Musician playing the five notes.
Softly, from inside the Silver shrine – The sound of
The Singer singing the five notes.
Silence.
The call is repeated, louder this time.
And again.
Silence.
The Tribes are scared, begin to back away.

Silver and Crimson Pontificators (*to their Tribes*) Stop!
(*Pointing/accusing each other.*) It's a trick! (*Furious, as*
some of their Tribes run away.) I command you to
stay!

A few of each Tribe stay, including The Acolytes and
The Traders.

Silver Pontificator A heathen trick to seize our land!
Crimson Pontificator A heathen trick to steal our crops!
Silver Pontificator And seduce our women.
Crimson Pontificator And corrupt our children!
Silver and Crimson Pontificators To the ways of their
heathen God!
Crimson Pontificator Take his sacred body to the safety
of the temple.
Silver Pontificator Take her sacred body to the safety of
the tabernacle.

The Tribes aren't too keen to go anywhere near the
shrines.

Silver and Crimson Pontificators (*to The Acolytes*) Open
the shrine. (*To The Traders.*) Help them!

The Acolytes and The Traders open the shrines.

They are both empty.
The Musician is heard playing.
The Singer is heard singing.
The Tribes run away as the Pontificators shout.

Silver and Crimson Pontificators God be praised! He/She
has ascended to Heaven!

The Traders gesture that they don't believe a word of it
and follow The Tribes offstage. The Pontificators and
The Acolytes stand alone in the silence.
Sound of The Musician playing from the empty
shrine.
Sound of The Singer singing from the empty shrine.
The sounds are repeated, moving towards each
other.
The Pontificators and The Acolytes look from the
shrines to the river, following the sound of the music
and the singing as it travels into the trees.
They get really scared when the playing and the
singing merge into one in the trees, where they know
The Singer and The Musician actually died.
The merged music and singing soar.
The sound distorts.
The sky darkens.
The Pontificators and The Acolytes flee.

The ghostly, ghastly shades of The Singer and The
Musician walk out of the trees, hand in hand, towards
the audience.
Immediate Blackout.

The next day dawns. A bleak cold light.
The Three Kritters enter with barrow and baskets.
As The Storyteller goes on telling her tale, they
un-create the garden – return the stage to the original
empty space surrounded by stark, bare trees.

The Storyteller And the flowers, gifts and offerings on the shrines, blackened and shrivelled and crumbled to dust.

And a bitter wind blew the dust over the garden and the orchard and the river

And the plants and fruits of the land, the trees and the water festered and died.

And mould rotted the stores of corn, barley, wheat and rye.

And nothing would grow again in the poisoned earth.

And the stench of decay floated in the air and on the stagnant river.

And famine and pestilence reduced The Tribes to skin and bone.

The very old and the the very young were among the first to die.

Some survived, but not many.

And those who did, abandoned the poisoned garden for ever.

And followed The Kritters into the big wide world beyond.

As The Landkritter, The Treekritter and The Water-kritter exit, The Kritter enters, carrying a small sack.

The Kritter Not much food left round here. Maggoty old grain from an abandoned farm.

The Girl The war is heading this way. Everybody's leaving.

The Kritter If the Kritters had inherited the earth instead of you lot, there would be no such thing as war.

The Girl Their descendants fight among themselves too.

The Kritter But not in the name of a celestial God. What sort of a reason is that?

The Girl Did The Singer and The Musician stay in the garden? Is the garden still in the world somewhere?

The Kritter Ask her. She's The Storyteller.

The Storyteller When our ancestors left the garden, some went north, some went south, some went east, some went west. And the two tribes became many tribes all over the big wide world.

The Kritter Where they carried on the ancient tradition of waging war on each other.

The Storyteller Didn't I just hear you say that I was The Storyteller round here?

The Kritter As the only one who can cook round here, I'll go and see if I can find any wild herbs that have survived the war. Catmint and camomile are particularly good in grain stew with maggots.

He exits, muttering.

The Girl He just made that up, didn't he?

The Storyteller He's cooked some very tasty meals over the years, with ingredients you might not want to know about.

The Girl What I really want to know is where the garden is. Maybe after all this time it has gone back to the beautiful place it once was. Maybe we could find it. Maybe we could live there.

The Storyteller Maybe.

The Girl But you don't know for sure, do you?

The Storyteller Nobody knows for sure. Though some claim they do. All I can tell you is that religions all over the world, north, south, east and west, tell tales of a mythical garden. And claim it as their own. And being human, they disagree about exactly where the garden was, where it still might be, who shall inherit it, who shall not.

Some of the Storytellers say that when we corrupted it, we were banished from the garden for ever.

Other Storytellers say that when we die, we shall ascend to the garden that awaits us in Heaven. But only if we have lived the good life according to the teachings of whatever One-True-God they believe in.

The stories of who this All-Powerful-God is and where he came from vary, depending on which Pontificator is telling the tale.

It's much the same tale worldwide, with regional variations.

And yes, there are Storytellers who believe that the garden is still here, somewhere in the big wide world. But we've forgotten where it used to be or have lost the way to find it.

The Girl What do you believe? That the garden is lost for ever? That it is waiting for us in Heaven? That it is still here, somewhere in the big wide world? What version of this tale did The Kritter's last Storyteller pass on to you?

The Storyteller The version that was passed on to her by the Storyteller who went before her.

The Girl You said you would pass it on to me.

The Storyteller So I did.

The Girl So, tell me the rest of it. Tell me what happened after the Kritters and the two Tribes left the garden. Did the ghosts of the lovers go on singing and playing together?

The Storyteller There was silence in the deserted garden for a year and a day. And then The Singer and The Musician appeared again, among the trees. And according to legend, when they discovered that The Tribes had fled, they followed them into the big wide world.

And every year and a day, ever since, the lovers reappear, and they sing and play together.

The Girl Where?

The Storyteller Different places, different times. Could be anywhere. Could be right here.

Listen to me, child. Listen and never forget.

If you ever hear the lovers singing and playing together, the sound will come from behind you. Don't be seduced by the music. Don't look back. Walk away from them. And don't look back.

The Girl Why not?

The Storyteller They love only each other.

But if you turn and look at them, they will tell you that *you* are their heart's desire. And you will see them as they once were. And you will fall in love. And they will smile at you and kiss you. And they will tell you that they have to go away, but they will promise to return for you in a year and day.

And in a year and a day, those on this earth who truly love you, will be the mourners at your funeral.

A small pause, as The Girl takes this in.
The Kritter returns with a bunch of bedraggled greenery.

The Kritter There's a little stream back there. Let's wash and dress for dinner.

The Girl I don't feel very hungry any more.

The Kritter You told her, then?

The Storyteller Yes.

The Kritter After we've eaten, get her to tell you one of her happy stories. Come on, the pair of you. Cheer up. Chop-chop. Onwards and upwards.

The Storyteller You are a wondrous creature. And I love you to bits.

The Kritter Don't be soft.

But he returns her smile.
The Girl looks at them and smiles. She is standing behind them.
They all have their backs to the grove of bare trees.
From the trees, the sound of The Singer and The Musician is heard.

They come out of the trees, singing and playing together, alive as they once were, not the shades they have become.
The Girl half-turns her head, seduced by the music.
The Storyteller turns, flings her arms around the girl, stops her from looking back.

The Storyteller Don't look back at them! Look at me! Look at me.

But The Storyteller is now looking at The Singer and The Musician.
She pushes the girl away, into the arms of The Kritter.
He holds The Girl to him, to prevent her from looking at the lovers.
The Singer and The Musician smile at The Storyteller for a long moment.

The Singer/The Musician You are my heart's desire.

They kiss The Storyteller and walk back into the trees.
The Kritter releases The Girl. She runs to The Storyteller.
The Girl Don't die. Please don't die.

The Storyteller stretches out her arms. Places the palm of her hands on each side of The Girl's face. Looks into her eyes. Blows three times into The Girl's face.

The Storyteller I pass my spirit to you. With The Kritter. Hush, child. Don't cry. Everybody has to die sometime. And we will have a year and a day together. Time enough for me to pass on to you all the other old stories that were passed on to me.

She places The Girl's hand in The Kritter's hand.
A sign/gesture between The Storyteller and The Kritter, acknowledging the passing/the new beginning.

The Kritter What sort of Storyteller will you be, I wonder? A gadabout or a stay-at-home?

The Girl Don't know yet.

The Kritter Let's you and I discuss it over dinner.

The Kritter leads The Girl offstage.
The Storyteller watches them as they exit, then turns to the audience.

The Storyteller Remember me. And don't forget – onwards and upwards. Don't be seduced by the music. Don't look back.

As the lights dim slowly on The Storyteller, the haunting sound of The Singer and The Musician is heard from behind the audience – secret lovers calling to each other as at the beginning of the play.
The singing and the music merge into one.
A terrible scream. Immediate blackout.

End.

Production Notes

Christina Reid loves ghost stories and graveyards. Once she was told a story at a centre for artists in Tyrone Guthrie's old home by the storyteller Mervyn Wall. It was about a graveyard where you mustn't linger because you will hear someone behind you. This was the inspiration for her play, which contains stories within stories framed by the Storyteller.

THE CHALLENGES

Staging the play offers the following challenges:

- How to make the river look interesting.

- How to make the sound move through the auditorium and across the stage without necessarily using speakers.

- What to do with the props – a minimalist approach?

- How to make the comedy work and balance it with the ghost story.

- How to manage the stepping-stones

- How to create and dismantle the shrines.

- How to make the Kritters distinctive from each other.

- How to work with a large cast to avoid a pile-up and how to get them on and off.

- How to fit into a smaller space.

- How to work with a smaller cast.

- How to vanish in a small space.

- How to engage your company to frighten people.

- How to manage the modern/old-fashioned mix.

You could use an alternative instrument to the tin whistle so long as it can produce an eerie quality of sound.

'Na-na na-na-na' is a sound used by children worldwide. There is a strong narrative progression in the sound. Simple and haunting, it is part of the story and must not be altered.

You don't necessarily need musical instruments for the song and dance routines. Make the most of the rhythms.

EXERCISE

Move 'in the quality of' things – such as ice, thick black tar, soggy cardboard, snowflakes falling. Find the quality and the rhythmic movement. Work wrists and fingers.

Move as in an environment surrounded by thick gases, finding pockets of air and moving them round the body.

THE CHARACTERS

THE STORYTELLER AND THE KRITTER   Christina has a sense the Kritter should be male, the Storyteller female.

The relationship between the Storyteller and the Kritter is key. The Kritter is more a person than an ape. The Kritter doesn't die; has had several storytellers and is about to get another one. There is love between them. They are equals – two parts of a whole, symbiotic. The gesture of 'moving on' is important. (At the end of the play, after a year and a day the new storyteller will pass on the stories.)

The Storyteller might have a longer-then-human lifespan. She's not paid, but is given food and shelter. Kritter is down-to-earth. He's definitely not a servant or a pet. He looks after the Storyteller and does things for her that she can't do, like cooking. You don't need to make her appear old or a crone – rather, accentuate her knowledge, bring out a quality of 'otherness'.

Avoid using mask or heavy make-up for the Kritters – it's important to see facial expressions. Find different ways of developing these characters through movement.

THE TRIBES   They are divided and separated by religion and lifestyle, but they are essentially the same people with a common ancestry. Don t give the tribes different physical properties. If you have a mixed-race cast, give that mix to both tribes.

Christina was told as a child in Belfast that Catholics had their eyes set close together and wrote this into a previous play. The actor who spoke the lines (who was Catholic) said she had heard that it was Protestants who had their eyes set close together . . . Christina changed the line.

EXERCISE

Split into groups of three and make a triangle. Apex is leader, others mirror movements. Leader passes clearly to another, re-form triangle and carry on as seamlessly as possible. Keep as a group, travel but keep in shape.

Next stage: merge two groups into one triangle, one person as leader, two behind and three at back. Leader passes to outside edge to re-form behind them. The structure can then be more informal, moving as a tight group and stopping. Explore different rhythms, end the exercise by having the two groups facing each other.

THE SINGER AND MUSICIAN   They fall in love immediately and absolutely the moment they set eyes on each other. Look at stories and films which describe and show love at first sight.

Don't signal to the audience that the lovers will meet a bad end. It should come as a terrible shock.

PONTIFICATORS   Villainous and greedy for wealth and power. Will go to any extreme to keep control over their tribe.

ACOLYTES   Oily, ambitious, on the make, prepared to obey orders and do the dirty work.

TRADERS   Earthy. Crafty. Not great believers in any god, but quick to spot a money-making opportunity in religious fervour.

Each Pontificator, Acolyte and Trader will, when it suits them, collude and conspire secretly with their counterpart in the other tribe.

SETTING

The action takes place in a devastated war zone and in a beautiful lush garden with trees, a river and stepping stones. Use these locations for strong entrances and useful acting areas rather than just dressing.

It is important to mark the difference between the cold war-torn world and the warmth of the world in the garden.

Stark, bare trees can be changed to summer simply by putting colour onto them with lighting. Props can be added or mimed.

Workshop facilitated by Josie Rourke and Dominic LeClerc, with notes taken by Sally Naylor

Participating Schools and Companies

The Abbey School Reading
The Academy at Peckham
ACS Cobham International
    School
Alderbrook Actors Theatre
Arc Youth Company
The Arnewood School
Arnold School Blackpool
Astor College for the Arts

Bablake School
The Basement
The Beacon Youth Theatre
Bedford College
Bilimankhwe Youth Theatre
Bishop Thomas Grant School
Bishop's Stortford College
Boston Theatre Company
Bournemouth School for Girls
Brentwood Youth Theatre
Brewery Arts Centre Youth
    Theatre Kendal
Bristol Old Vic Youth Theatre
British School of Brussels
The BRIT School for Performing
    Arts and Technology
Brockhill Park Performing Arts
    College: NoName Theatre
Buckingham School
Burntwood School

Callington Community College:
    Young and Unique
The Canterbury High School

Cardinal Newman R C
    Secondary School
The Carriageworks
The Castle Arts Centre
    Youth Theatre
Castleford High School
Castle Vale School
CATS Youth Theatre
    Southampton
Chaucer Business and
    Enterprise College
Cheadle and Marple Sixth
    Form College
Chingford Foundation
    Secondary School
City College Norwich
Clacton County High School
Claremont High School
The Clarendon School:
    Culture Box
Coleg Sir Gar
Conquest Youth Theatre
Coopers Technology College
Coulsdon College
County Carlow Youth Theatre
Craigholme School
CRE8 Yeovil
The Crestwood School

Doncaster College
Doyly Arts Peterborough
Dukeries Community College
Dumont High School Youth
    Theatre New Jersey

Earlsfield School
Edge of Reason from Brigshaw
  High School
Ellesmere College

Forest Gate Community School
Fowey Community College

The Gantry Youth Theatre
Garforth Green Lane Primary
  School
George Greens School
George Heriot's School Drama
Glenthorne High School
Grenville College
Griese Youth Theatre
Guernsey College of Further
  Education

Hampshire Collegiate School
Hampstead Fine Arts
Hampstead Theatre Youth
  Theatre
Hanger Farm Arts Centre
The Harrodian School
Harrogate Youth Theatre
Hatfield Visual Arts College
Headington School
Hemel Hempstead School
Hemsworth Arts and
  Community College
Hertswood Lower School
Hope Valley College
Hornsey School for Girls
The Howard School
Huddersfield Technical College
Hull Collegiate School

Imp Theatre Lincoln
Independent Youth Theatre
  Dublin

Invicta Grammar School

Jacksons Lane Youth Theatre
Jigsaw Youth Theatre Company

Kennet School
Kidbrooke School
Kilcullen Town Hall Theatre
Kildare Youth Theatre
Kings College for the Arts and
  Technology
Kingston College

Lambeth College
Langley Park School For Girls
Langley School
Leicester Haymarket Theatre
  Young Blood
The Lindsey School and
  Community Arts College
  Cleethorpes
Lingfield Notre Dame Senior
  School
Lister Community School
Llanelli Youth Theatre
Longley Park Sixth Form
  College
The Lowry Youth Theatre
  Salford
Lyceum Youth Theatre
  Edinburgh

Manor College of Technology
Marple Hall School
Marshalls Park School
Masquerade Theatre Company
  Malta
Millfield School
The Mountbatten School

Nescot College

Northampton School for Girls Youth Theatre
Notre Dame Senior School
Nuffield Youth Theatre
Nunthorpe School Youth Theatre

Oakham School
Oslo International School, International String of Lights

The Park High School
Performance Academy (Newcastle College)
Performance Lab @ Roundabout Youth Theatre
Peter Symonds College
Peterborough High School
The Petersfield School Senior Youth Theatre
Portlaoise Parochial Hall
Portlaoise Youth Theatre
Portsmouth High School
Preston Manor High School
Prior Pursglove College
Pump House CYT
Pump House Theatre and Arts Centre
The Purbeck School

Queen Mary's College

Range High School
Razed Roof Harlow
Redruth School
Regent College
Revolution Arts Academy
Roundabout Youth Theatre
Royal and Derngate Youth Theatre
The Royal High School Bath GDST (Senior School)

RSAMD YouthWorks Drama

Sacred Heart RC High School
St Aelred's Technology College
St Augustine's High School
St Bernard's School
St Edmund Arrowsmith High School
St George's College
St Julian's School
St Martin in the Fields High School For Girls
St Martin's School
St Mary's RC Comprehensive School
St Mary's Youth Theatre
St Monica's High School
St Peter's School
Sandbach School
Sedgehill School
Selah Youth Theatre
Shenfield High School
Sheredes School
Shetland Arts
Shotton Hall
Sir Christopher Hatton School
Sir Frederic Osborn School
Skelmersdale College
Southwark College
South West Youth Theatre
Stafford Gatehouse Youth Theatre
Salisbury Playhouse Stage 65 Youth Theatre
Stage by Stage Music Theatre School
Stephen Joseph Theatre
Stoke Damerel Community College
Stokesley School

Subject2change

Tarleton High School
The Television Workshop
  Birmingham
The Television Workshop Leeds
The Television Workshop
  Nottingham
Terry O'Toole Theatre
Tewkesbury School
Theatre Royal Bury
  St Edmunds Youth Group
Thomas Hardye School
Thomas Lord Audley School
  and Language College
Thornden School
Traverse Theatre

Varndean School

Walthamstow Academy
Washington School
West Thames College
The Westgate School
Weydon School
Wired Youth Theatre
Wolfreton School
Woolston High School
Wymondham High School

Yew Tree Youth Theatre
Young Actors Theatre
Young Actors Company
Ysgol Aberconwy
Yvonne Arnaud Youth Theatre

REGIONAL PARTNERS AND VENUES

Bath Theatre Royal
Brighton Dome
Bristol Old Vic
Cork Everyman Palace Theatre
Edinburgh Royal Lyceum Theatre
Kendal Brewery Arts Theatre
London Arcola Theatre
London Hampstead Theatre
London Lyric Hammersmith
Newcastle Theatre Royal
Northampton Royal & Derngate
Norwich Playhouse & The Garage
Salford The Lowry
Scarborough Stephen Joseph Theatre
Southampton Nuffield
Wellingborough Castle Arts Centre

The Connections Series